PSALMS FOR TODAY

FULL MUSIC EDITION

Edited by
Michael Perry and David Iliff

in association with CPAS

Hodder & Stoughton
LONDON SYDNEY AUCKLAND TORONTO

Also from Jubilate Hymns, published by Hodder and Stoughton:

Hymns for Today's Church
Carols for Today
Church Family Worship
Songs from the Psalms

Copyright Information
Every effort to trace copyright-holders and to obtain permission has been made; the
publishers would welcome details of any errors or omissions. Corrections will be
incorporated into future reprints. This title is available in the USA from Hope
Publishing Company, Carol Stream, Illinois 60188, USA.

British Library Cataloguing in Publication Data

Psalms for Today
  1. Psalms, English
  I. Perry, Michael   II. Iliff, David

ISBN 0 340 50700 4 hbk
     0 340 52826 5 pbk

CONTENTS

	Page
Preface	v
Using *Psalms for Today*	vii

	Number
The Psalms	1–150
The Canticles	151–164
Other Liturgical Hymns	165–167
Liturgical Psalms	8L–150L

	Page
Legal Information, Notes and Acknowledgements	357
Themes Index to the Psalms and Canticles	359
Liturgical Index to the Psalms and Canticles	371
Morning and Evening Prayer Index to the Canticles	372
Lectionary Index to the Psalms and Canticles	374
Alphabetical Index to Tunes	377
First Lines Index to the Psalms and Canticles	379
Holy Communion Rite A (Congregational Prayers)	382
Morning or Evening Worship (Congregational Prayers)	385

PREFACE

The Psalms are an inheritance of the Christian Church, and its basic hymn book. Many if not most of the hymns we sing – certainly the lasting ones – owe their existence to a psalm. Psalms are the encouragement of our spiritual growth, the reminder of God's omnipotence and ever-presence; they are the celebration of our life in Christ and the consolation of our dying.

How were the Psalms first used? A good proportion of them have notes as to their dedication or origin, and about how they are to be performed. Terms which apparently refer to instruments and tunes are obscure so that, on the whole, their interpretation is conjectural. There is little doubt about 'with stringed instruments' (Psalm 4); but 'for the flutes' is just one possible rendering of a phrase which occurs only in Psalm 5. The sense of the Hebrew 'choral' directions is similarly uncertain. But they do suggest energy, variety, and special use for certain occasions. Most of our evidence for the purpose and early use of psalms comes from the text itself. For instance, there is a huge difference between a psalm of individual confidence or sorrow, and a psalm of communal thanksgiving.

Individual psalms – for instance, the laments – are often packed by the psalmist with human experiences, evidently to meet the pastoral situation of various individuals. Whoever was the contemporary custodian of the psalms at temple or shrine, meeting-place or (later) synagogue, would thus be equipped to articulate the unexpressed needs of the worshipper – not only in public services, but also in private counselling.

In the course of our work on *Psalms for Today* we were tempted to omit some examples as too individualistic, or too specific to translate into anything a congregation would wish to sing. Psalms must say what we want to say to God, or be vehicles of God's word to us – often both; the uncritical recitation of *every* psalm no longer appeals. A closer look assured us that many of the psalms more difficult to render have much to say to a society beset by personal frustrations and anxieties, and can in worship be most expressive of our human condition. We found ways to generalise – '*When* the waters cover me' (69A) – to distil the essence of a psalm, and so to claim it with integrity for congregational use.

At the other end of the scale are the great communal worship songs – many apparently tied to a recurring event or festival. The clearest example is Psalm 118. Here the temple congregation gives thanks, and sings 'God's love is eternal'; the symbolic would-be worshipper stands at the door and asks for entrance. Persons in authority assert: 'This is the gate of the Lord; only the righteous can come in'. God's goodness and salvation is declared by the worshipper. There is a blessing: 'May God bless the one who comes in the name of the Lord'. Then action begins; the master of ceremonies orders: 'With branches in your hands, start the festival and march round the altar'. How did we ever imagine that this psalm might be treated as a straight poem, let alone that it should be chanted – including this stage instruction – in complete ignorance of its intended setting and without distinction of one part from another?

These examples serve to demonstrate the varied texture of the Psalms – a diversity which needs to be reflected in the breadth of treatment given by such a collection for the church as *Psalms for Today*. Here are all manner of psalm versions: some strictly to metre, others responsive, and yet others pointed for chanting or arranged for choral speaking. The music includes popular hymn tunes and other familiar melodies, new tunes and special settings. All are employed to reflect the spirit and enhance the mood of the text. According to the tradition of metrical psalmody we have permitted the 'Christianising' of psalms in some cases – not least when the content has long been appreciated as pointing to the coming Messiah.

As many psalms as could reasonably be offered in a form for worship are represented in *Psalms for Today* – the more versatile psalms by several versions. Always we looked for one version that could be readily used without notice or rehearsal. After that we felt at liberty to extend the range by more adventurous treatment. In this volume we insisted upon competent music and well-crafted text. For occasions where a freer musical style and an informal verbal expression is appropriate, we defer to our companion publication *Songs from the Psalms*. For churches where both hymns and songs are in use there is a combined words edition.

Authors and editors alike must acknowledge the debt to earlier collections of psalm versions – even from the uncharted past – whose extensive influence on the church's music is seen in its liturgies and hymn books. In the early 1970s our first – sometimes heavy-handed – efforts in *Psalm Praise* gave us a taste for the spiritual profundity of our source material in the Hebrew Scriptures, and a love for the words and music of worship. For this we owe special thanks to Michael Baughen, Chairman of Jubilate Hymns and Bishop of Chester, who drew us together on that project, and to the Church Pastoral Aid Society who first published our work. As the years have gone by other writers and musicians have associated themselves with us. We hope that our own standards have improved as we have seen our work in use; and that thereby we have become better practitioners, and not merely theorists. Not one of our humble attempts at paraphrase can match the worth of the Psalms themselves, nor be allowed to displace the translated text in Christian devotion. But we offer them for worship and by way of introduction. All the while, the Psalms, profound, unsurpassable, have been a challenge and an example to our writing. It is something of their profundity and not our own transient views that we have sought to offer in *Psalms for Today*.

We thank most sincerely our Jubilate colleagues, whose help and advice has been unstinting; the wider group of associate writers and musicians whose skills and gifts we have been able to call upon; our energetic publishers; and that inner group of Jubilate staff without whose talent and devotion we would have ceased to function long ago.

MICHAEL PERRY, Tonbridge
DAVID ILIFF, Brussels
Epiphany 1990

USING *PSALMS FOR TODAY*

In the Church of England

The practice of chanting pointed psalms only came into general use in parish churches during the latter part of the nineteenth century. This style is found beautiful and helpful by many, but it has to be acknowledged that more worshippers are defeated by the technicalities of pointing and wish consequently to discontinue the use of psalms.

The move towards Parish Communion as the main Sunday service has reduced the opportunity for psalm and canticle singing. Morning and Evening Prayer (Matins and Evensong) traditionally provided for three or four canticles to be sung, and because these services are used less often, the Psalter has become much less well-known.

The Church of England has in fact lost part of the genius of its heritage. The recital of the psalms at the offices according to a regular pattern dates back to very early times. The Book of Common Prayer Psalter ensures the public reading of every psalm once a month. But quite apart from tradition, the persistent omission of the Psalms deprives the Church of a pillar of its spirituality. As a consequence the Church is unable to offer the resources of the Psalms, which so squarely face up to the human condition, as it tries to meet the needs of the present secular generation. Where is the remedy?

The Anglican congregation today has much more influence in what it says and sings in church. Through the Parochial Church Council, changes of direction in worship have to be agreed with the incumbent, with the bishop as final arbiter. The incumbent, who has theological training and professional liturgical and pastoral advice to offer, will be allowed to lead if the PCC is wise; and the incumbent will keep the musician in his confidence if he has sense and foresight. An awareness by the minister, musician and church council of the gradual demise of the Psalms is important. *Psalms for Today* may be used to remedy this situation. How can it best be used?

We suggest that the choice of psalms from *Psalms for Today* follows the promptings of the Lectionary, or matches the minister's or preacher's chosen theme. The Themes Index, the Liturgical Index and the Lectionary Index will help with subjects and seasons.

Experienced practitioners will know that it is unwise to introduce too many new tunes at once – especially where there is neither choir nor active tradition of congregational singing. Most of the metrical versions in *Psalms for Today* are cross-referenced to known hymn tunes, and may be used this way while the book is being introduced. There is, however, a danger here: the peril of monotony if every psalm version is set to a known hymn tune. With choices from the hymn book already made, Morning or Evening Prayer (Matins or Evensong) could end up in effect with seven hymns! The Psalms need to contrast with the hymns on such an occasion. The 'known' hymn tunes here set or recommended should therefore be used for psalms with economy and good judgement.

To provide a different style of music from the traditional hymn, extensive use has been made of folk-song tunes, early nineteenth century American tunes, responsive tunes, and tunes newly-composed. Chants for pointed versions of well-known psalms and canticles are also provided. They are printed without definite note values in order to encourage singing in rhythms dictated by natural speech rather than those imposed by a beat. A choir practising chanted psalms and canticles is recommended to *say* the words through, at a deliberate pace, before singing them. This will make clear where natural emphases should come and these should be incorporated as far as possible in the sung performance.

With such variety there is considerable scope for balanced choice in a service where more than one psalm/canticle is needed.

Some churches will wish to use this Psalm book exclusively. Others, especially where the song genre is popular, may prefer to use our companion volume *Songs from the Psalms* in conjunction. The words edition is a combined one, and includes songs based on psalms as well as the texts set here in *Psalms for Today*. This means there need be only one financial outlay involved in equipping the congregation. The two music books have been kept separate, to keep costs lower and because the musical styles are different. Using both music books (one words book) gives even greater flexibility in choice and balance.

In the Free Churches

Today's Free Churches, whose forebears developed metrical psalmody, received from them a host of psalm texts. But they did not feel the obligation to use them systematically, as Anglicans used the psalter. In the eighteenth century, the flowering of hymnody in the Free Churches tended to eclipse the metrical psalms – although Spurgeon's *Our Own Hymn-book* (1866) devoted its first 150 numbers to a complete metrical psalter, and *Wesley's Hymns* (1889) still had a large selection of metrical psalms. Many of the traditional texts are rigidly long metre or common metre, and this gives them a bland, even monotonous, feel. Their dated appeal, and the absence of any system of psalm use in the less structured worship of the Free Churches led to their gradual demise.

The losers are the congregation, because they no longer have that close acquaintance with the spirituality of the Psalms which is the inheritance of all Christendom. *Psalms for Today* presents churches and congregations with an opportunity to put the matter right. Published and recognised hymn-writers of the leading denominations have united to craft new psalm versions. The work spans twenty years. We hope that congregations which have embraced new hymns and Christian songs will warm to these texts which combine a fresh approach with biblical statements of faith, worship and aspiration.

Psalms may be chosen to match the movement of worship in the Free Churches: Approach to Worship/Thanksgiving; Scripture Reading and Teaching; Prayer and Intercession; Praise; Proclamation, Challenge and Dedication. The thematic index will offer the minister or group leader a considerable resource for combining worship with teaching.

More recently there has been a call in Free Church circles for spoken material suitable for use by minister and congregation – something almost unheard of even ten years ago. Words are wanted which involve the people and demonstrate that verbal worship is not just the province of the minister. But for the Free Churches, to return to the slavish commitment to repetition of traditional texts (and archaism) that has been the diet of the established church until now simply would not do. A contemporary and much more participatory diet is required. We believe that the *Psalms for Today* appendix of forty spoken psalm versions goes some way towards meeting that demand.

Our hope is that *Psalms for Today* will be warmly received in the Free Churches, not only because it can enable greater congregational participation, but also because it makes accessible the incomparable spirituality of the Psalms.

In the Roman Catholic Church

Until the Second Vatican Council, the Roman Catholic Church used almost exclusively Gregorian psalm-tones, with antiphons before and after each psalm. This world-wide practice employed the Latin text whenever a monastic or neo-monastic office was sung. The exception was the Gelineau form of vernacular psalmody which is now little used;

although it is more prevalent in the United States than in the United Kingdom. At Mass, a psalm-verse or two would be sung during the Gradual or Alleluia between the readings (again with a Latin text), using either very florid plainchant or, less often, polyphonic or fauxbourdon settings. These chants were reserved for the choir.

Since Vatican II, the Sunday and Weekday Lectionary has contained a responsive psalm after the first reading at Mass. A congregational response occurs every four or six lines; the normal practice is for the congregation to sing the refrain, and for a cantor – or a group of cantors – to sing the verses. A substantial majority of the psalm-tones used are of the 'reciting note with termination' type. There is now an increasing use of psalm *tunes* (tones in regular metres).

As regards translation, the Grail version is almost universal for the English-speaking world (the USA also uses NAB). Specific examples of the Gelineau form (for which the Grail text was designed) still appeal, though the generality does not. Probably it was ahead of its time, becoming available before the use of the vernacular at Mass. By the time that departure was authorised, taste and opinion had moved on; the text, however, has remained.

Less than half of English-speaking Catholic congregations sing any psalm at all, the responsive psalm being said. And, although various styles of psalm are attempted by forward-looking Catholics, these are often employed for exits, entrances, communion etc. and do not occupy the traditional positions in the service.

For monastic, or neo-monastic, offices today, most communities sing the psalms in English, using similar tones to those mentioned above; some communities still preserve some Latin psalmody to Gregorian tones mixed in with vernacular psalmody (though not normally within the same office).

It is remarkable, then, that each tradition – Roman Catholic, Free Church, and Anglican – has lost a significant element of the 'word' service developed by the early Church from their Hebrew inheritance. There are riches to be rediscovered!

Practical Points
None of the performance directions given with the psalm versions are intended to be prescriptive. Indications of speed, or of division of verses between men and women, for example, should be adapted to suit particular local circumstances.

● **Metrical Settings**
Many of these are in four-part harmony but it is suggested that when new tunes are introduced they are sung initially in unison. When descants are used all other voices should sing the melody in unison.

● **Pointed Settings to Chants**
(a) The rhythm and speed of chanting should be that of clear, deliberate speech. Notes in the chants are purposely printed without indication of value in beats.
(b) Normally a breath should be taken at the end of each line. Occasionally an asterisk or double space between words indicates a break.
(c) A dot indicates the division of syllables in a bar when there are more than two syllables.
(d) *Second part* indicates that the music should be begun half-way through the chant.
(e) If it is wished to say rather than sing the psalm the use of bold type indicates how the words may be divided between two groups or between leader and congregation.

● **Responsorial Settings**
Settings such as 42B, 47B, 117B are not necessarily intended for choir alone. The choir may sing the verse sections with the congregation joining in the repeated refrains.

PSALMS, CANTICLES

AND LITURGICAL HYMNS

If we love the word of God

1A

Fullness 7 6 7 6

Words: from Psalm 1
Michael Perry
Music: Noël Tredinnick

1 If we love the word of God and____
2 If we shun the sin - ners' way and____
3 If we do these things we'll find rich____

heed it day__ and__ night; if we make God's truth our
spurn their false__ ad - vice; if we turn from God - less
bless - ings as__ we__ go; then we'll flour - ish like a

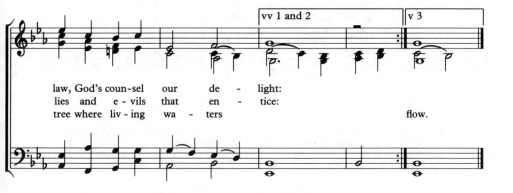

vv 1 and 2   v 3

law, God's coun-sel our de - light:
lies and e - vils that en - tice:
tree where liv - ing wa - ters   flow.

Alternative tune: Dartmeet, *Songs from the Psalms* 1A

1B(i)

The Law of God

Bibury 8 8 8 8 (LM)

Words: from Psalm 1
Brian Foley
Music: David Iliff

1 The Law of God is life to choose, the
2 The Law of God is no mere list of
WOMEN 3 The Will of God must be our will, to

Will of God is joy to see, the Word of God is
things to do and not to do, but God's per-fect-ion—
wish, to want, to do, to be; and with the mind of

truth to speak, the Love of God brings love to be!
this a-lone the yes and no of all we do!
God, to think, and through the eyes of God, to see!

MEN
4 The Word of God, the voice of God,
was through his Servant-Prophets heard,
in time, foretelling One-to-Come –
his Servant-Son, his living Word!

ALL
5 The Love of God is God himself –
most precious gift that he can give! –
to be in us the cause of love,
to fill with love the life we live!

6 Then make the Law of God our law,
the Will of God our chosen ways,
the Word of God our firmest faith,
and God himself our endless praise!

The Law of God

Melcombe 8 8 8 8 (LM)

Words: from Psalm 1
Brian Foley
Music: S Webbe the elder (1740–1816)

1 The Law of God is life to choose, the
2 The Law of God is no mere list of
WOMEN 3 The Will of God must be our will, to

Will of God is joy to see, the Word of God is
things to do and not to do, but God's per - fect - ion-
wish, to want, to do, to be; and with the mind of

truth to speak, the Love of God brings love to be!
this a - lone the yes and no of all we do!
God, to think, and through the eyes of God, to see!

MEN
4 The Word of God, the voice of God,
was through his Servant-Prophets heard,
in time, foretelling One-to-Come –
his Servant-Son, his living Word!

ALL
5 The Love of God is God himself –
most precious gift that he can give! –
to be in us the cause of love,
to fill with love the life we live!

6 Then make the Law of God our law,
the Will of God our chosen ways,
the Word of God our firmest faith,
and God himself our endless praise!

1C   Blessed are they

Coln Rogers 3 9 3 6 3 7 8 5

Words: from Psalm 1
Paul Wigmore
Music: John Barnard

1 Blessed are they who lis-ten not to e-vil coun-sel,
2 Blessed are they, for as a tree by streams of wa-ter
3 Blessed are they though sin-ners like the chaff be scat-tered,

turn a - side from ev - ery thought of sin:
spreads its leaves in boun - ti - ful dis - plays,
blessed are they though winds of judge-ment blow;

day and night, the law of God their mak - er
bears and yields its rip - ened fruit in sea - son —
from the Lord, up - on his right-eous ser - vants,

is their joy and me - di - ta - tion, well of life with - in.
so shall they in ev - ery call - ing pros - per all their days.
lov - ing care and ten - der mer - cies ev - er - more shall flow.

How many are against me, Lord

Solothurn 8 8 8 8 (LM)

Words: from Psalm 3
Christopher Idle
Music: Swiss traditional melody
arranged C H Kitson (1874–1944)

1 How many are a - gainst me, Lord: how
2 But you are round me, Lord, my shield; but
3 I go to rest, and sleep in peace – I

ma - ny fierce at - tacks rise up! They say 'God will not
you, my glo - ry, lift my head! You hear me from your
wake a - gain; God keeps me safe: ten thou - sand shall not

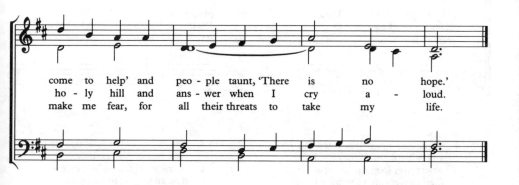

come to help' and peo - ple taunt, 'There is no hope.'
ho - ly hill and ans - wer when I cry a - loud.
make me fear, for all their threats to take my life.

4 Arise, O Lord, to rescue me:
arise and save me, O my God!
You silence all my enemies
till scorn and spite are all destroyed.

5 Your blessings, Father, grant to us;
your help, O Saviour, still be ours:
O Holy Spirit, fill our lives –
to God be glory, love, and praise!

4A   O God, defender of the poor

Liverpool   8 6 8 6 (CM)

Words: from Psalm 4
Christopher Idle
Music: American folk melody
arranged John Barnard

1 O God, de-fen-der of the poor, have
2 How long will peo-ple choose vain things, love
3 The saints, O Lord, you set a-part by

mer-cy when I pray: you lis-tened to my
emp-ty words and wrong? They scorn to serve the
grace to be your own: let sin-ners trem-ble,

prayer be-fore Lord, hear my prayer to-day!
King of kings O liv-ing God, how long?
search their hearts, and bow be-fore your throne.

WOMEN

4 While many pray that you will bless
   and bring them all they need,
   unless they long for holiness
   their prayers are vain indeed.

MEN

5 Your light, O Lord, let us receive,
   your face within us shine:
   for richer is the joy you give
   than all their corn and wine.

ALL

6 And even when I turn to sleep
   your blessings still increase,
   for you alone, O Lord, will keep
   your child in perfect peace.

Alternative tune: Abridge, *Hymns for Today's Church* 374

Lord, as I wake

Bolnhurst 8 8 8 8 (LM)

Words: from Psalm 5
Brian Foley
Music: Paul Edwards

1 Lord, as I wake I turn to you, your -
2 There is no bless - ing, Lord, from you for____
3 Your lov - ing gifts of grace to me, those____
4 Lord, make my life a life of love, keep____

- self the first thought of my day;____ my king, my God, whose help is
those who make their will their way,____ no praise for those who will not
fa - vours I could ne - ver earn,____ call for my thanks in praise and
me from sin in all I do;____ Lord, make your law my on - ly

sure,____ your - self the help____ for which I pray.
praise,____ no peace for those____ who will not pray.
prayer,____ call me to love____ you in re - turn.
law,____ your will my will,____ for love of you.

Words: from the *New Catholic Hymnal*
© 1971 Faber Music Ltd, 3 Queen Square,
London WC1N 3AU

Music: © Paul Edwards/Jubilate Hymns †

Lord, as I wake

Daniel 8 8 8 8 (LM)

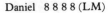

Words: from Psalm 5
Brian Foley
Music: Irish traditional melody
arranged David Iliff

1 Lord, as I wake I turn to you, your -
2 There is no bless - ing, Lord, from you for
3 Your lov - ing gifts of grace to me, those
4 Lord, make my life a life of love, keep

- self the first thought of my day; my king, my God, whose
those who make their will their way, no praise for those who
fa - vours I could ne - ver earn, call for my thanks in
me from sin in all I do; Lord, make your law my

help is sure, your - self the help for which I pray.
will not praise, no peace for those who will not pray.
praise and prayer, call me to love you in re - turn.
on - ly law, your will my will, for love of you.

Words: from the *New Catholic Hymnal*
© 1971 Faber Music Ltd, 3 Queen Square,
London WC1N 3AU

Music arrangement: © David Iliff/Jubilate Hymns †

O gracious Lord

St Alphege 7 6 7 6

Words: from Psalm 6
Michael Perry
Music: H J Gauntlett (1805–1876)

1 O gra - cious Lord, be near me! My
2 'How shall the voice you gave me sing
3 I knew the fear of dy - ing, and

soul cries out, 'How long? When will you turn to
prais - es from the dead? Re - turn, O Lord, and
sor - row filled my eyes; but God who hears my

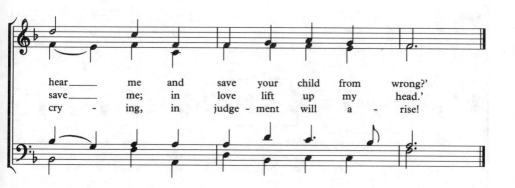

hear_____ me and save your child from wrong?'
save_____ me; in love lift up my head.'
cry - ing, in judge - ment will a - rise!

Alternative tune: Kocher, *Hymns for Today's Church* 530

I will give thanks

Hiding-place

Words: from Psalm 7
Michael Perry
Music: David Iliff

Refrain
UNISON

I will give
thanks to the Lord most high; — I will sing praise to his right-eous name. *Fine*

Verse

1 I have no strength but___ yours,___ O
2 To love that will not___ cease_____ I
3 My God, my sove - reign___ still,_____ my

God, my hid - ing - place; you snatch me from the
owe my life, my___ all;___ and just - ly if I
shield, my joy, my___ crown: you hon - our those who

This Psalm version can be sung without the refrain to Venice,
Psalms for Today 133A(ii), *Hymns for Today's Church* 34.

Music: © David Iliff/Jubilate Hymns †

Words: © Michael Perry/Jubilate Hymns †

li - on's__ claws__ and save me by your__ grace.__
break God's peace__ then pun - ish - ment will__ fall.__
do your__ will,__ you tread the e - vil__ down.__

OPTIONAL HARMONY for Verse 2

2 To love that will not cease____ I
will not cease____

owe my life, my all;__ and just - ly if I
life, my all;

break God's peace__ then pun - ish - ment will fall.__
break God's peace then pun - ish - ment will fall.__

The Harmony and Unison versions are harmonically compatible.

8A(i)   Lord, how majestic is your name

Jacob's Well 8 7 8 7

Words: from Psalm 8
Fred Kaan
Music: Barry Rose

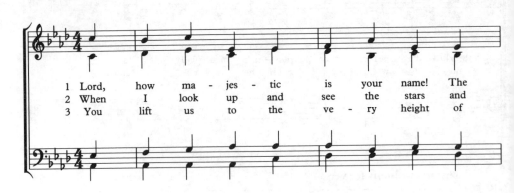

1 Lord, how ma - jes - tic is your name! The
2 When I look up and see the stars and
3 You lift us to the ve - ry height of

earth and sky a - dore you, the mouths of ba - bies
think of space un - end - ing, I mar - vel that you
your cre - a - tive like - ness, just as you raised your

sing your praise and child - ren dance be - fore you.
come and care, us with your love be - friend - ing.
Son from death to Eas - ter's wide - a - wake - ness.

12

Lord, how majestic is your name

Ach, Gott und Herr   8 7 8 7

Words: from Psalm 8
Fred Kaan
Music: *Neu Leipziger Gesangbuch* 1682
arranged J S Bach (1685–1750)

1 Lord, how ma - jes - tic___ is___ your name! The
2 When I look up and___ see___ the stars and
3 You lift us to the___ ve - ry height of

earth_ and_ sky a - dore_____ you, the mouths of ba - bies
think_ of___ space un - end - ing, I mar - vel that you
your_ cre - a - tive_ like - ness, just as you raised your

sing___ your_ praise and child - ren dance be - fore_____ you.
come_ and_ care, us with your love_ be - friend - ing.
Son_ from_ death to Eas - ter's wide - a - wake - ness.

Words: © Stainer & Bell Ltd,
82 High Road, London N2 9PW

8B(i)

With wonder, Lord

Manton Hollow 8 8 8 4

Words: from Psalm 8
Brian Foley
Music: John Barnard

UNISON

1 With won - der, Lord, we see your works,_____ we
(2 With) won - der, Lord, we see your works,_____ and
(3 The) stars that fill the skies a - bove,_____ the
(4 We) praise your works, yet we our - selves_____ are
(5 All) you have made is ours to rule,_____ the

see the beau - ty you have made;_____ this earth, the skies, all things that
child-like in our joy we sing_____ to praise you, bless you, mak - er,
sun and moon which give our light,_____ are your de - sign - ing for our
works of won - der made by you;_____ not far from you in all we
birds and beasts at will to tame,_____ all things to or - der for the

vv 1-4

are in beau-ty made.
Lord of ev - ery-thing.
use and our de - light.
are and all we do.

v 5

2 With
3 The glo - ry of your name.
4 We
5 All

Music: © John Barnard/Jubilate Hymns †

14

Words: © 1971 Faber Music Ltd,
3 Queen Square, London WC1N 3AU

With wonder, Lord

8B(ii)

Es ist kein Tag 8 8 8 4

Words: from Psalm 8
Brian Foley
Music: J D Meyer (1692)

1 With won - der, Lord, we see your works, we see the beau - ty you have made; this earth, the skies, all things that are in beau - ty made.

2 With won - der, Lord, we see your works, and child - like in our joy we sing to praise you, bless you, mak - er, Lord of ev - ery - thing.

3 The stars that fill the skies a - bove, the sun and moon which give our light, are your de - sign - ing for our use and our de - light.

4 We praise your works, yet we our - selves are works of won - der made by you; not far from you in all we are and all we do.

5 All you have made is ours to rule, the birds and beasts at will to tame, all things to or - der for the glo - ry of your name.

Alternative tune: Almsgiving, *Hymns for Today's Church* 287

15

O Lord our Governor

Words: Psalm 8
from *The Liturgical Psalter*
David Frost and others
Music: G M Garrett (1834–1897)
Descant: John Barnard

DESCANT

O Lord our Gover-nor: how glorious is your name in all the earth!

1 O ' Lord our ' Governor:
   how glorious is your ' name in ' all the ' earth!
2 Your majesty above the heavens is ' yet re'counted:
   by the ' mouths of ' babes and ' sucklings.

Second part
3 You have founded a strong defence a'gainst your ' adversaries:
   to quell the ' ene·my ' and · the a'venger.

4 When I consider your heavens the ' work of · your ' fingers:
   the moon and the stars which ' you have ' set in ' order,
5 what is man   that you should be ' mindful ' of him:
   or the son of ' man that ' you should ' care for him?

6 Yet you have made him little ' less · than a ' god:
   and have ' crowned him · with ' glory · and ' honour.
7 You have made him the ' master · of your ' handiwork:
   and have put all things in sub'jection · be'neath his ' feet,

8 all ' sheep and ' oxen:
   and all the ' creatures ' of the ' field,
9 the birds of the air and the ' fish · of the ' sea:
   and everything that moves in the pathways ' of the ' great ' waters.

Second part
10 O ' Lord our ' Governor:
    how glorious is your ' name in ' all the ' earth!

    Glory to the Father and ' to the ' Son:
    and ' to the ' Holy ' Spirit;
    as it was in the be'ginning · is ' now:
    and shall be for ' ever. ' A'men.

Confitebor tibi

Words: from Psalm 9
Michael Perry
Music: David Llewellyn Green

Slow waltz tempo

mp

Con ped.

℞ Refrain
UNISON

I praise you, Lord, with all__ my heart, re - joic - ing

Fine Verse
SOLO (OR UNISON SEMI-CHORUS)

in__ your won - ders!_____ 1 Your jus - tice is per - fect, your

2 You gov - ern the peo - ples, you

p

rit. *D.℞ al Fine*

judge-ments are true; the wick-ed have fall - en, their names are for - got-ten.

help the op - pressed; and no - one who seeks you is ev - er for - sak - en.

Alternative tune: *Songs from the Psalms 9*

10(i) In my hour of grief or need

Lewknor 7 7 7 7

Words: from Psalm 10
Timothy Dudley-Smith
Music: John Barnard

DESCANT
6 Then shall vice and false-hood fail, truth and right-eous-

UNISON
1 In my hour of grief or need when a friend is
2 When the powers of e-vil ride through the world in
6 Then shall vice and false-hood fail, truth and right-eous-

-ness pre-vail, all his ran-somed
friend in-deed, now, when Sa-tan
o-pen pride, flaunt-ed sins and
-ness pre-vail, all his ran-somed

peo-ple sing___ God, their ev-er-last-ing King!
walks a-broad, be not far from me, O Lord.
boast-ed shame bring con-tempt up-on your name —
peo-ple sing God, their ev-er-last-ing King!

v 6

18

3 When the god-less man is strong;— when his mouth is
4 When the poor be-comes his prey,— when the weak are
5 Powers of dark-ness bring to grief,— break the hold of

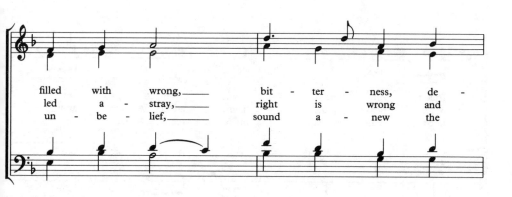

filled with wrong,_____ bit - ter - ness, de -
led a - stray,_____ right is wrong and
un - be - lief,_____ sound a - new the

D.C. for verse 6

- ceit and fraud,__ be not far from me, O Lord.
truth is lies =___ then, O Lord our God, a - rise!
quick - ening word =___ rise and come a - mong us, Lord!

The Unison and Harmony versions are harmonically compatible.
The Unison version should be used for the accompaniment throughout.

In my hour of grief or need

Heinlein 7 7 7 7

Words: from Psalm 10
Timothy Dudley-Smith
Music: *Nürnbergisches Gesangbuch* 1676
attributed to M Herbst (1654–1681)

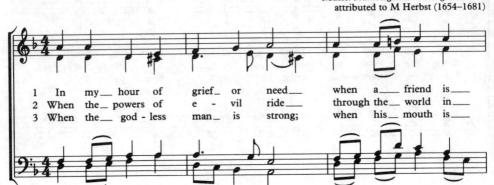

1 In my hour of grief or need when a friend is
2 When the powers of evil ride through the world in
3 When the godless man is strong; when his mouth is

friend in - deed, now, when Sa - tan
o - pen pride, flaunt - ed sins and
filled with wrong, bit - ter - ness, de -

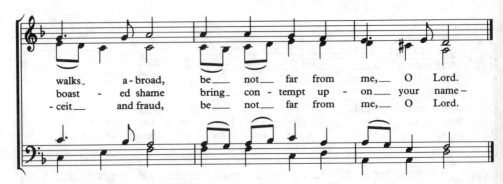

walks a-broad, be not far from me, O Lord.
boast - ed shame bring con-tempt up - on your name –
-ceit and fraud, be not far from me, O Lord.

4 When the poor becomes his prey,
   when the weak are led astray,
   right is wrong and truth is lies –
   then, O Lord our God, arise!

5 Powers of darkness bring to grief,
   break the hold of unbelief,
   sound anew the quickening word –
   rise and come among us, Lord!

6 Then shall vice and falsehood fail,
   truth and righteousness prevail,
   all his ransomed people sing
   God, their everlasting King!

I find my refuge in the Lord

Everberg 8 8 8 8 (LM)

Words: from Psalm 11
Basil Bridge
Music: David Iliff

1 I find my re - fuge in the Lord, no
2 The Lord is in his ho - ly place, en -
3 He knows what I through shame con - ceal, yet

fears shall make me fly a - way: the moun - tains hide the hunt - ed
- throned on high, yet near at hand; both saint and sin - ner come to
of - fers me this cup of grace: his Spi - rit's fire will cleanse and

bird; his truth stands firm – with him I stay.
face his judge - ment, in his pres - ence stand.
heal, the up - right shall be - hold his face.

Alternative tunes: Bow Brickhill or Breslau, *Hymns for Today's Church* 146

12A   God will arise

Salvum me fac

Words: from Psalm 12
Michael Perry
Music: Anthony Greening

God will a-
Man.

-rise be - cause the weak are___ cry - ing,

Ped.

God will a - rise be - cause the need - y ___ call,

Fine

God will a-rise who_ knows and_ loves them all.

Verses

1 Flaw - less are God's migh - ty words — sil - ver forged in_ fire,_____
2 When the wick-ed strut a - bout, when they take the_ sword,_____

mf

D.C.

sham - ing ev - ery_ e - vil tongue, ev - ery dark de - sire._____
hear your peo - ple_ in their pain, come to us, O_ Lord!_____

Optional Harmony version for Refrain overleaf

23

The accompaniment on pages 22 and 23 should be used with this version.

The promises of God

Bramdean 8 8 8 7

Words: from Psalm 12
Keith Landis
Music: Barry Rose

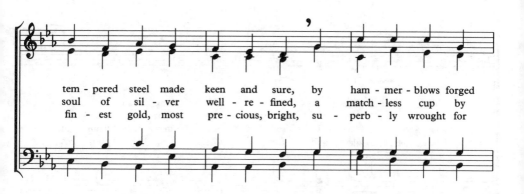

1 The pro - mis - es of God are pure, as tem - pered steel made keen and sure, by ham - mer - blows forged to en - dure, a sword for my de - fend - ing.

2 The pro - mis - es of God re - mind my soul of sil - ver well - re - fined, a match - less cup by Love de - signed, di - vine e - lix - ir blend - ing.

3 The pro - mis - es of God are right, as fin - est gold, most pre - cious, bright, su - perb - ly wrought for my de - light, a crown of life un - end - ing.

13A   How long will you forget me, Lord

Bangor 8 6 8 6 (CM)

Words: from Psalm 13
Christopher Idle
Music: from W Tans'ur's *Harmony of Syon* 1734

1 How long will you_ for - get me,_ Lord, and
2 Look on my need,_ O Lord my_ God who
3 Look on their threats_ and hear my_ cry, and
4 But since I trust_ your con - stant_ love my

hide_ your_ face a - way? How_ long shall e - vils_
grants my_ ev - ery breath; give_ light that I may_
ans - wer_ when I call: or_ they will claim the_
heart_ is_ glad and free to_ sing the prais - es_

tear_ my_ heart and_ trou - bles_ fill my day?
see_ your_ light, not sleep the_ sleep of death.
vic - to - ry who_ long to_ see me fall.
of_ the_ Lord for_ all your_ grace to me.

The fool whose heart declares in pride

14

Detroit   8 6 8 6 (CM)

Words: from Psalm 14
Stephen Wilcockson
Music: *Supplement to the Kentucky Harmony* 1820
arranged David Iliff

1 The fool whose heart declares in pride, 'There
2 For all have sinned and turned from God, not
3 Do they not know, can they not tell, who
4 Now come, O Lord, your peo-ple bless, and

is no God to fear,' for-gets the Lord's all-
one has kept God's way; cor-rupt a-like, not
plan to crush the poor, that God is with the
pu-ri-fy from wrong, that we may make your

-see-ing eye who finds no good-ness here:
one does good—we all have gone a-stray.
right-eous still, their re-fuge ev-er sure?
right-eous-ness our ev-er-last-ing song!

Alternative tune: Stracathro, *Psalms for Today* 165B(ii), *Hymns for Today's Church* 144

15A Lord, who may dwell within your house

Withington 8 6 8 8 8 6

Words: from Psalm 15
Paul Wigmore
Music: John Barnard

1 Lord, who may dwell with - in your house and on__ your ho - ly
2 All those who love their neigh-bour well, who hate__ the way of

hill? All those who walk a blame - less way, who
sin, who hon - our all that fear the Lord, whose

love the right, who win the day with truth - ful words and,
pro - mise is a bind - ing cord, who help, and seek no

come what may, will speak no word of ill:
rich re - ward – these, Lord, you wel - come in.

Lord, who may venture where you dwell 15B

Wells House 8 8 8 8 (LM)

Words: from Psalm 15
David Preston
Music: David Iliff

UNISON

1 Lord, who may ven-ture where you dwell, or wor-ship on your ho - ly hill? The
2 They ne - ver do their neigh-bour wrong, and ut - ter no ma - li-cious word; the
3 They keep their oath at a - ny cost, and glad - ly lend, but not for gain; they

pure in heart, whose spot - less lives by word and deed o - bey your will.
sin-ner's fol - ly they des - pise, but hon - our those who fear the Lord.
hate all bribe - ry: come what may, se - cure for ev - er they re-main.

Alternative tune: Breslau, *Hymns for Today's Church* 146

16A   I set the Lord before my eyes

Palace Green   8 7 8 7 8 8 7

Words: from Psalm 16
Owen Dowling
Music: Michael Fleming

1 I set the Lord be-fore my eyes, and look in long-ing to him;
2 The One who takes the fear from death turns dark-ness in-to dawn-ing;

Christ calls me dai-ly to a-rise from fear and an-xious striv-ing.
my spi-rit and my mind give birth to prais-es fresh each morn-ing.

At my right hand he al-ways moves, the path through dark-ened plac-es shows,
All night-ly fears will now de-part, for hope se-cure with-in the heart

UNISON

his hold is firm, con-sol - ing.
is found with Christ's ap-pear - ing.

Alternative tune: Luther, *Psalms for Today* 29A, *Hymns for Today's Church* 189

Music: © Royal School of Church Music,
Addington Place, Croydon, Surrey CR9 5AD

Cogenhoe 6 5 6 5

Words: from Psalm 17
David Mowbray
Music: Paul Edwards

UNISON

1 Lord of all my foot - steps, watch - ing from a - bove,
2 O - thers moved by ma - lice spread un - truths a - round:
3 For their hope is rich - es, time will yet des - troy;

keep me in the safe - ty of your per - fect love.
shall their schemes not fal - ter and their plans re - bound?
you are all my trea - sure and my last - ing joy.

Alternative tune: Caswall, *Hymns for Today's Church* 126

18A
I love you, O Lord

Jane 8 8 8 8 D

Words: from Psalm 18
Christopher Idle
Music: David Peacock

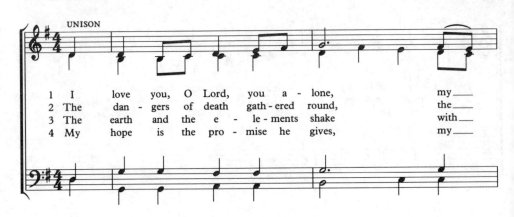

1 I love you, O Lord, you a - lone, my__
2 The dan - gers of death gath - ered round, the__
3 The earth and the e - le - ments shake with__
4 My hope is the pro - mise he gives, my__

re - fuge on whom I de - pend; my ma - ker, my sav - iour, my
waves of des - truc - tion came near; but in my des - pair - ing I
thun - der and light - ning and hail; the cliffs and the moun - tain-tops
life is se - cure in his hand; I shall not be lost, for he

own,__ my hope and my trust with-out end._____ The
found__ the Lord who re-leased me from fear._____ I
break__ and mor - tals are fee - ble and pale._____ His
lives!__ He comes to my aid – I shall stand!_____ Lord

Alternative tune: Trewen, *Hymns for Today's Church* 449

Lord   is   my strength and my   song,_____ de -
called for his help   in   my   pain,_____ to
jus - tice is   full   and com - plete,_____ his
God, you are power - ful to   save,_____ your

- fen - der and guide of my ways;   my   mas - ter to whom I be -
God my sal - va - tion I cried;   he   brought me his com - fort a -
mer - cy to us has no end;   the   clouds are a path for his
Spi - rit will spur me to pray;   your   Son has de - feat - ed the

- long,   my   God who shall have all my praise.
- gain,   I   live   by the strength he sup - plied.
feet,   he   comes on the wings of the wind.
grave: I   trust and I praise you to - day!

18B(i)

I love you, Lord

Northwood 8 8 8 8 (LM)

Words: from Psalm 18
Keith Landis
Music: David Iliff

UNISON

1 I love you, Lord, my strength and rock, my
2 My God, my ref - uge and my shield, my

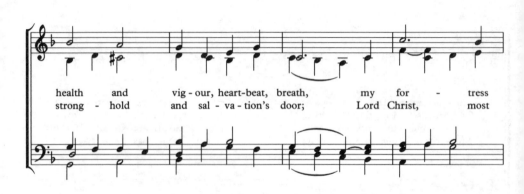

health and vig - our, heart-beat, breath, my for - tress
strong - hold and sal - va - tion's door; Lord Christ, most

and de - liv - er - er from death of life and life of death!
wor-thy to be praised, all these you are, yet more – much more!

I love you, Lord

Church Triumphant 8 8 8 8 (LM)

Words: from Psalm 18
Keith Landis
Music: J W Elliott (1833–1915)

1 I love you, Lord, my strength and rock, my __
2 My God, my re - fuge and my shield, my __

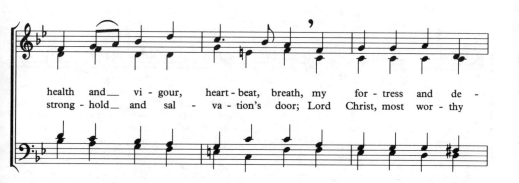

health and __ vi - gour, heart - beat, breath, my for - tress and de -
strong - hold __ and sal - va - tion's door; Lord Christ, most wor - thy

- liv - er - er from death of life and life of death!
to be praised, all these you are, yet more – much more!

19A We look into your heavens

The Linden Tree 8 7 8 7

Words: from Psalm 19
Fred Pratt Green
Music: Old German melody
arranged John Barnard

1 We look in-to your heavens and see your glo-ry
2 We look in-to our way-ward hearts: how wise-ly
3 From mer-cy what have I to hide? You hold me
4 That you ap-prove my spo-ken word, my thoughts and

in cre-a - tion — there's not a sun or
you di-rect us! Your law is where our
back from sin - ning. O let me not be
my be-hav - iour, will be your ser - vant's

ga - lax - y but speaks our a - dor - a - tion.
jus - tice starts, its clear com-mands pro-tect us.
ruled by pride, where sin has its be - gin - ning.
great re - ward, my Sun, my Shield, my Sav - iour!

Alternative tune: St Columba, *Hymns for Today's Church* 404

Music arrangement: © John Barnard/Jubilate Hymns †

Glory and praise to God

Water-End

Words: from Psalm 19
Christopher Idle
Music: Geoffrey Shaw (1879–1943)

1 Glo - ry and praise to God! All the skies sing praise –
2 Glo - ry and praise to God for his per - fect law,

songs from the sun and moon, from the nights and days: No hu-man voice is
mak - ing the sim - ple wise and the wav-erer sure. Sweet-er than hon - ey -

there, no mor-tal speech is heard; still through the depths of space speeds the
- comb, rich-er than pur-est gold; praise for re-demp-tion's plan which the

sound - ing word. Up comes the morn - ing sun for his migh - ty
words un - fold. Lord, keep my heart from sin – you have set me

race, and the Lord shines on us with his truth___ and grace.
free: be my life and my light; Je-sus, shine___ on me.

19C   # God's glory fills the heavens

St Patrick   8 8 8 8 D

Words: from Psalm 19
Carl P Daw Jnr
Music: Irish traditional hymn melody
arranged C V Stanford (1852–1924)

1 God's glo - ry fills the heavens with hymns, the domed sky
2 God's per - fect law re - vives the soul, its pre - cepts
3 God's ser - vant may I ev - er be this world my

bears the Ma - ker's mark; new prais - es sound from
make the sim - ple wise, its just com - mands re -
joy, that word my guide: O cleanse me, Lord, from

day to day and e - cho through the know - ing dark. With -
- joice the heart, its truth gives light un - to the eyes. For
se - cret sin; de - li - ver me from sel - fish pride. Ac -

-out a word their songs roll on — in - to all lands their
ev - er shall this_ law en - dure — un - blem - ished, right - eous,
-cept my thoughts and_ words and deeds; let them find fav - our

voic - es run; and with____ a____ champ - ion's strength and
true, com - plete; no gold____ was__ ev - er found so
in your sight — for you____ a - lone___ can make me

grace__ from_ farth - est__ heaven comes forth the sun.
fine,_ no__ ho - ney_ in____ the comb more sweet.
whole,_ O__ Lord my_ re - fuge and my might.

20A   May the Lord God hear you pray

Queen's Terrace 7 7 7 7

Words: from Psalm 20
Michael Perry
Music: Norman Warren

Andante

1 May   the Lord God   hear you pray,   may   God's strength be
2 May   God give you   all__ you need,   may   God make your
3 Now   we see the   Lord can save,   now   the trem-bling

yours to-day;   may   God bless you__   from a-bove,
plans suc-ceed;   may   God guide you__   all__ your days,
heart is__ brave;   now   we know that__   Love will hear:

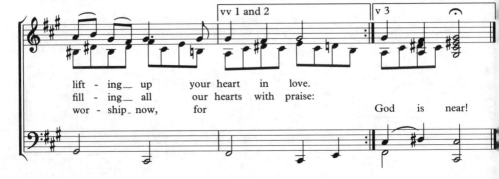

vv 1 and 2   v 3

lift-ing__ up   your heart in love.
fill-ing__ all   our hearts with praise:
wor-ship__ now,   for   God is near!

Alternative tune: Song 13, *Hymns for Today's Church* 235

With all your heart rejoice

St Austin 8 6 8 6 (CM)

Words: from Psalm 21
David Mowbray
Music: English traditional melody
arranged David Iliff

1 With all your heart re - joice, and sing to
2 A hap - py king who trusts in God, his
3 Yet who, ex - cept the Lord most high, may
4 The King of kings, the Christ of God, to

God the Lord of all! His mer - cy, like a
shin - ing crown se - cure! His face is bright, his
bear the e - ter - nal name, or reign in un - spoilt
whom all power is given! Rise, then, with spi - rit

moun - tain spring, brings life to great and small.
prayers are heard, his throne shall long en - dure.
ma - jes - ty a - bove our world - ly shame?
un - de - terred, and join the praise of heaven!

Alternative tune: St Fulbert, *Hymns for Today's Church* 168

22A(i)   Why, God, have you forsaken me

Attercliffe 8 8 8 8 (LM)

Words: from Psalm 22
Brian Foley
Music: Derek Williams

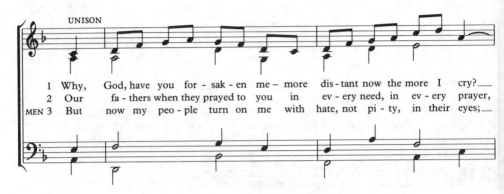

1 Why, God, have you for-sak-en me – more dis-tant now the more I cry?___
2 Our fa-thers when they prayed to you in ev-ery need, in ev-ery prayer,
MEN 3 But now my peo-ple turn on me with hate, not pi-ty, in their eyes;___

___ Must I, a-lone un-ans-wered, go like one un-loved, a-lone to die?
___ were heard by you and saved by you, and ne-ver doubt-ed that you care!
___ and all who see me, see in me no man, a worm that they des-pise!

WOMEN
4 Let God deliver him, they say;
his God would save him, was his claim!
They only wait to see me die;
they share my clothing in a game!

MEN
5 My hands and feet they bind to wound;
my bones they number, and each breath,
until with burning thirst I taste
the bitter agony of death!

WOMEN
6 My God, I trust you, trust you still –
be near, be near to hear my prayer!
I know that all who hope in you
are safe in death from death's despair.

ALL
7 Then I and all who live for you,
this day and till the end of days,
will tell of ever-answered prayer,
and pray this world's most thankful praise!

Why, God, have you forsaken me   22A(ii)

Ombersley 8 8 8 8 (LM)

Words: Brian Foley
Music: W H Gladstone (1840–1891)

1 Why, God, have you for - sa - ken me –
more dis - tant now the more I cry? Must I, a - lone un -
- ans - wered, go like one un - loved, a - lone to die?

2 Our fa - thers when they prayed_ to you
in ev - ery need, in ev - ery prayer, were heard by you and
saved_ by you, and ne - ver doubt - ed that you care!

MEN 3 But now my peo - ple turn__ on me
with hate, not pi - ty, in their eyes; and all who see me,
see__ in me no man, a worm that they des - pise!

WOMEN

4 Let God deliver him, they say;
his God would save him, was his claim!
They only wait to see me die;
they share my clothing in a game!

MEN

5 My hands and feet they bind to wound;
my bones they number, and each breath,
until with burning thirst I taste
the bitter agony of death!

WOMEN

6 My God, I trust you, trust you still –
be near, be near to hear my prayer!
I know that all who hope in you
are safe in death from death's despair.

ALL

7 Then I and all who live for you,
this day and till the end of days,
will tell of ever-answered prayer,
and pray this world's most thankful praise!

23A(i) The Lord my shepherd rules my life

Bedfordshire May-Day Carol 8 6 8 6 (CM)

Words: from Psalm 23
Christopher Idle
Music: English traditional melody
arranged Paul Edwards

1 The Lord my shepherd rules my life and gives me all I need; he leads me by refreshing streams, in pastures green I feed.

2 The Lord revives my failing strength, he makes my joy complete; and in right paths, for his name's sake, he guides my faltering feet.

3 Though in a valley dark as death, no evil makes me fear; your shepherd's staff protects my way, for you are with me there.

4 While all my enemies look on
you spread a royal feast;
you fill my cup, anoint my head,
and treat me as your guest.

5 Your goodness and your gracious love
pursue me all my days;
your house, O Lord, shall be my home –
your name, my endless praise.

6 To Father, Son and Spirit, praise!
to God, whom we adore,
be worship, glory, power and love,
both now and evermore!

The Lord my shepherd rules my life   23A(ii)

Brother James' Air   8 6 8 6 8 6

Words: from Psalm 23
Christopher Idle
Music: J L Macbeth Bain (c1840–1925)
arranged John Barnard

1 The Lord my shep - herd rules my life and_ gives me all I_ need;
2 The Lord re - vives my_ fail - ing strength, he_ makes my joy com - plete;
3 Though in a val - ley_ dark as death, no_ e - vil makes me_ fear;

he leads me by_ re - fresh-ing streams, in_ pas-tures green I_ feed;
and in right paths, for_ his name's sake, he_ guides my fal - tering feet;
your shep-herd's staff_ pro - tects my way, for_ you are with me_ there;

he leads me by re - fresh-ing streams, in pas-tures green I feed.
and in right paths, for his name's sake, he guides my fal-tering feet.
your shep-herd's staff pro - tects my way, for you are with me there.

4 While all my enemies look on
   you spread a royal feast;
   you fill my cup, anoint my head,
   and treat me as your guest;
      you fill my cup, anoint my head,
      and treat me as your guest.

5 Your goodness and your gracious love
   pursue me all my days;
   your house, O Lord, shall be my home –
   your name, my endless praise;
      your house, O Lord, shall be my home –
      your name, my endless praise.

6 To Father, Son and Spirit, praise!
   to God, whom we adore,
   be worship, glory, power and love,
   both now and evermore;
      be worship, glory, power and love,
      both now and evermore!

Alternative tune: Shoreham-by-Sea, *Songs from the Psalms* 23A

23B   O Lord my Shepherd, lead me

Willard   10 10 10 10

Words: from Psalm 23
Pearl Beasley
Music: Keith Landis
arranged Peter Cutts

1 O Lord my shep-herd, lead me in your ways
2 When deep-est dark-ness falls a-round my head,
3 You wel-come me to share the ho-ly feast,

  to cool-ing streams where I shall drink and live;
  I need not fear with you close by my side;
  you of-fer me for-give-ness and your love;

  to pas-tures green where I may spend my days
  and all a-long the sto-ny road I tread
  and with your good - ness all my days are blessed =

  in per-fect peace that on-ly you can give.
  you will be there to strength-en and to guide.
  un-til at last I reach your home a-bove.

Alternative tune: Eventide, *Hymns for Today's Church* 425

The Lord is my Shepherd

Words: Psalm 23
from *The Liturgical Psalter*
David Frost and others
Music: T A Walmisley (1814–1856)

1 The Lord ˈ is my ˈ shepherd:
therefore ˈ can I ˈ lack ˈ nothing.

2 He will make me lie down in ˈ green ˈ pastures:
and ˈ lead me · beˈside still ˈ waters.

3 He will reˈfresh my ˈ soul:
and guide me in right pathways ˈ for his ˈ name's ˈ sake.

4 Though I walk through the valley of the shadow of death
I will ˈ fear no ˈ evil:
for you are with me
your ˈ rod · and your ˈ staff ˈ comfort me.

5 You spread a table before me
in the face of ˈ those who ˈ trouble me:
you have anointed my head with oil ˈ and my ˈ cup · will be ˈ full.

6 Surely your goodness and loving-kindness will follow me *
all the ˈ days · of my ˈ life:
and I shall dwell in the ˈ house · of the ˈ Lord for ˈ ever.

Glory to the Father and ˈ to the ˈ Son:
and ˈ to the ˈ Holy ˈ Spirit;
as it was in the beˈginning · is ˈ now:
and shall be for ˈ ever. ˈ Aˈmen.

24A   Lift up your heads

Wootton 8 6 8 6 (CM)

Words: from Psalm 24
David Mowbray
Music: Paul Edwards

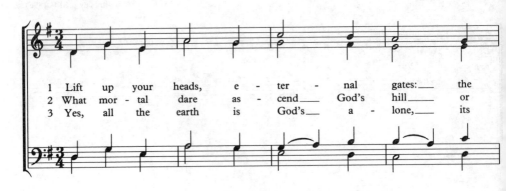

1 Lift up your heads, e - ter - nal gates:___ the
2 What mor - tal dare as - cend___ God's hill___ or
3 Yes, all the earth is God's___ a - lone,___ its

Lord___ our God___ draws near; the King of glo - ry
reach___ that ho - ly place? Not those who plan___ their
com - pass far___ and wide, and in that King___ up -

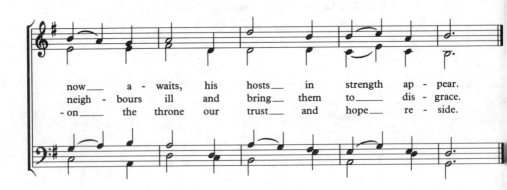

now___ a - waits, his hosts___ in strength ap - pear.
neigh - bours ill and bring___ them to___ dis - grace.
-on___ the throne our trust___ and hope___ re - side.

Alternative tune: Nativity, *Hymns for Today's Church* 206

Fling wide the gates

Crucifer   10 10 and refrain

Words: from Psalm 24
Michael Perry
Music: S H Nicholson (1875–1947)

Fling wide the gates, un - bar the an - cient doors; sa - lute your king___ in his___ tri - um - phant cause!

1 Now___ all the world___ be - longs to Christ our Lord: let___
2 Who___ has the right___ to___ wor - ship him to - day? All___
3 He___ comes to save___ all___ those who trust his name, and___
4 Who___ is the vic - tor___ glor - ious from the fight? He___

all___ cre - a - tion___ greet the liv - ing Word!
those___ who___ glad - ly___ serve him and o - bey.
will___ de - clare___ them___ free from guilt and shame.
is___ our___ king, our___ life, our Lord, our right!

Music: © Hymns Ancient & Modern Ltd,
St Mary's Works, St Mary's Plain, Norwich, Norfolk NR3 3BH

The earth is the Lord's

Words: Psalm 24
from *The Liturgical Psalter*
David Frost and others
Music: J Barnby (1838–1896)

1 The earth is the Lord's and ˈ all · that is ˈ in it:
   the compass of the ˈ world and ˈ those who ˈ dwell therein.

2 For he has founded it up ˈ on the ˈ seas:
   and esˈtablished it · upˈon the ˈ waters.

3 Who shall ascend the ˈ hill · of the ˈ Lord:
   or who shall ˈ stand · in his ˈ holy ˈ place?

4 He that has clean hands and a ˈ pure ˈ heart:
   who has not set his soul upon idols
   nor ˈ sworn his ˈ oath · to a ˈ lie.

5 He shall receive ˈ blessing · from the ˈ Lord:
   and recompense from the ˈ God of ˈ his salˈvation.

6 Of such a kind as this are ˈ those who ˈ seek him:
   those who seek your ˈ face O ˈ God of ˈ Jacob.

7 Lift up your heads O you gates
   and be lifted up you everˈlasting ˈ doors:
   and the King of ˈ glory ˈ shall come ˈ in.

8 Who is the ˈ King of ˈ glory?
   the Lord strong and mighty *
   the ˈ Lord ˈ mighty · in ˈ battle.

9 Lift up your heads O you gates
   and be lifted up you everˈlasting ˈ doors:
   and the King of ˈ glory ˈ shall come ˈ in.

10 Who is the ˈ King of ˈ glory?
   the Lord of hosts ˈ he · is the ˈ King of ˈ glory.

   Glory to the Father and ˈ to the ˈ Son:
   and ˈ to the ˈ Holy ˈ Spirit;
   as it was in the beˈginning · is ˈ now:
   and shall be for ˈ ever. ˈ Aˈmen.

All my soul to God I raise

St Petersburg 7 7 7 7 7 7

Words: from Psalm 25
Timothy Dudley-Smith
Music: D Bortnianski (1752–1825)

1 All my soul to God I raise: Be my guard-ian
2 Gra-cious-ly my sins for-give; Help me by your
3 Mer-cies ma-ni-fold ex-tend, Not as judge but
4 Shel-tered safe when trou-bles fret, Trust-ing God I

all my days. Con-fi-dent in hope I rest,
truth to live. In your foot-steps lead me, Lord,
faith-ful friend. O my Sav-iour, hear my prayer,
tri-umph yet! Un-dis-mayed in him I stand,

Dai-ly prove your path is best. Ev-er work in
Joy re-newed and hope re-stored, Know-ing ev-ery
Pluck my feet from ev-ery snare; Qui-et-ude be
Vic-tor on-ly by his hand. Wor-ship, hom-age,

me your will, Faith-ful to your pro-mise still.
sin for-given, Learn-ing all the ways of heaven.
mine at last, Rest from all my guil-ty past.
love and praise, All my soul, to God I raise.

Following the psalmist, this text is abecedarian.
Alternative tune: Ratisbon, *Hymns for Today's Church* 266

26   To lead a blameless life

Talbot Woods   8 6 8 6 (CM)

Words: from Psalm 26
Michael Perry
Music: Michael Dawney

UNISON

1 To lead a blame-less life, O Lord, to trust you with-out fear,
3 Let this be my su-preme de-sire, my ob-ject and my prayer,

to bring my hum-ble heart to you and know your love is near:
un-til I stand be-fore your throne to glo-ri-fy you there!

HARMONY

2 To walk be-fore you__ in the truth, to__ shun the e-vil ways,__

to come in-to your house to pray and__ shout a-loud your praise:

The Harmony version is not harmonically compatible with the Unison setting.

Alternative tune: St Peter, *Hymns for Today's Church* 211

God is my strong salvation

27A

Christus der ist mein Leben 7 6 7 6

Words: from Psalm 27
J Montgomery (1771–1854)
Music: M Vulpius (c1560–1616)
arranged David Iliff

1 God is my strong salvation — what
2 Though hosts encamp around me, firm
3 Place on the Lord reliance, my
4 His might my heart shall strengthen, his

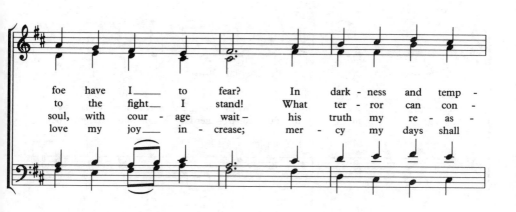

foe have I to fear? In darkness and tempta-
to the fight I stand! What terror can confound
soul, with courage wait — his truth my reassur-
love my joy increase; mercy my days shall length-

- ta - tion my light, my help is near:
- found me, with God at my right hand?
- sur - ance when faint and desolate:
length - en, the Lord will give me peace.

28(i)

O Lord, my rock

Somerset 8 6 8 8 6

Words: from Psalm 28
Michael Perry
Music: Somerset folk song
arranged David Iliff

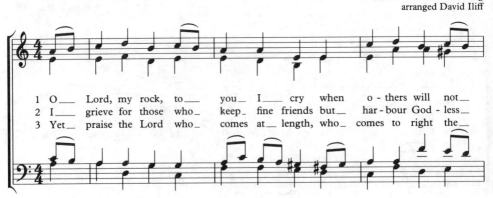

1 O__ Lord, my rock, to__ you__ I__ cry when o - thers will not__
2 I__ grieve for those who__ keep__ fine friends but__ har - bour God - less__
3 Yet__ praise the Lord who__ comes at__ length, who__ comes to right the__

hear;_____ to__ you I lift my__ hands on high– your__
schemes;_____ who__ use your works for__ worth - less ends, to__
wrong:_____ to__ you our shep - herd__ and our strength be__

arms are al - ways near, O Lord, your__ arms are al - ways__ near.
squan - der on their dreams, O Lord, to__ squan - der on their__ dreams.
praise in joy - ful song, O Lord, be__ praise in joy - ful__ song!

O Lord, my rock

St Bernard 8 6 8 6 (CM)

Words: from Psalm 28
Michael Perry
Music: *Tochter Zion* Cologne 1741

1 O Lord, my rock, to___ you I cry when
2 I grieve for those who___ keep fine friends but
3 Yet praise the Lord who___ comes at length, who

o - thers will not hear; to you I lift my
har - bour God - less schemes; who use your works for
comes to right the wrong: to you our shep - herd

hands on high — your arms are al - ways___ near.
worth - less ends, to squan - der on their___ dreams.
and our strength be praise in joy - ful___ song!

Alternative tune: Nicolaus, *Psalms for Today* 157A, *Hymns for Today's Church* 606

29A   Let all in heaven and earth unite

Luther   8 7 8 7 8 8 7

Words: from Psalm 29
Basil Bridge
Music: *Geistliche Lieder* Wittenberg 1535

1 Let all in heaven and earth unite in this, our joyful
     du - ty; to praise our God, the Lord of might, the source of truth and
     beau - ty; the rumb - ling thun - der's awe - some voice, the
     light-ning flash, both cry, 'Re - joice! Come, give him praise and glo - ry!'

2 God's voice is e - choed by the seas, in storms, their power un -
     - furl - ing, in winds that lash the ce - dar trees and set the de - sert
     swirl - ing; it stirs the might - y o - cean deep, the
     hills like star - tled cat - tle leap: come, give him praise and glo - ry!

Alternative tune: Palace Green, *Psalms for Today* 16A, *Hymns for Today's Church* 189

56

I worship you, O Lord

Bishop Tucker 6 6 6 6 6 6

Words: from Psalm 30
J E Seddon (1915–1983)
Music: Norman Warren

30A

1 I worship you, O Lord, for you have raised me up; I
cried to you for help, and you re-stored my life. You
brought me back from death and saved me from the grave.

WOMEN 2 Sing prais-es to the Lord, all those who know his name: for
while his wrath is brief, his fav-our knows no end. Though
tears may flow at night, the morn-ing brings new joy.

MEN 3 I said, 'I am so strong I ne-ver shall be moved!' But
you, Lord, shook my life my heart was in dis-tress. I
cried for you to help and plead-ed for your grace:

ALL 4 My mourn-ing you have turned to danc-ing and to joy; my
sad-ness you dis-pelled as glad-ness filled my soul. And
so I'll sing your praise, my God, through all my days!

31A   I come to you for shelter, Lord

Ye banks and braes   8 8 8 8 D (DLM)

Words: from Psalm 31
Basil Bridge
Music: Scottish traditional melody
arranged David Iliff

1 I come to you___ for shel - ter,
2 Your stead - fast love___ is my___ de -

Lord:___ de - liv - er me___ from ev - ery
-fence, my ha - ven from___ the strife___ of

snare. In you___ I find___ true li - ber -
tongues. You see___ my need,___ you hear___ my

-ty;___ I rest___ my spi - rit in___ your care. Your
cry,___ you turn my sor - rows in - to songs. May

lov - ing - kind - ness cheers my heart;___ you
all your peo - ple glad - ly come,___ and

know___ the hurts,___ the deep___ dis - tress! My
seek - ing, find___ you and___ a - dore: to

times___ are in___ your hand — I trust___ your
Fa - ther, Son___ and Spi - rit give___ all

ne - ver - fail - ing faith - ful - ness.
praise___ and glo - ry ev - er - more.

32A(i) How glad are those with peace of mind

Buttermere 8 8 8 8 (LM)

Words: from Psalm 32
David Mowbray
Music: John Barnard

UNISON

1 How glad are those with peace of mind, their past wrong-
(2 While ev - ery) wrong lay un - con - fessed, their spi - rits
(3 With your great) wis - dom, Lord, we pray, help us to

- do - ings left be - hind; their sins for - giv - en by the Lord – they stand, re -
knew no last - ing rest; but shed - ding tears of hon - es - ty they reached the
walk life's path to - day! How glad are those with peace of mind, their past wrong-

vv 1 and 2

- joic - ing in their God! 2 While ev - ery
place of heart - felt joy. 3 With your great

v 3

- do - ings left be - hind!

How glad are those with peace of mind 32A(ii)

Hawkhurst 8 8 8 8 (LM)

Words: from Psalm 32
David Mowbray
Music: H J Gauntlett (1805–1876)

1 How glad are those with peace of mind, their
2 While ev - ery wrong lay un - con - fessed, their
3 With your great wis - dom, Lord, we pray, help

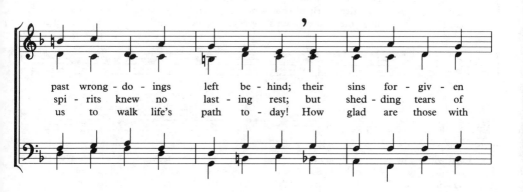

past wrong - do - ings left be - hind; their sins for - giv - en
spi - rits knew no last - ing rest; but shed - ding tears of
us to walk life's path to - day! How glad are those with

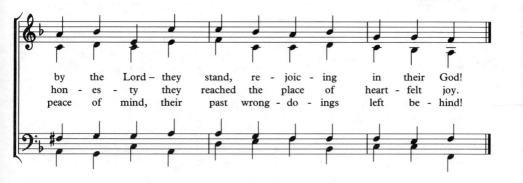

by the Lord – they stand, re - joic - ing in their God!
hon - es - ty they reached the place of heart - felt joy.
peace of mind, their past wrong - do - ings left be - hind!

Alternative tune: St Laurence, *Hymns for Today's Church* 133

33A Bring songs of joy to God

Words: from Psalm 33
Paul Wigmore
Music: Stephen Matthews

Lardergate 888888

1 Bring songs of joy to God the Lord who saves and keeps you by his word; bring all your skill to harp and lyre, delight the Lord with purest sound; let music high to heaven rebound, your praising hearts a joyful choir.

2 The Lord's own word is right and true, unfaithful deeds he will not do; his justice, righteousness and love flow freely from his gracious hand, enriching life till all the land reveals a holy treasure trove.

3 By merest breath he brought to birth the starlit skies about the earth; to him, the oceans vast and wild are in their raging little more than water gathered in a store or given to a thirsty child.

4 Come, fear the Lord! Hope in his love,
revere his word, his mercy prove;
then you will know his power to save,
to overrule the evil plan.
His watching eyes, since earth began,
care for the lives whose breath he gave.

5 With songs of joy to God the Lord
who saves and keeps us by his word
we bring our voices, harp and lyre,
whose music shall to heaven rebound.
We trust in God: in him is found
true love that sets our hearts on fire.

Alternative tune: Surrey, *Hymns for Today's Church* 117

Tell his praise

Alleluia 8 7 8 7 D

Words: from Psalm 34
Timothy Dudley-Smith
Music: S S Wesley (1810–1876)

34A

1 Tell his praise in song and sto - ry, bless the Lord with heart and voice:
2 To the Lord whose love has found them cry the poor in their dis - tress;
3 Taste and see! In faith draw near him, trust the Lord with all your powers;
4 In our need he walks be - side us, ears a - lert to ev - ery cry;

in my God is all my glo - ry, come be - fore him and re - joice.
swift his an - gels camped a - round them prove him sure to save and bless.
seek and serve him, love and fear him, life and all its joys are ours –
watch - ful eyes to guard and guide us, love that whis - pers, 'It is I.'

Join to praise his name to - ge - ther, he who hears his peo - ple's cry;
God it is who hears our cry - ing though the spark of faith be dim:
true de - light in ho - ly liv - ing, peace and plen - ty, length of days:
Good shall tri - umph, wrong be right - ed, God has pledged his pro - mised word;

tell his praise, come wind or wea - ther, shin - ing fa - ces lift - ed high.
taste and see! Be - yond de - ny - ing blessed are those who trust in him.
come, my child - ren, with thanks-giv - ing bless the Lord in songs of praise.
so with ran - somed saints u - ni - ted join to praise our liv - ing Lord.

Alternative tune: Wealdstone, *Hymns for Today's Church* 41

34B   I'll praise the Lord

Great Cheverell   10 10 7 8 10

Words: from Psalm 34
Paul Wigmore
Music: John Barnard

1 I'll praise the Lord for ev - er and
2 I sought the Lord, he an - swered my
3 O taste and see how gra - cious the
4 The Lord re - deems the faith - ful who

ev - er, my soul shall_ boast of his won - der - ful name:
call - ing, de - liv - ered_ me from my in - ner-most fears:
Lord___ is - se - cure are_ they who take re - fuge in him:
serve___ him, and those who_ trust him he ne - ver con-demns:

Glo - ri - fy the Lord with me; ex - alt his name, for great is he! I'll
great_ is___ he!

praise the Lord___ for___ ev - er and ev - er.

before verse 2

mp

before verse 3

p

before verse 4

f

after verse 4

ff   *molto rall.*

65

36   No fear of God

Sherington   8 6 8 8 6

Words: from Psalm 36
Christopher Idle
Music: Paul Edwards

1 No fear of God be-fore the eyes,＿ no pe-ni-tence with-
2 Your love, O Lord, shall ne-ver sleep,＿ nor shall your mer-cy
3 Be-neath the sha-dow of your wings＿ our re-fuge is most
4 Con-ti-nue, Lord, your love to me,＿ for you are all my

-in:＿ such is the one no long-er wise, whose
cease;＿ your truth is like the migh-ty deep, and
sure;＿ re-freshed by your re-viv-ing springs and
trust;＿ grant us the light we need, to see how

words are trea-che-ry and lies, who ne-ver grieves for sin.
like the rock-y moun-tain steep your stead-fast right-eous-ness.
all the joy your mer-cy brings our fu-ture is se-cure.
good you are, and still shall be to those you count as just.

Alternative tune: Binney's, *Hymns for Today's Church* 553

66

Commit your way to God

Summercourt 8 8 8 8 (LM)

Words: from Psalm 37
Michael Perry
Music: English traditional melody
arranged David Iliff

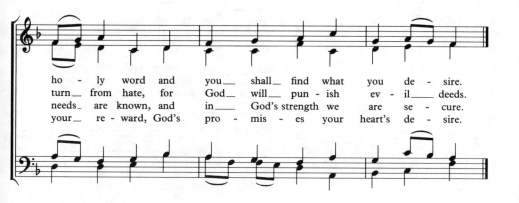

1 Com - mit your way to God the Lord – your
2 Be still be - fore the Lord and wait, and
3 Sal - va - tion comes from God a - lone – the
4 Com - mit your way to God the Lord, to

cause will shine as bright as fire; de - light to do God's
do not fret when wrong suc - ceeds; re - frain from an - ger,
faith - ful know their help is sure; to hea - ven all our
peace and truth and grace as - pire: then mer - cy shall be

ho - ly word and you shall find what you de - sire.
turn from hate, for God will pun - ish ev - il deeds.
needs are known, and in God's strength we are se - cure.
your re - ward, God's pro - mis - es your heart's de - sire.

Alternative tune: Wareham, *Hymns for Today's Church* 331

38 Lord, will you turn from your anger

Langleigh 11 10 11 10

Words: from Psalm 38
Mollie Knight
Music: Kenneth W Coates

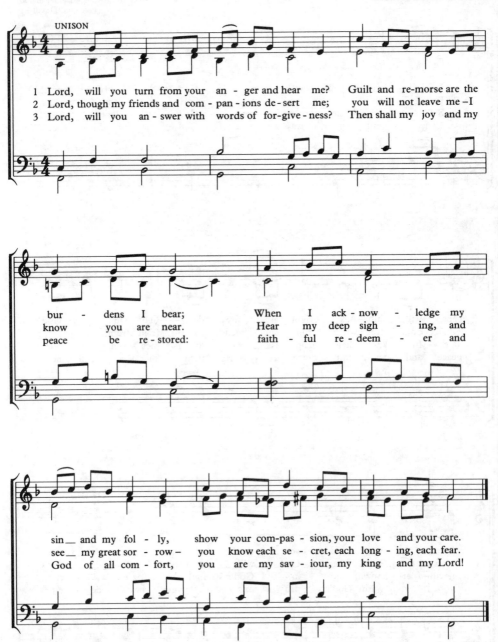

1 Lord, will you turn from your an - ger and hear me? Guilt and re-morse are the
2 Lord, though my friends and com - pan - ions de - sert me; you will not leave me – I
3 Lord, will you an - swer with words of for-give - ness? Then shall my joy and my

bur - dens I bear; When I ack - now - ledge my
know you are near. Hear my deep sigh - ing, and
peace be re - stored: faith - ful re - deem - er and

sin __ and my fol - ly, show your com-pas - sion, your love and your care.
see __ my great sor - row – you know each se - cret, each long - ing, each fear.
God of all com - fort, you are my sav - iour, my king and my Lord!

Alternative tune: O quanta qualia, *Hymns for Today's Church* 252

Joyous Peace 6 5 6 5 D

Words: from Psalm 39
David Mowbray
Music: Hu Te-ai
arranged John Barnard

1 Silent, I have waited, counting out my days; questions overwhelm me, set my heart ablaze. Measured by God's greatness human lives are small; wealth departs, and beauty like a flower will fall.

2 Suffering, leaden-weighted, drags my spirit low: God in heaven, have mercy, let your healing flow! All my hope I fasten on your strength-ening word = lift your hand in blessing, let my prayer be heard!

Alternative tune: North Coates, *Psalms for Today* 162B(ii), *Hymns for Today's Church* 384

40A

To the Lord I looked

Nannerch 8 7 8 7 8 7

Words: from Psalm 40
Paul Wigmore
Music: John Barnard

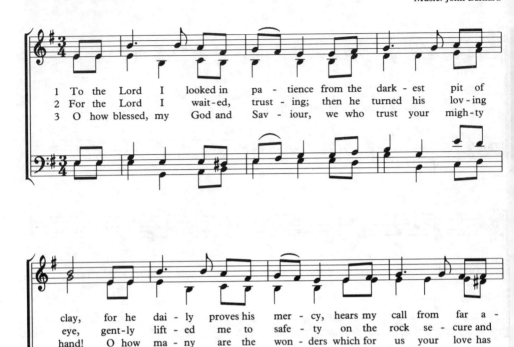

1 To the Lord I looked in pa – tience from the dark – est pit of
2 For the Lord I wait – ed, trust – ing; then he turned his lov – ing
3 O how blessed, my God and Sav – iour, we who trust your migh – ty

clay, for he dai – ly proves his mer – cy, hears my call from far a –
eye, gent – ly lift – ed me to safe – ty on the rock se – cure and
hand! O how ma – ny are the won – ders which for us your love has

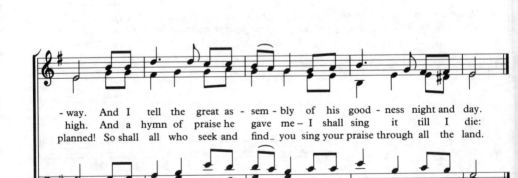

- way. And I tell the great as – sem – bly of his good – ness night and day.
high. And a hymn of praise he gave me – I shall sing it till I die:
planned! So shall all who seek and find_ you sing your praise through all the land.

Alternative tune: Mannheim, *Hymns for Today's Church* 525

Like the deer

Howerton 8 8 7 7

From Psalm 42
Words and music: Keith Landis
Music arranged David Iliff

42A

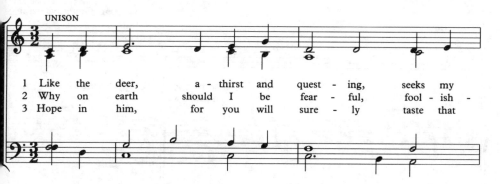

1 Like the deer, a - thirst and quest - ing, seeks my
2 Why on earth should I be fear - ful, fool - ish -
3 Hope in him, for you will sure - ly taste that

soul for God, un - rest - ing, wide a - wake or in my
- ly down - cast and tear - ful? In my Sav - iour I have
ri - ver flow - ing pure - ly, bright as crys - tal from his

dreams, long - ing for life - giv - ing streams.
found God who keeps me safe and sound.
throne, God for ev - er seen and known!

42B

O put your trust in God

Tamié Tone

Words: from Psalm 42
from *The Liturgical Psalter*
David Frost and others
Music: Tamié tone
arranged Anthony Greening

Music arrangement: © Anthony Greening

mf

O put your trust in God the liv - ing God:_____ God: I'll_____

D.C.

— I'll praise him yet,_____ my sav - iour and my God.

— praise him yet, my sav - iour and my God.

> O put your trust in God the living God:
> I'll praise him yet, my saviour and my God.

1 As a deer longs for the ׀ running ׀ brooks:
  so longs my soul for ׀ you O ׀ God.
  My soul is thirsty for God * thirsty for the ׀ living ׀ God:
  when shall I come and ׀ see his ׀ face?
     O put your trust . . .

2 My tears have been my food ׀ day and ׀ night:
  while they ask me all day long 'Where now ׀ is your ׀ God?'
  Why are you so full of ׀ heaviness · my ׀ soul:
  and why so un׀quiet with׀in me?
     O put your trust . . .

3 Surely the Lord will grant his loving mercy ׀ in the ׀ day-time:
  and in the night his song will be with me
  a prayer to the ׀ God · of my ׀ life.
  Why are you so full of ׀ heaviness · my ׀ soul:
  and why so un׀quiet with׀in me?
     O put your trust . . .

43A   O Light and Truth of God

Norwich 6 7 6 7 8 7

From Psalm 43
Words and music: Keith Landis
Music arranged Jeffrey Rickard

1 O___ Light and Truth of God, the world is dark a-round me; deep__ pit-falls, bat-tle-fields, and mor-tal foes_____ sur-round me: you are my Way as bright as day— all oth-er ways con-found me!

2 O___ high and ho-ly hill, O land of peace and rest-ing— God's love-ly dwel-ling place, the goal of all___ my quest-ing: in you I'll find a home as-signed, a man-sion for my guest-ing!

3 Be___ not cast down my soul, go to his al-tar sing-ing, with__ in-stru-ment__ and voice your gift of mu-sic bring-ing; e-ter-nal joy my lips' em-ploy with al-le-lu-ias ring-ing!

When my bitter foes surround

Carsaig 7 7 7 5

Words: from Psalm 43
Michael Perry
Music: G Thalben-Ball (1896–1987)

1 When my bit - ter foes___ sur - round,___ when their
2 When deep sor - rows o - ver - power,___ when life's
3 Then shall fer - vent prayers a - vail,___ then shall

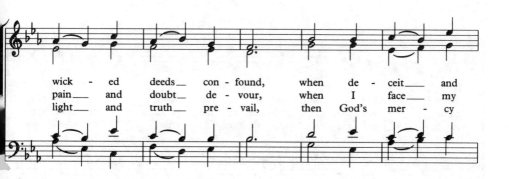

wick - ed deeds___ con - found, when de - ceit___ and
pain___ and doubt___ de - vour, when I face___ my
light___ and truth___ pre - vail, then God's mer - cy

lies___ a - bound, I___ will hope___ in God.___
dark - est hour,___ I___ will trust___ in God.___
will___ not fail: ___ I___ will praise___ my God.

Alternative tune: Capetown, *Psalms for Today* 124A(ii), *Hymns for Today's Church* 12

44 We have heard, O Lord our God

Great Glen 7 6 8 8 6

Words: from Psalm 44
Michael Perry
Music: Peter White

UNISON

1 We have heard, O Lord our God, the sto - ry of your
2 You are great, O Lord our God, we trust - ed in your
3 Yet to - day, O Lord our God, the weak – who once were

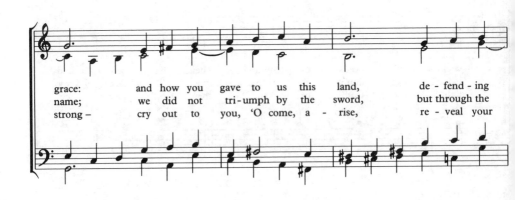

grace: and how you gave to us this land, de - fend - ing
name; we did not tri - umph by the sword, but through the
strong – cry out to you, 'O come, a - rise, re - veal your

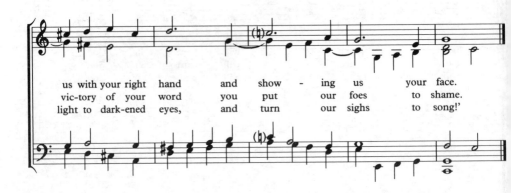

us with your right hand and show - ing us your face.
vic-tory of your word you put our foes to shame.
light to dark-ened eyes, and turn our sighs to song!'

Alternative tune: *Songs from the Psalms* 44

Let those with voices sing

Marlborough Gate 6 6 6 6 8 8

Words: from Psalm 45
David Mowbray
Music: Wayne Marshall

1 Let those with voi - ces__ sing,_____ as if in - spired to
2 With scep - tre in his__ hand_____ our king will__ reign in
3 A - noint - ed thus to__ serve,_____ and set a - part__ on
4 So let his pa - lace__ ring_____ with roy - al__ praise to -

write_____ the prais - es__ of__ our king, our heart__ and
peace;_____ no e - vil__ can__ with - stand his sword of
high,_____ our king yet__ stoops to love, to hear__ his
- day;_____ let sons and__ daugh - ters bring their gifts__ with -

soul's__ de - light:
right - eous - ness.   Be - fore his__ throne the
peo - ple's cry.
- out__ de - lay!

na - tions__ fall and throng to__ crown him Lord of all.

Alternative tune: Gopsal, *Psalms for Today* 47A, *Hymns for Today's Church* 180

46A God is our strength and refuge

Dam Busters March 7 7 7 5 7 7 11

Words: from Psalm 46
Richard Bewes
Music: E Coates (1886–1958)
arranged John Barnard

1 God is our strength and re-fuge, our pres-ent help in trou-ble;
and we there-fore will not fear, though the earth should change!
Though moun-tains shake and trem-ble, though swirl-ing floods are rag-ing,
God the Lord of hosts is with us ev-er-more!

The Harmony version is harmonically compatible with the Unison setting.

46B   God is our refuge and strength

Words: Psalm 46
from *The Liturgical Psalter*
David Frost and others
Music: Martin Luther (1483–1546)
Descant: S H Nicholson (1875–1947)

1 God is our ˈ refuge · and ˈ strength:
  a very ˈ present ˈ help in ˈ trouble.
2 Therefore we will not fear though the ˈ earth be ˈ moved:
  and though the mountains are ˈ shaken · in the ˈ midst · of the ˈ sea;

Second part
3 though the waters ˈ rage and ˈ foam:
  and though the mountains quake at the ˈ rising ˈ of the ˈ sea.

4 There is a river whose streams make glad the ˈ city · of ˈ God:
  the holy dwelling-place ˈ of the ˈ Most ˈ High.
5 God is in the midst of her
  therefore she shall ˈ not be ˈ moved:
  God will ˈ help her · and at ˈ break of ˈ day.

6 The nations make uproar and the ˈ kingdoms · are ˈ shaken:
  but God has lifted his ˈ voice · and the ˈ earth shall ˈ tremble.
7 The Lord of ˈ hosts is ˈ with us:
  the God of ˈ Jacob ˈ is our ˈ stronghold.

8 Come then and see what the ˈ Lord has ˈ done:
  what destruction he has ˈ brought upˈon the ˈ earth.
9 He makes wars to cease in ˈ all the ˈ world:
  he breaks the bow and shatters the spear
  and burns the ˈ chari·ots ˈ in the ˈ fire.

10 'Be still and know that ˈ I am ˈ God:
  I will be exalted among the nations
  I will be exˈalted · upˈon the ˈ earth.'
11 The Lord of ˈ hosts is ˈ with us:
  the God of ˈ Jacob ˈ is our ˈ stronghold.

  Glory to the Father and ˈ to the ˈ Son:
  and ˈ to the ˈ Holy ˈ Spirit;
  as it was in the beˈginning · is ˈ now:
  and shall be for ˈ ever. ˈ A·men.

Take heart and praise our God

47A

Gopsal 6 6 6 6 8 8

Words: from Psalm 47
David Mowbray
Music: melody and bass G F Handel (1685–1759)

1 Take heart and praise our God; re - joice and clap your
2 Take heart, but sing with fear, ex - alt his wor - thy
3 Take heart for fu - ture days, for tasks as yet un -
4 Take heart and trust in God the Fa - ther and the

hands – his power our foe sub - dued, his
name; with mind a - lert and clear now
- known – the God whose name we praise is
Son – God is our strength and shield, his

mer - cy ev - er stands:
ce - le - brate his fame: let trum - pets sound and
seat - ed on the throne:
Spi - rit guides us on:

peo - ple sing, the Lord through all the earth is king!

47B God is the king of all the earth

Words: from Psalm 47
from *The Liturgical Psalter*
David Frost and others
Music: John Barnard

1st time: CHOIR God is the king of all the earth – O
2nd time: ALL

praise him in a well-wrought psalm.

CHOIR 1 O

clap your hands, all you peo - ples, _ and cry a-loud to God with

shouts of joy:_ for the Lord Most High is to be feared — he is a great king

o - ver all___ the earth.

ALL God is the king of

all the earth — O praise him in a well-wrought psalm.

CHOIR 2 He cast down peo-ples un-der us,_ and the na - tions be -

-neath our feet; he chose us a land for our pos-ses - sion that was the pride of

Ja - cob whom — he loved. ALL God is the king of

all the earth – O praise him in a well-wrought psalm.

CHOIR 3 God has gone up — with the sound of re - joic - ing,

and the Lord_ to the blast of the horn: O sing prais - es, sing

prais-es to God;_ O sing prais - es, sing prais - es to_____ our

DESCANT 2nd time

King. ALL God is the king of all the earth – O

praise him in a well-wrought psalm.

Great is the Lord

48A

La Corbière 8 8 8 8 (LM)

Words: from Psalm 48
Christopher Idle
Music: Norman Warren

UNISON

1 Great is the Lord! His praise is great on Zi - on's
2 God is the Tower whose strength was shown when Sa - tan's
3 Our ears have heard, our eyes have seen what God the

mount, his ho - ly place; the roy - al ci - ty crowns the
ar - mies threat-ened harm; they gath - ered round, and looked, and
Lord of Hosts has done; with - in these walls we ce - le -

earth and shines on all with ra - diant grace.
ran like boats be - fore the driv - ing storm.
- brate his stead - fast love, his age - less throne.

4 God is the Judge whose mighty name
across the world with praise shall ring:
for his resplendent victories
let Zion shout and Judah sing!

5 God is the King whose kingdom's power
we see built up on every side;
we tell our children of our God
who will for ever be our Guide.

Alternative tune: Truro, *Hymns for Today's Church* 31

What riches on this earth

Golden Hill 6 6 8 6 (SM)

Words: from Psalm 49
Paul Wigmore
Music: *Kentucky Harmony* 1816
arranged David Iliff

49A

1 What rich - es___ on this earth___ can
2 What wis - dom___ in this life___ can
3 What rich - es___ come from God___ when
4 And wis - dom___ I shall know___ when

buy one___ hu - man breath?___ No wealth brings im - mor -
know the___ mind of God?___ No sage can___ tread the
his de - sire is mine;___ his will un - locks a
he re - deems my soul;___ for at his___ throne the

-ta - li - ty, no trea - sure___ hin - ders___ death.___
paths of___ thought where our Cre - a - tor___ trod.___
trea - su - ry, his love re - veals___ a___ shrine!___
mor - tal___ mind is sanc - ti - fied___ and___ whole.___

Alternative tune: Franconia, *Hymns for Today's Church* 110

49B
O people, listen

Wharfdale 11 10 11 10

Words: from Psalm 49
Michael Perry
Music: Norman Warren

Gently flowing

1 O   peo - ple, lis - ten – hear God's wis - dom   cry - ing!_____ Al -
2 For   God will take the ho - ly   in - to   hea - ven,_____ by
3 To   Fa - ther, Son and Spi - rit be the   glo - ry!_____ Come,

- though the dark-ness comes to rich and poor,___ and no - thing mor-tal can sur - vive our
grace re-deem the faith-ful from the grave;___ we leave be - hind us all this world has
wor - ship and a - dore the ho - ly Name;___ let wis - dom think up-on our hu - man

dy - ing,_____ yet in the morn-ing jus - tice shall en - dure:
giv - en,_____ and trust God's migh - ty power to love and save!
sto - ry,_____ and faith our ev - er - liv - ing God pro-claim.

Alternative tune: Highwood, *Psalms for Today* 138A, *Hymns for Today's Church* 422

Let God, who called the worlds to be

50A

A babe is born 8 8 8 8 (LM)

Words: from Psalm 50
David Mowbray
Music: English traditional melody
arranged David Iliff

1 Let God, who called the worlds to be, a-rise in all-con-sum-ing fire to judge the peo-ple right-eous-ly, and faith-less ones with awe in-spire.

2 This God is ours, and yet we break the co-ve-nant made long a-go; God's words we fool-ish-ly for-sake, God's ways we have re-fused to know.

3 For though our lips have preached God's law, our err-ing hearts have scorned the Name; we choose the thief and slan-der-er as friends, and so in-crease our shame.

4 What then shall God the Lord de-mand? Not gifts or lav-ish of-fer-ing, but vows and pro-mis-es per-formed, and lives from which true prais-es spring!

Alternative tune: Solothurn, *Psalms for Today* 3A, *Hymns for Today's Church* 276

God speaks – the Lord of all the earth

Christmas Eve 8 6 8 6 D (DCM)

Words: from Psalm 50
Michael Perry
Music: English traditional melody
arranged David Iliff

1 God speaks – the Lord of___ all the earth, and calls the world to hear:
2 'Yet___ hon - our me, ful - fil your vow, in truth pre-pare the road –

what glo - ry shines, what light springs forth, to draw the peo - ple near!
so___ to the faith - ful___ I will show the sav - ing grace of God.'

Says God, the right - eous one, the___ wise, 'Your wor-ship I de - cline;
Then lift your hearts and___ voi - ces___ high to___ Fa - ther and to Son

I have no need of___ sa - cri-fice for all the___ world is mine.'
and Spi - rit – Three in___ ma - jes-ty, our God for___ ev - er One!

God, be merciful to me

Aberystwyth 7 7 7 7 D

Words: from Psalm 51
adapted from *The Psalter* 1912
in this version Word & Music
Music: J Parry (1841–1903)

51A

1 God, be merciful to me,
let your love my refuge be;
my offences wash away,
cleanse me from my sin today.
My transgressions I confess,
grief and guilt my soul oppress;
I have sinned against your grace
and provoked you to your face.

2 Wash me, wash me pure within,
cleanse, O cleanse me from my sin:
in your righteousness I trust,
in your judgements you are just.
Come, salvation to impart,
teach your wisdom to my heart;
make me pure, your grace bestow,
that your mercy I may know.

3 Gracious God, my heart renew,
make my spirit right and true;
from my sins O hide your face,
blot them out in boundless grace.
Cast your servant not away,
let your Spirit with me stay;
make me joyful, willing, strong,
teach me your salvation's song!

51B

Have mercy on me O God

Words: from Psalm 51
from *The Liturgical Psalter*
David Frost and others
Music: David Iliff

Have mercy on me O God in your en┃during ┃ goodness:
according to the fulness of your compassion * ┃
blot out ┃ my of┃fences.
Wash me thoroughly ┃ from my ┃ wickedness:
and ┃ cleanse me ┃ from my ┃ sin.

For I acknowledge ┃ my re┃bellion:
and my ┃ sin is ┃ ever · be┃fore me.
Against you only have I sinned *
and done what is evil ┃ in your ┃ eyes:
so you will be just in your sentence
and ┃ blameless ┃ in your ┃ judging.

Purge me with hyssop and I ┃ shall be ┃ clean:
wash me and I ┃ shall be ┃ whiter · than ┃ snow.
Create in me a clean ┃ heart O ┃ God:
and re┃new a · right ┃ spirit · with┃in me.

Do not cast me ┃ out · from your ┃ presence:
do not take your ┃ holy ┃ spirit ┃ from me.
O give me the gladness of your ┃ help a┃gain:
and sup┃port me · with a ┃ willing ┃ spirit.

You take no pleasure in sacrifice or ┃ I would ┃ give it:
burnt ┃ offerings · you ┃ do not ┃ want.
The sacrifice of God is a ┃ broken ┃ spirit:
a broken and contrite heart O God ┃ you will ┃ not de┃spise.

Glory to the Father and ┃ to the ┃ Son:
and ┃ to the ┃ Holy ┃ Spirit;
as it was in the be┃ginning · is ┃ now:
and shall be for ┃ ever. ┃ A┃men.

Why in the dawning

52

Flanders 10 10 10 10

Words: from Psalm 52
Paul Wigmore
Music: David Iliff

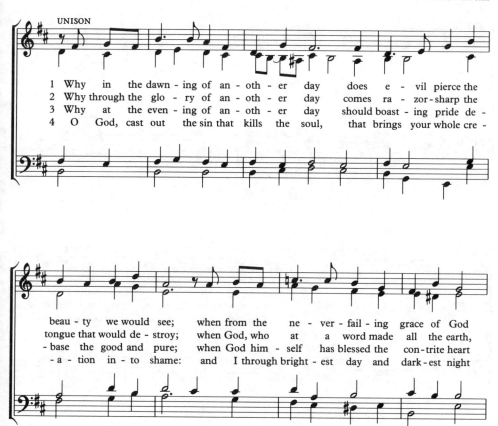

UNISON

1 Why in the dawn - ing of an - oth - er day does e - vil pierce the
2 Why through the glo - ry of an - oth - er day comes ra - zor-sharp the
3 Why at the even - ing of an - oth - er day should boast - ing pride de -
4 O God, cast out the sin that kills the soul, that brings your whole cre -

beau - ty we would see; when from the ne - ver - fail - ing grace of God
tongue that would de - stroy; when God, who at a word made all the earth,
- base the good and pure; when God him - self has blessed the con - trite heart
- a - tion in - to shame: and I through bright - est day and dark - est night

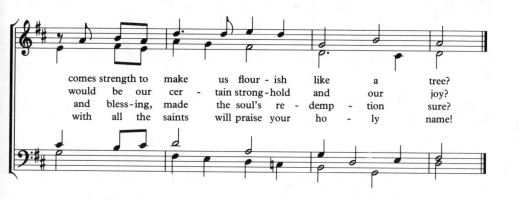

comes strength to make us flour - ish like a tree?
would be our cer - tain strong-hold and our joy?
and bless - ing, made the soul's re - demp - tion sure?
with all the saints will praise your ho - ly name!

Alternative tune: Farley Castle, *Hymns for Today's Church* 361

53

Only the fool will say

Astwood 10 10 10 10

Words: from Psalm 53
Michael Perry
Music: Paul Edwards

1 On - ly the fool will say 'There is no God'; on - ly the one whose
2 On - ly from Zi - on shall sal - va - tion come; on - ly in God we

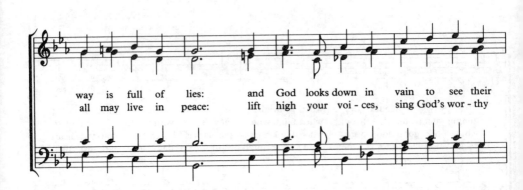

way is full of lies: and God looks down in vain to see their
all may live in peace: lift high your voi - ces, sing God's wor - thy

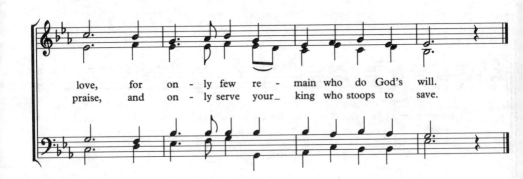

love, for on - ly few re - main who do God's will.
praise, and on - ly serve your king who stoops to save.

Alternative tune: *Songs from the Psalms* 53

Save me, O God, hear my prayer 54(i)

Heather 7 7 7 7

Words: from Psalm 54
Michael Perry
Music: Norman Warren

1 Save me, O God, hear my prayer, o - pen your
2 Yet shall the Lord be my help – strong is the

ears to my cry; keep me when e - vils pre -
one who sus - tains; offer - ings of love I will

- vail, strength - en my hand from on high.
bring God who e - tern - al - ly reigns!

54(ii) Save me, O God, hear my prayer

Knightwood 7 7 7 7

Words: from Psalm 54
Michael Perry
Music: Hugh Benham

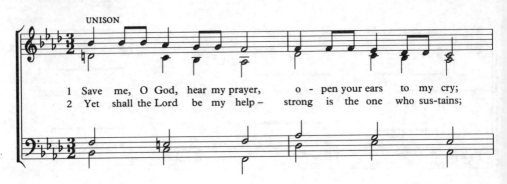

1 Save me, O God, hear my prayer, o - pen your ears to my cry;
2 Yet shall the Lord be my help – strong is the one who sus-tains;

keep me when e - vils pre-vail, strength-en my hand from on high.
offer - ings of love I will bring God who e - ter - nal - ly reigns!

O for the wings to fly afar

Shepherd Boy's Song 8 6 8 6 (CM)

Words: from Psalm 55
David Mowbray
Music: J H Alden (1900–1976)

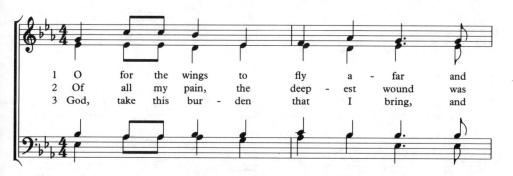

1 O for the wings to fly a - far and
2 Of all my pain, the deep - est wound was
3 God, take this bur - den that I bring, and

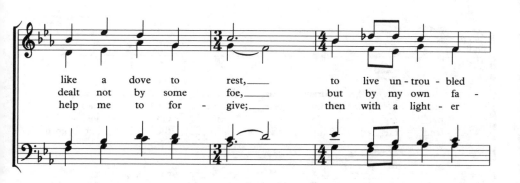

like a dove to rest,___ to live un - trou - bled
dealt not by some foe,___ but by my own fa -
help me to for - give;___ then with a light - er

by the care which_ brings us to___ the___ test.
- mi - liar friend with_ whom I loved_ to___ go.
heart, I'll sing and_ to your glo - ry___ live!

Alternative tune: Metzler, *Hymns for Today's Church* 178

56A Be merciful to me, O God

Bangor 8 6 8 6 (CM)

Words: from Psalm 56
Paul Wigmore
Music: W Tans'ur's *Harmony of Syon* 1734

1 Be mer - ci - ful____ to me, O____ God – for those_ who_ harm draw near; they_ turn my words of____ good_ in - tent, they_ fill my___ day with fear.

2 I fear the hurt - ful word of____ scorn, I dread_ the_ mock - ing gaze, the_ deed that comes of____ cru - el - ty, the_ hat - red___ it be - trays.

3 But when I am____ a - fraid, O____ God, I'll put_ my_ trust in you: if____ God im - mor - tal____ strength - ens_ me, what_ harm can_ mor - tals do?

4 My tears are gone = now lead me, Lord, de - fend_ me_ in the strife: for____ then in your great_ strength I'll_ walk led____ by the_ Light of Life.

Be gracious to me, Lord

Boundless love 6 6 8 6 (SM)

Words: from Psalm 57
Michael Perry
Music: Norman Warren
arranged John Barnard

1 Be gra - cious to me, Lord,____ and
2 Though snares are set for me,____ yet
3 My soul, a - wake and sing,____ God's

hold my spi - rit fast,____ that I may shel - ter
will I sleep in peace,____ for I have asked the
bound - less love re - call;____ ex - alt God's name a -

by your side un - til the storm is____ past.
care of God whose love shall ne - ver____ cease.
- bove the skies, God's glo - ry o - ver____ all!

Alternative tune: Holyrood, *Hymns for Today's Church* 497

60   We are a land divided

Potterne 7 6 7 6 D

Words: from Psalm 60
Michael Perry
Music: John Barnard

UNISON

1 We are a land di - vid - ed, un - wor-thy of you,
2 Our God is strong to— save us and— tread the e - vil

Lord, and yet by_ your great mer - cy our_ peace can_ be re -
down, to raise the cause of jus - tice and_ gain the_ vic-tor's

- stored. Though we in - vite your an - ger and fail to do your
crown. Sing glo - ry— to the_ Fa - ther, bring wor-ship to the

will, yet if we_ turn and fear you your love can_ tri-umph still.
Son, a - dore the_ Ho - ly Spi - rit: praise God the Three-in - One!

Alternative tune: Aurelia, *Hymns for Today's Church* 501

Listen to my prayer, Lord

Listening 6 5 6 5

Words: from Psalm 61
J E Seddon (1915–1983)
Music: Norman Warren

1 Lis - ten to my prayer,— Lord,— hear my hum - ble
2 In earth's far - thest cor - ner— you will hear my
MEN 3 You have been my shel - ter— when the foe was

cry:— when my heart is faint - ing,—
voice:— set me on your rock,— Lord,—
near,— as a tower of re - fuge—

vv 1-5 / v 6

to your throne I fly.—
then I shall re - joice.— be my songs of praise!
shield - ing me from fear.—

WOMEN
4 I will rest for ever
in your care and love,
guarded and protected
as by wings above.

ALL
5 All that I have promised,
help me to fulfil;
and in all who love you
work your perfect will.

6 May your truth and mercy
keep me all my days;
let my words and actions
be my songs of praise!

Alternative tune: Caswall, *Hymns for Today's Church* 126 or *Songs from the Psalms* 61A

61B(i)
O God, hear me calling

Love's Gift   11 11 11 11

Words: from Psalm 61
Paul Wigmore
Music: English traditional melody
arranged David Iliff

1 O God, hear me calling and answer, I pray!
No distance can silence the words that I say,
no mountain, no ocean can hinder my prayer
when deep is my sorrow and dark my despair.

2 When trouble comes near me and enemies taunt,
Lord, you are the fortress no evil can daunt;
and safe on the rock that is higher than I
your strength is my hope as you answer my cry.

3 For Lord you have heard all the vows I have made =
my thoughts and intentions when homage I paid;
with all who have lived by the fear of your name,
Lord, grant all my prayers as your praise I proclaim.

4 I long for the day when your dwelling is mine,
your wings for a shelter, your presence a shrine;
I praise you on earth for your mercy and grace:
what blessings I'll sing when I look on your face!

O God, hear me calling

Stowey 11 11 11 11

Words: from Psalm 61
Paul Wigmore
Music: English traditional melody
arranged Norman Warren

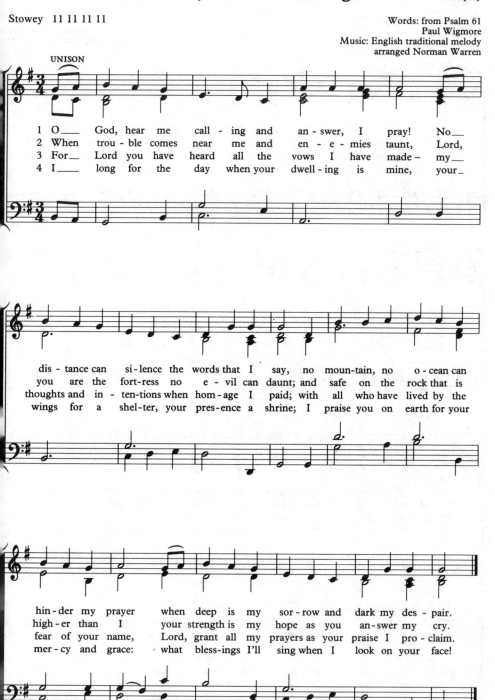

UNISON

1 O___ God, hear me call - ing and an - swer, I pray! No___
2 When trou - ble comes near me and en - e - mies taunt, Lord,
3 For___ Lord you have heard all the vows I have made – my___
4 I___ long for the day when your dwell - ing is mine, your_

dis - tance can si - lence the words that I say, no moun-tain, no o - cean can
you are the fort - ress no e - vil can daunt; and safe on the rock that is
thoughts and in - ten-tions when hom - age I paid; with all who have lived by the
wings for a shel - ter, your pres-ence a shrine; I praise you on earth for your

hin - der my prayer when deep is my sor - row and dark my des - pair.
high - er than I your strength is my hope as you an - swer my cry.
fear of your name, Lord, grant all my prayers as your praise I pro - claim.
mer - cy and grace: what bless-ings I'll sing when I look on your face!

62A

Rest in God

Michael 8 7 8 7 3 3 7

Words: from Psalm 62
David Mowbray
Music: Herbert Howells (1892–1983)

UNISON

1 Rest in God, our God _ most migh - ty _ thanks and praise to
2 Trust no more in doubt-ful _ rich - es, part with those who
3 In the past the Lord has _ spo - ken through his pro-phets
4 Glo - ry be to God _ the _ Fa - ther, glo - ry be to

him _ be-long; from the Lord comes our sal - va - tion,
work _ de-ceit: God him - self is our re - ward - er,
and _ the law, shin - ing lan - tern for our jour - ney,
God _ the Son, glo - ry be to God the Spi - rit _

he re - mains our strength and song. Si - lent - ly
throned up - on his judge - ment seat. Mer - cy waits
where no path was known be - fore. Hope a - gain!
ev - er Three and ev - er One. Trust God still,

none but _ he waits, our rock _ and shield _ to be.
at his _ gates for each one _ who false - hood hates.
Fears are _ vain – God's re - new - ing power _ is plain.
do his _ will; hold to him through good _ and ill!

My soul is at rest in God

From Psalm 62
Taizé
Words and music: Jacques Berthier

62B

The accompaniment is suitable for the Verses as well as the Refrain.
The Refrain may be sung before and after each verse
or additionally as an accompaniment to each verse.

Words and music: © 1982, 1983 and 1984 Les Presses de Taizé (France)
Published by Wm Collins Sons & Co Ltd
(USA) GIA Publications,
7404 South Mason Avenue, Chicago, Illinois 60638

63A

God is my great desire

Leoni 6 6 8 4 D

Words: from Psalm 63
Timothy Dudley-Smith
Music: from a synagogue melody for the Yigdal (doxology)
transcribed M Lyon (1751–1797)
adapted T Olivers (1725–1799)

1 God is my great de - sire, his face I seek the first; to
2 God is my true de - light, my rich - est feast his praise, through
3 God is my strong de - fence in ev - ery e - vil hour; in

him my heart and soul a - spire, for him I thirst. As
si - lent watch - es of the night, through all my days. To
him I face with con - fi - dence the temp - ter's power. I

one in de - sert lands, whose ve - ry flesh is flame, in
him my spi - rit clings, on him my soul is cast; be -
trust his mer - cy sure, with truth and tri - umph crowned: my

burn - ing love I lift my hands and bless his name.
- neath the sha - dow of his wings he holds me fast.
hope and joy for ev - er - more in him are found.

106

O God, you are my God

63B

Temple Guiting 6 6 10 5

Words: from Psalm 63
Paul Wigmore
Music: John Barnard

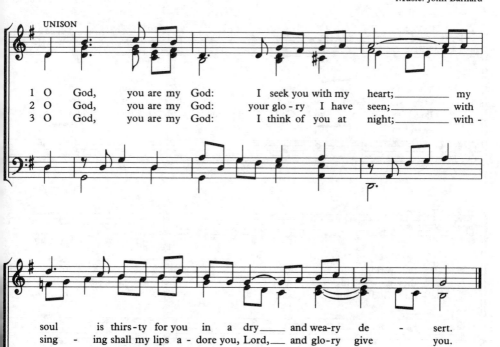

1 O God, you are my God: I seek you with my heart;_____ my
2 O God, you are my God: your glo - ry I have seen;_____ with
3 O God, you are my God: I think of you at night;_____ with -

soul is thirs-ty for you in a dry_____ and wea-ry de - sert.
sing - ing shall my lips a - dore you, Lord,_____ and glo-ry give you.
- in the sha-dow of your wings I stay,_____ and you de - fend me.

4   O God, you are my God:
    the victory is yours;
    all evil by your justice overthrown
      in holy anger.

5   As long as I shall live
    my lips will sing your praise;
    my hungry soul will feast upon your love,
      and glorify you.

65A God whose praise is sung in Zion

Bennelong 878787

Words: from Psalm 65
David Mowbray
Music: Robert Boughen

UNISON

1 God whose praise is sung in Zi - on, Lord who calls the worlds to be; ma - ker of the moun-tain ran - ges, mas - ter of the roar - ing sea: we, with saints of ev - ery na - tion, sing your praise, who sets us free.

2 Vi - sit, Lord, the earth to bless it, pros - per all the grow - ing corn; let the val - leys fill with laugh - ter and the lambs be safe - ly born; farm-er's year with good - ness, till the days of plen-ty dawn;

3 Glo - ry be to God the Fa - ther, glo - ry be to God the Son, Glo - ry be to God the Spi - rit, ev - er Three and ev - er One! Earth's cre - a - tor, Lord, life - giv - er, let your work through us be done!

Alternative tune: Rhuddlan, *Hymns for Today's Church* 195

108

You are to be praised O God

65B

Words: from Psalm 65
from *The Liturgical Psalter*
David Frost and others
Music: G M Garrett (1834–1897)

You are to be praised O ˈ God in ˈ Zion:
to you shall vows be paid ˈ you that ˈ answer ˈ prayer.
Those who dwell at the ends of the earth are aˈfraid at · your ˈ wonders:
the dawn and the ˈ evening ˈ sing your ˈ praises.

You tend the ˈ earth and ˈ water it:
you ˈ make it ˈ rich and ˈ fertile.
You crown the ˈ year · with your ˈ goodness:
and the tracks where you have ˈ passed ˈ drip with ˈ fatness.

The pastures of the ˈ wilderness · run ˈ over:
and the ˈ hills are ˈ girded · with ˈ joy.
The meadows are ˈ clothed with ˈ sheep:
**and the valleys stand so thick with corn
they ˈ shout for ˈ joy and ˈ sing.**

**Glory to the Father and ˈ to the ˈ Son:
and ˈ to the ˈ Holy ˈ Spirit;
as it was in the beˈginning · is ˈ now:
and shall be for ˈ ever. ˈ Aˈmen.**

66A Praise our God with shouts of joy

Harts 7 7 7 7

Words: from Psalm 66
Christopher Idle
Music: B Milgrove (1731–1810)

1 Praise our God with shouts of joy, sing the glo - ry of his name; join to lift his prais - es high, through the world his love pro - claim.

2 Come and see what God has done by the power of his right hand; see the bat - tles he has won by his word of swift com - mand.

3 God has tamed the rag - ing seas, carved a high - way through the tide, paid the cost of our re - lease, come him - self to be our guide.

4 God has put us to the test,
  bringing us through flood and fire
  into freedom, peace, and rest,
  for our good is his desire.

5 He has not despised my prayer
  nor kept back his love from me;
  he has raised me from despair –
  to our God all glory be!

Mercy, blessing, favour, grace

Urchfont 7 7 7 7

Words: from Psalm 67, *Deus misereatur*
Timothy Dudley-Smith
Music: John Barnard

UNISON

1 Mer - cy, bless - ing, fa - vour, grace,   sav - ing power to us be shown;
2 Shout in tri - umph, sing in praise! Peo - ples all, pro - claim his worth:
3 Har - vests year by year pro - claim bless - ings new in plen - ty poured;

bright - ness of the Fa - ther's face to the na - tions now be known.
just and right - eous are his ways, sov - ereign Lord of all the earth.
all the earth shall fear his name, all his peo - ple praise the Lord.

Alternative tune: Savannah, *Hymns for Today's Church* 150

67B   May God be gracious

Universa Laus   10 10 10 10

Words: from Psalm 67, Deus misereatur
Stephen Horsfall
Music: Anthony Greening

1 May God be gracious, may we see his face;
2 He holds our future safe within his hand;

through-out the wide world may his power be known. May all the
he judges rightly and he guides our ways. Earth yields its

nations trust his saving grace, and come to worship,
increase — God will bless our land: may all his people,

and come to worship him before his throne.
may all his people give him thanks and praise!

Original key: D♭

Alternative tunes: Ellers, *Hymns for Today's Church* 281, St Agnes, *Hymns for Today's Church* 406

Let God be gracious to us

67C

Words: Psalm 67, *Deus misereatur*
from *The Liturgical Psalter*
David Frost and others
Music: J Nares (1715–1783)

1 Let God be gracious to ' us and ' bless us:
and make his ' face ' shine up'on us,
2 that your ways may be ' known on ' earth:
your liberating ' power · a'mong all ' nations.

3 Let the peoples ' praise you · O ' God:
let ' all the ' peoples ' praise you.
4 Let the nations be ' glad and ' sing:
for you judge the peoples with integrity
and govern the ' nations · up'on ' earth.

5 Let the peoples ' praise you · O ' God:
let ' all the ' peoples ' praise you.
6 Then the earth will ' yield its ' fruitfulness:
and ' God our ' God will ' bless us.

Second part
7 God ' shall ' bless us:
and all the ' ends · of the ' earth will ' fear him.

Glory to the Father and ' to the ' Son:
and ' to the ' Holy ' Spirit;
as it was in the be'ginning · is ' now:
and shall be for ' ever. ' A'men.

DESCANT for verse 7

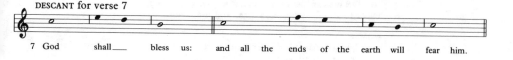

7 God   shall___   bless   us: and   all   the   ends   of   the   earth   will   fear   him.

Words: From *The Psalms: A New Translation for Worship*
© English text 1976, 1977 David L Frost, John A Emerton,
Andrew A Macintosh, all rights reserved
© pointing 1976, 1977 Wm Collins Sons & Co Ltd,
8 Grafton Street, London W1X 3LA

68A

Let God arise

Song 46   10 10

Words: from Psalm 68
Christopher Idle
Music: Orlando Gibbons (1583–1625)

ALL 1 Let God a - rise!___ his e - ne - mies be gone
WOMEN 2 Make known the Lord,___ and sound his name a - loud
MEN 3 Fa - ther and judge,___ he gave the world his law

and melt like wax be - fore the ho - ly One.
to praise the king who rides up - on the cloud.
with free - dom, love and jus - tice for the poor.

WOMEN
4 God marched ahead, strong shepherd of his flock;
the heavens opened; earth in terror shook.

MEN
5 God spoke the word, and faithful was the band
of those who took his truth to every land.

ALL
6 See God ascend, with captives as his prize,
and gifts for all who shall in him arise.

WOMEN
7 Bless day by day the living God who saves,
who raises up his people from their graves.

MEN
8 Draw near his throne: musicians lead our song!
all nations, tribes, and races join the throng.

WOMEN
9 All strength is his! the rebels reign no more;
he scatters all who take delight in war.

MEN
10 God rules on high, and mighty is his voice:
to God be praise; in God we shall rejoice.

ALL
11 Glory to God, creator, saviour, friend
whose greatness, love, and wisdom never end.

Verses with italicized numbers may be omitted.

When the waters cover me

Salvum me 7 4 7 7 7 4

Words: from Psalm 69
Michael Perry
Music: David Llewellyn Green

69A

1 When the waters cover me, save me, O
2 You know all my guilty fears, thank you, O

God; when I look and cannot see,
God, you have heard with open ears,

when I seek what cannot be, when my
you have seen my contrite tears, you will

friends abandon me, save me, O God.
bless me all the years, thank you, O God.

May be sung a tone higher in G minor when performed by choir alone.

Come quickly, Lord

Splendour 8 8 8 8 (LM)

Words: from Psalm 70
Bert Polman
Music: M Praetorius (1571–1621)
adapted from *Piae Cantiones* 1582
arranged David Iliff

1 Come quick - ly, Lord, to res - cue me, and has - ten to my help, I pray. May all who seek to take my life be put to shame with - out de - lay.

2 May all who seek your name re - joice, your praise in gra - ti - tude re - cord. May those who love your sav - ing power say ev - er - more, 'Ex - alt the Lord!'

3 Yet I am poor and need - y, Lord: be quick to hear my ur - gent plea. You are my help, my Sav - iour God! Do not de - lay; re - mem - ber me.

Music arrangement: © David Iliff/Jubilate Hymns †

Words: © 1987 CRC Publications,
2850 Kalamazoo SE, Grand Rapids, Michigan 49560, USA

From time beyond my memory

Passons 8 8 8 8 (LM)

Words: from Psalm 71
Michael Perry
Music: Keith Landis
arranged Jack Noble White

UNISON

1 From time be - yond my me - mo - ry your
2 But when the years are pass - ing by as
3 We praise you, God, the ho - ly One, pro -
4 Sing glo - ry to the Fa - ther, Son — and

love has been my rock, O Lord; since child-hood days I
friends de - part and spi - rits fail: O God, come quick - ly
- claim your love from day to day; ex - alt your tri - umphs
to the Spi - rit glo - ry be; let psalms to God on

trust - ed you, and in my youth de - clared your word.
to my side, that in your strength I may pre - vail.
to the skies and trust your mer - cy, come what may:
earth be - gun re - sound through all e - ter - ni - ty!

Alternative tunes: Eisenach, *Hymns for Today's Church* 64, O Tannenbaum, *Songs from the Psalms* 71A

72   To those who rule our land

Maiden Way   6 6 8 8 6

Words: from Psalm 72
Michael Perry
Music: E Routley (1917–1982)

UNISON

1 To those who rule our land, give jus-tice, love and truth; so help them to de-fend the poor, to keep us safe, to guard the law, and pros-per at your

hand: 2 Let mer - cy all their days fall

as re - fresh - ing showers; so guide the peo - ple with your light that

we may flour - ish in your sight, and earth be filled with praise!

Surely God the Lord is good

Calon Lân 7 7 7 7 D

Words: from Psalm 73
Michael Perry
Music: J Hughes (1873–1932)
arranged John Barnard

1 Sure-ly God the Lord is good,— guid-ing all whose hearts are pure;— at God's hands we take our food,— in God's love we are se-cure:— vain-ly do the heath-en cry,— 'Can the Most High watch us all?' Shamed by that— all-see-ing eye— soon the boast-ing proud will fall.

2 When my stum-bling foot-steps tire,— strength-en me in all I do—— earth has no more I de-sire;— whom have I in heaven but you?— Though my flesh and heart shall fail,— you sup-ply— im-mor-tal needs; with your help— I shall pre-vail— and pro-claim your per-fect deeds.

3 Yes, this earth-bound fan-ta-sy— shall dis-perse when you a-rise;— when you come to wel-come me— to your home be-yond the skies.— Glo-ry be to God to-day,— ev-ery heart by grace for-given; souls re-deemed and an-gels say,— Glo-ry in the high-est heaven!

Alternative tune: Hollingside, *Hymns for Today's Church* 438

O God, we thank you

Cople 8 8 8 8 (LM)

Words: from Psalm 75
Michael Perry
Music: Paul Edwards

1 O God, we thank you that your name is known and
2 The proud you cau - tion not to boast, the wick - ed,
3 We come be - fore you, God of gods – your power shall

feared through all the earth; your sen - tence waits the ap -
not to raise their eyes; for you are king from
cut the wick - ed down; we wor - ship you as

- point - ed time and thun - der brings your judge - ments forth.
east to west, and you a - lone shall have the praise!
Lord of lords – you lift us up to share your throne!

Alternative tune: Winchester New, *Hymns for Today's Church* 112

76(i) Silent the earth when God arose

St Bartholomew's Pico Rivera   8 6 8 6 (CM)

Words: from Psalm 76
David Mowbray
Music: Keith Landis
arranged Betty Pulkingham

UNISON

1 Si - lent the earth___ when___ God___ a - rose
2 So let earth's ty - rants___ gaze___ in fear,
3 Let God be praised, Je - ru - sa - lem,

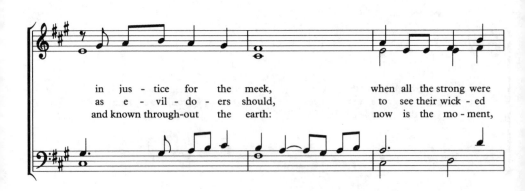

in jus - tice for the meek,   when all the strong were
as e - vil - do - ers should,   to see their wick - ed
and known through-out the earth: now is the mo - ment,

cast a - side   and mer - cy spared the weak.
deeds trans - formed   to pro - vi - den - tial good.
now the time   to tell God's sov - ereign worth!

Silent the earth when God arose 76(ii)

Plumstead 8 6 8 6 (CM)

Words: from Psalm 76
David Mowbray
Music: John Joubert
commissioned for *The Cambridge Hymnal*

1 Si - lent the earth when God a - rose
2 So let earth's ty - rants gaze in fear,
3 Let God be praised, Je - ru - sa - lem,

in jus - tice for the meek,____ when all the strong were
as e - vil - do - ers should,____ to see their wick - ed
and known through-out the earth:____ now is the mo - ment,

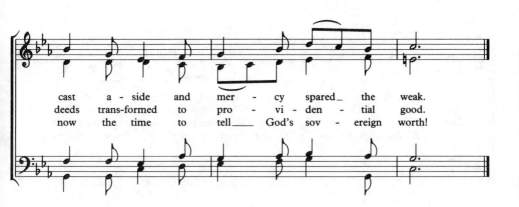

cast a - side and mer - cy spared__ the weak.
deeds trans-formed to pro - vi - den - tial good.
now the time to tell__ God's sov - ereign worth!

Alternative tune: Richmond, *Hymns for Today's Church* 541

77   I cried out for heaven to hear me

Now join we   9 8 9 8

Words: from Psalm 77
Michael Perry
Music: Michael Metcalf

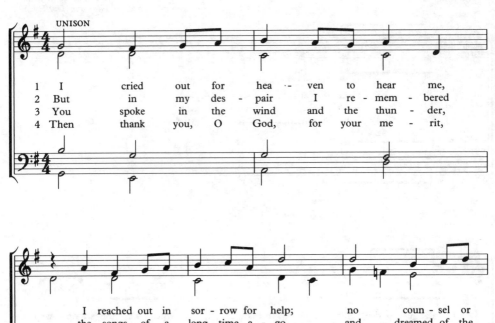

UNISON

1   I   cried   out   for   hea - ven   to   hear   me,
2   But   in   my   des - pair   I   re - mem - bered
3   You   spoke   in   the   wind   and   the   thun - der,
4   Then   thank   you,   O   God,   for   your   me - rit,

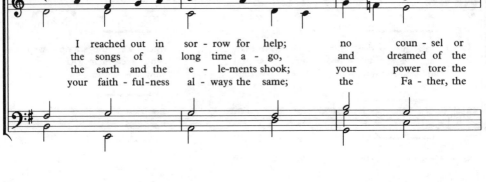

I reached out in   sor - row for help;   no   coun - sel or
the songs of a   long time a - go,   and   dreamed of the
the earth and the   e - le-ments shook;   your   power tore the
your faith - ful-ness   al - ways the same;   the   Fa - ther, the

com - fort would cheer me,   my   spi - rit a - ban - doned all hope.
ma - jes - ty splen-doured   of   God the al - migh - ty, the true:
wa - ters a - sun - der,   as   Shep - herd, you guid - ed your flock.
Son and the Spi - rit –   one   Lord o - ver all. Praise your name!

We will tell each generation

Restoration 8 7 8 7

Words: from Psalm 78
Michael Perry
Music: *The Southern Harmony* 1835
arranged John Barnard

1 We will tell each___ ge - ne - ra - tion
2 Tell the times of___ our re - bel - ling –
3 Tell how once, when___ spite and ter - ror
4 Tell the grace that___ falls from hea - ven,

all that you, our___ God, have done; how you called and
how we wan - dered_ from your way, how your law___ our
threat - ened to en - gulf our land, you de - fend - ed
an - gels' food as___ faith's re - ward; tell how sins___ may

led our___ na - tion, chose us out___ to be your own:
love com - pel - ling taught us hum - bly to o - bey:
us with___ vi - gour, saved us by___ a migh - ty hand.
be for - giv - en through the mer - cy of the Lord.

Alternative tune: Stuttgart, *Hymns for Today's Church* 8

80(i) God of hosts, you chose a vine

Catherine 7 7 7 7

Words: from Psalm 80
David Mowbray
Music: Richard Connolly

1 God of hosts, you chose a vine meant to __ bear the
2 Like a ce - dar, it grew strong – deep its __ roots, its
3 Des - o - late, to God we cry: 'Spare us __ from the
4 Turn us too, for we have failed, faith - ful - ness has

fin - est __ wine, __ set it in a pro - mised
ten - drils __ long; __ yet, in en - vy those a -
e - ne - my!' __ God of hosts, turn back a -
not __ pre - vailed; __ vi - sit, Lord, and heal your

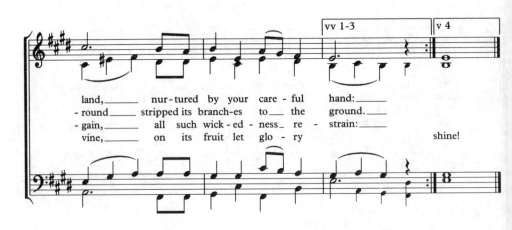

vv 1-3   v 4

land, __ nur - tured by your care - ful hand: __
- round __ stripped its branch - es to __ the ground. __
- gain, __ all such wick - ed - ness __ re - strain: __
vine, __ on its fruit let glo - ry   shine!

God of hosts, you chose a vine

80(ii)

St Bees 7 7 7 7

Words: from Psalm 80
David Mowbray
Music: J B Dykes (1823–1876)

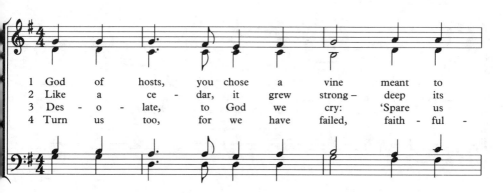

1 God of hosts, you chose a vine meant to
2 Like a ce - dar, it grew strong – deep its
3 Des - o - late, to God we cry: 'Spare us
4 Turn us too, for we have failed, faith - ful -

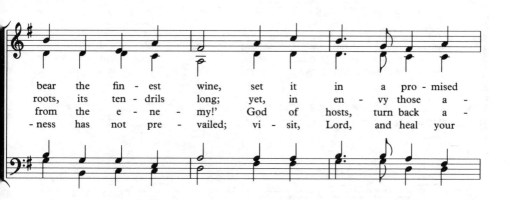

bear the fin - est wine, set it in a pro - mised
roots, its ten - drils long; yet, in en - vy those a -
from the e - ne - my!' God of hosts, turn back a -
- ness has not pre - vailed; vi - sit, Lord, and heal your

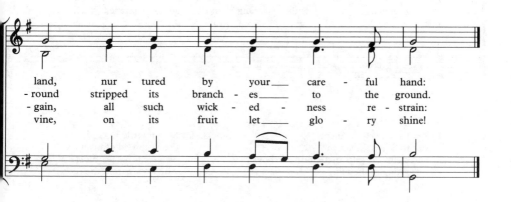

land, nur - tured by your___ care - ful hand:
- round stripped its branch - es___ to the ground.
- gain, all such wick - ed - ness re - strain:
vine, on its fruit let___ glo - ry shine!

81 Sing merrily to God

Speen 6 6 8 6 (SM)

Words: from Psalm 81
David Mowbray
Music: Anthony Greening

1 Sing merrily to God whose arm has done great things, and play with all the skill you have on trumpet, pipe and strings.

2 Remember Israel's plight in Egypt's far-off land: how God, unaided, rescued them with strong and outstretched hand.

3 Remember too their pride, their murmurings on the way; recall how they forsook the Lord and chose to disobey.

4 Let us not act like them,
but walk in faith again
and claim the gifts that God will shower
refreshing as the rain.

5 Sing merrily to God,
the Shepherd of his flock
who feeds his people, as of old,
with honey from the rock.

Alternative tune: Narenza, *Psalms for Today* 163B, *Hymns for Today's Church* 568

God is king – be warned, you mighty

Llanymawddwy 8 7 8 7 D

Words: from Psalm 82
Michael Perry
Music: David Preston

1 God is king – be warned, you_ migh-ty; God is judge through all the land:
2 There are lands that have no_ hon - our, hear no wis - dom, see no light;

or - der your af - fairs with jus - tice, rule with firm but_ gen - tle_ hand.
blind, they stum-ble in the_ dark-ness, lea - der - less, they shake with fright.

Help the weak, sup - port the_ need - y, take to heart the fa - ther - less;
Trem-ble, all you migh-ty_ rul - ers; ev - ery na - tion, know God's worth:

prove the rights of those who_ suf - fer, meet the poor in their dis - tress.
power and wealth are God's pos - sess - ion, who a - lone shall judge the_ earth!

Alternative tune: Gott Will's machen, *Psalms for Today* 100A(ii), *Hymns for Today's Church* 360

84A   How lovely is your dwelling-place

Melchbourne 8 4 8 8 4

Words: from Psalm 84
Barbara Woollett
Music: Paul Edwards

1 How love - ly is your dwell - ing - place, O Lord__ most
2 The spar - row comes to build her nest, O Lord__ most
3 Your peo - ple come to you a - gain, O Lord__ most

high,__ we long to know more of your grace, and
high,__ and in your house finds peace and rest: so
high,__ for here we feel your strength, like rain re -

yearn to see you face to face, O Lord__ most high!
may we too be ev - er blessed, O Lord__ most high!
- fresh - ing us through toil and pain, O Lord__ most high!

4 In fellowship your love we share,
   O Lord most high;
far better is one day of prayer
than any spent in worldly care,
   O Lord most high!

5 How lovely is your dwelling-place,
   O Lord most high;
we bring you all our trust and praise,
and ask your blessing on our days,
   O Lord most high!

O Lord, the mansions where you dwell   84B

QEGS 8 8 8 8 (LM)

Words: from Psalm 84
Paul Wigmore
Music: Gareth D Green

1 O Lord, the man - sions where you dwell are ov - er - flow - ing
with your love; while here on earth my soul knows
well of last - ing joy in heaven a - bove.

2 And, Lord, my heart and flesh cry out in long - ing for that
ho - ly place; an end to sor - row, sin and
doubt, the re - ve - la - tion of your face.

3 One day with - in your courts, O Lord, one day set free from
ev - ery fear, one day with your dear name ad -
- ored is bet - ter than a thou - sand here.

4 For those, O Lord, who trust in you: di - rect their eyes to
see your ways, their heart to love, their hands to
do, their head to bow, their lips to praise.

Alternative tune: St Laurence, *Hymns for Today's Church* 512

84C   How lovely is your dwelling-place

Words: Psalm 84
from *The Liturgical Psalter*
David Frost and others
Music: C H H Parry (1848–1918)

1 How lovely ' is your ' dwelling-place:
   O ' Lord ' God of ' hosts!
2 My soul has a desire and longing to enter the ' courts · of the ' Lord:
   my heart and my flesh re'joice · in the ' living ' God.

3 The sparrow has found her a home
   and the swallow a nest where she may ' lay her ' young:
   even your altar   O Lord of ' hosts ' my ' King · and my ' God.
4 Blessed are those who ' dwell in · your ' house:
   they will ' always · be ' praising ' you.

5 Blessed are those whose ' strength · is in ' you:
   in whose ' heart · are the ' highways · to ' Zion;
6 who going through the valley of dryness
   find there a spring from ' which to ' drink:
   till the autumn ' rain shall ' clothe it · with ' blessings.

Second part
7 They go from ' strength to ' strength:
   they appear every one of them before the ' God of ' gods in ' Zion.

8 O Lord God of hosts ' hear my ' prayer:
   give ' ear O ' God of ' Jacob.
9 Behold O God ' him who · reigns ' over us:
   and look upon the ' face of ' your a'nointed.

10 One day in your courts is ' better · than a ' thousand:
    I would rather stand at the threshold of the house of my God
    than ' dwell · in the ' tents of · un'godliness.
11 For the Lord God is a rampart and a shield
    the Lord gives ' favour · and ' honour:
    and no good thing will he withhold from ' those who ' walk in ' innocence.

Second part
12 O Lord ' God of ' hosts:
    blessed are those who ' put their ' trust in ' you.

    Glory to the Father and ' to the ' Son:
    and ' to the ' Holy ' Spirit;
    as it was in the be'ginning · is ' now:
    and shall be for ' ever. ' A'men.

When this land knew

Great Oxendon   10 10 10 10

Words: from Psalm 85
Christopher Idle
Music: Paul Edwards

UNISON

1 When this land knew God's gra-cious love out-poured   guilt was re -
2 But now where wrong so fla-grant-ly has trod   will you for
3 O let me hear God's word of sweet com-mand: peace to his
4 That day draws near when truth will join with grace,   jus-tice and

- moved and cap-tive lives re - stored; then was drawn back the
ev - er pun-ish with your rod? Once more re - vive us!
saints, sal - va-tion is at hand; peace to his peo - ple,
peace will meet in love's em - brace; faith on the earth, and

an - ger of the Lord, his peo - ple par - doned, their sins___ for-giv-en.
Give us life, O God! Give joy for an - guish; for wrath,___ sal - va-tion.
glo - ry in our land for those who fear him, who turn___ and wor-ship.
from his ho-ly place he comes in glo - ry, the right - eous Sav-iour.

Alternative tune: Sine Nomine, *Hymns for Today's Church* 567

86A(i)

Hear me, O Lord

Pamela   10 8 10 8

Words: from Psalm 86
Michael Perry
Music: Gareth D Green

1 Hear me,   O Lord,   and re - spond to my   prayer,
2 Bring me   your joy   as I   wor - ship you, Lord,_
3 Give me   a sign   of your   good-ness, O Lord,_

guard well   my life,   for I   love_____ you:__
come to   my heart,   for I   need_____ you;__
grant me   the strength   that o - beys_____ you:__

no - thing com - pares with the won - ders you do,___
teach me your way, let me walk in your truth =
you are com - pas - sion, a - bound - ing in love,___

vv 1 and 2   v 3

for there is no___ god a - bove you.
I can-not fail when I heed you.
you are my king, and I   praise you.

OPTIONAL DESCANT for verse 3. (Instrumental or vocal sung to 'Ah')

86A(ii)

Hear me, O Lord

Thursford Green   10 8 10 8

Words: from Psalm 86
Michael Perry
Music: Derek Williams

UNISON

1 Hear me, O Lord, and re - spond to my prayer,
2 Bring me your joy as I wor - ship you, Lord,
3 Give me a sign of your good - ness, O Lord,

guard well my life, for I love you: no - thing com-pares with the
come to my heart, for I need you; teach me your way, let me
grant me the strength that o - beys you: you are com-pas - sion, a -

won - ders you do, for there is no god a - bove you.
walk in your truth – I can - not fail when I heed you.
- bound - ing in love, you are my king, and I praise you.

For all your boundless gifts

87(i)

Ridley 6 6 8 6 (SM)

Words: from Psalm 87
David Mowbray
Music: Christopher Blissard-Barnes
arranged John Barnard

1 For all your bound - less gifts___ we
2 So was Je - ru - sa - lem___ both
3 Through all our ci - ties, Lord,___ let
4 So trum - pet - ers shall sound___ and

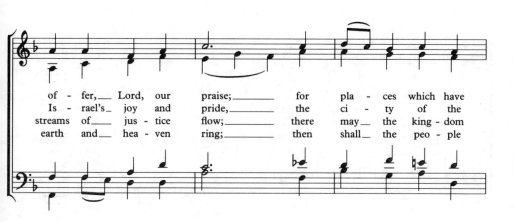

of - fer,__ Lord, our praise;___ for pla - ces which have
Is - rael's_ joy and pride,___ the ci - ty of the
streams of__ jus - tice flow;___ there may_ the king - dom
earth and__ hea - ven ring;___ then shall_ the peo - ple

shel - tered us and__ shaped our earth - ly days.
Lord_ most high where_ kings_ were born and died.
of___ your Christ - a___ spread - ing ce - dar_ grow.
say__ A - men and__ songs_ of glad - ness sing!

87(ii) For all your boundless gifts

St Ethelwald 6 6 8 6 (SM)

Words: from Psalm 87
David Mowbray
Music: W H Monk (1823–1889)

1 For all your bound - less gifts we
2 So was Je - ru - sa - lem both
3 Through all our ci - ties, Lord, let
4 So trum - pet - ers shall sound and

of - fer, Lord, our praise; for plac - es which have
Is - rael's joy and pride, the ci - ty of the
streams of jus - tice flow; there may the king - dom
earth and hea - ven ring; then shall the peo - ple

shel - tered us and shaped our earth - ly days.
Lord most high where kings were born and died.
of your Christ - a spread - ing ce - dar grow.
say A - men and songs of glad - ness sing!

Alternative tune: Dominica, *Hymns for Today's Church* 380

138

O Lord, the God who saves me

Blunham 7 6 7 6

Words: from Psalm 88
Michael Perry
Music: Paul Edwards

UNISON

1 O Lord, the God who saves me, to
2 Your an - ger lies up - on me, I
3 And shall the dead sing prais - es, and

you my spi - rit cries; my world is full of
can - not make a - mends; your waves, they o - ver -
can the dark - ness see your right - eous ways, your

vv 1-4 | v 5

trou - ble, and hope of mer - cy dies.
- whelm me, you take a - way my friends. grave!
won - ders, your faith - ful - ness to me?

4 I call to you in waking,
and seek you all day long:
O hear me, Lord and Saviour –
restore to me my song.

5 My God shall yet uplift me,
the Spirit come to save,
and Jesus my redeemer
shall tear me from the grave!

Alternative tune: Christus der ist mein Leben, *Psalms for Today* 27A

89A(i)

Timeless love

Patrixbourne 8 7 8 7 7 7

Words: from Psalm 89
Timothy Dudley-Smith
Music: John Barnard

DESCANT

Ah

UNISON

1 Time-less love! We sing the sto - ry, praise his won - ders, tell his

worth; love more fair than hea-ven's glo - ry, love more firm than an-cient

earth! Tell his faith - ful-ness a-broad: who is like him? Praise the Lord!

2 By his faith - ful - ness sur - round - ed, north and
3 Truth and right - eous - ness en - throne__ him, just and

south his hand pro - claim;___ earth and hea - ven formed and
e - qual are his ways;___ more than hap - py, those who

found - ed, skies and seas, de - clare his name!___ Wind and
own him, more than joy, their songs of praise!___ Sun and

storm o - bey his word:__ who is like him? Praise the Lord!
shield and great re - ward:__

The Harmony version is compatible with the Unison setting.

141

89A(ii)

Timeless love

Timeless love 8 7 8 7 7 7

Words: from Psalm 89
Timothy Dudley-Smith
Music: Norman Warren

1 Time-less love! We sing the sto - ry, praise his won - ders,_ tell his
2 By his faith - ful-ness sur - round-ed, north and south his_ hand pro -
3 Truth and right - eous-ness en - throne him, just and e - qual_ are his

worth;   love more fair   than hea - ven's   glo - ry, love more
- claim;   earth and hea - ven formed and found - ed, skies and
ways;   more than hap - py, those who own   him,   more than

firm   than an - cient   earth!   Tell his faith - ful - ness a -
seas,   de - clare his   name!   Wind and storm   o - bey his
joy,   their songs of   praise!   Sun and   shield   and great re -

- broad:
word: who is   like__ him? Praise_ the   Lord!
- ward:

Alternative tune: All Saints, *Hymns for Today's Church* 215

142

Our God eternal, reigning

Innsbruck 776778

Words: from Psalm 90
Timothy Dudley-Smith
Music: German traditional melody

1 Our God eternal, reigning, cre-
a-tion's life sustaining, our refuge and our home;
enthroned, in light surrounded, when earth was yet un-
founded, the living God, to him we come.

2 We fade, a dream that passes, like
withered meadow grasses when summer's sun has shone.
Before that face all-seeing of God who gave us
being we pass away and we are gone.

3 O God of mercy, hear us, in
steadfast love draw near us, from age to age the same;
that we, by grace defended, when earthly days are
ended may live to praise a Saviour's name.

90B   God everlasting, at your word

Orphan Girl   8 6 8 6 (CM)

Words: from Psalm 90
David Mowbray
Music: *Sacred Harp* 1902
arranged David Iliff

1 God ev - er - last - ing, at your word the
2 Our days like dreams come to an end, our
3 Teach us, good Lord, to count our days, to
4 Lord, at your hand we have re - ceived the

hills in splen - dour rise; they o - ver - sha - dow
sto - ry soon is told when strength is spent, and
che - rish ev - ery hour; to seek your will, to
cup of joy and pain: pour out the ful - ness

hu - man life whose glo - ry swift - ly dies.
beau - ty fades, and bo - dies have grown old.
do your work, and trust your migh - ty power.
of your grace and we shall sing a - gain!

Alternative tune: London New, *Hymns for Today's Church* 332

Safe in the shadow of the Lord 91A(i)

Creator God 8 6 8 6 (CM)

Words: from Psalm 91
Timothy Dudley-Smith
Music: Norman Warren

DESCANT

6 Safe in the sha - dow of the Lord, pos - sessed by

1 Safe in the sha - dow of the Lord, be - neath his
2 My hope is set on God a - lone though Sa - tan
MEN 3 From fears and phan - toms of the night, from foes a -

love di - vine, I trust in him, I

hand and power, I trust in him, I
spreads his snare; I trust in him, I
- bout my way, I

trust in him, and meet his love with mine, with mine.

trust in him, my for - tress and my tower.
to keep me in his care.
by dark - ness as by day.

WOMEN
4 His holy angels keep my feet
secure from every stone;
I trust in him,
I trust in him,
and unafraid go on.

ALL
5 Strong in the everlasting name,
and in my Father's care,
I trust in him,
I trust in him,
who hears and answers prayer.

6 Safe in the shadow of the Lord,
possessed by love divine,
I trust in him,
I trust in him,
and meet his love with mine.

91A(ii)   Safe in the shadow of the Lord

Stanton 8 6 8 6 (CM)

Words: from Psalm 91
Timothy Dudley-Smith
Music: John Barnard

UNISON

1 Safe in the sha - dow of the Lord, be - neath his
2 My hope is set on God a - lone though Sa - tan
MEN 3 From fears and phan - toms of the night, from foes a -

hand__ and power,
spreads his snare; I trust in him, I trust in
-bout__ my way,

him,
to keep me in__ his care.
by dark - ness as__ by day.
my for - tress and__ my tower.

WOMEN
4 His holy angels keep my feet
  secure from every stone;
    I trust in him,
    I trust in him,
  and unafraid go on.

ALL
5 Strong in the everlasting name,
  and in my Father's care,
    I trust in him,
    I trust in him,
  who hears and answers prayer.

6 Safe in the shadow of the Lord,
  possessed by love divine,
    I trust in him,
    I trust in him,
  and meet his love with mine.

Make music to the Lord

Rodmell 8 6 8 6 (CM)

Words: from Psalm 92
Christopher Idle
Music: English traditional melody
arranged David Iliff

1 Make mu - sic to the Lord__ most__ high whose__
2 Lord, when we see all you__ have__ done our__
WOMEN 3 The god - less mind will ne - ver__ know – be -

praise is__ our__ de - light: we__ sing your__ love__ as__
songs of__ joy__ re - sound: your__ hand - i - work, how__
- cause its sense__ is__ void – that__ though the__ wick - ed

day__ be - gins, your__ faith - ful - ness__ by__ night.
vast__ it__ is, your__ coun - sels, how__ pro - found!
spread like__ grass, they__ all shall be__ de - stroyed.

ALL
4 For ever, Lord, you are supreme;
   your throne remains on high
   while rebels meet eternal doom
   and evil-doers die.

MEN
5 But like the cedar and the palm
   the righteous stand serene;
   they flourish in the house of God,
   their leaves are fresh and green.

ALL
6 To fruitful age they still proclaim
   the Lord who makes them new –
   our God, in whom no wrong is found,
   my Rock, for ever true.

92A(ii)   Make music to the Lord

Bishopthorpe 8 6 8 6 (CM)

Words: from Psalm 92
Christopher Idle
Music: J Clarke (c1674–1707)

1 Make music to the Lord most high whose
2 Lord, when we see all you have done our
WOMEN 3 The godless mind will never know = be-

praise is our delight: we sing your love as
songs of joy resound: your hand-i-work, how
-cause its sense is void = that though the wick-ed

day begins, your faithfulness by night.
vast it is, your counsels, how profound!
spread like grass, they all shall be destroyed.

ALL
4 For ever, Lord, you are supreme;
  your throne remains on high
  while rebels meet eternal doom
  and evil-doers die.

MEN
5 But like the cedar and the palm
  the righteous stand serene;
  they flourish in the house of God,
  their leaves are fresh and green.

ALL
6 To fruitful age they still proclaim
  the Lord who makes them new –
  our God, in whom no wrong is found,
  my Rock, for ever true.

Clothed in kingly majesty

Kingly majesty 7 5 5

Words: from Psalm 93
Michael Saward
Music: Norman Warren
Harmony: John Barnard

1 Clothed in king-ly ma-jes-ty, robed in re-gal

power,___ God is o - ver all.

2 Lord of all, un-shake-a - ble,___ throned be-yond all
3 Great - er than the ri - ver's roar___ and the surg - ing
4 Change-less as his law's de-crees,___ crowned our ho - ly

time,___ God is o - ver all.___
sea,___
king,___

The Harmony and Unison versions are not harmonically compatible.

93B   God is King! The Lord is reigning

Crail 8 7 8 8 8 7 7 7

Words: from Psalm 93
Timothy Dudley-Smith
Music: Peter Cutts

1 God is King! The Lord is reign-ing, might and ma-jes-ty his robe;
to his seat on high as-cend-ed, gird-ed round with glo-ry splen-did,
there in time and space sus-tain-ing this our star-en-cir-cled globe.
Fore-or-dained and found-ed fast, ev-er-more his throne shall last!

2 God is King! In storm and thun-der wind and tide their war-fare wage;_
3 God is King! Let earth a-dore him—change-less still his sure de-cree.__

burst-ing seas and break-ers tower-ing, pound-ing surge the
Throned be-yond our mor-tal tell-ing, ho-li-ness and

rocks de-vour-ing, light-ning rend-ing skies a-sun-der,
truth his dwell-ing: come with tremb-ling hearts be-fore him,

o-cean's roar and tem-pest's rage. Might-ier_ far than_
bow the head and bend the knee, where the_ ran-somed

sea or_ sky_ stands the throne of God_ on_ high!
ev-er_ raise_ God's im-per-ish-a-ble_ praise!

The Harmony version is not harmonically compatible with the Unison setting.
Only one of the two interlined verses should be sung in harmony.

95A   Come with all joy to sing to God

Fulda 8 8 8 8 (LM)

Words: from Psalm 95, *Venite*
Christopher Idle
Music: W Gardiner *Sacred Melodies* 1815

1 Come with all joy to sing_ to God   our sav - ing
2 In ho - li - ness and light_ ar - rayed   a - bove all
WOMEN 3 The earth is his from east_ to west,   from o - cean -

rock,   the liv - ing Lord;   in glad thanks - giv - ing
gods that we_ have made   he is the one_ al -
- floor to moun - tain - crest;   he made the seas_ and

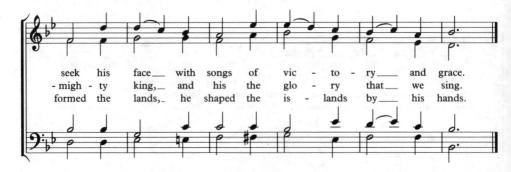

seek his face_ with songs of vic - to - ry_ and grace.
- migh - ty king,_ and his the glo - ry that_ we sing.
formed the lands,_ he shaped the is - lands by_ his hands.

MEN

4 Come near to worship! come with faith,
  bow down to him who gives us breath:
  God is our shepherd, he alone;
  we are his people, all his own.

WOMEN

5 But if you hear God's voice today
  do not reject what he will say:
  when Israel wandered from God's path
  they suffered forty years of wrath.

MEN

6 That generation went astray,
  they did not want to know his way;
  they put their saviour to the test,
  and saw his power, but lost their rest.

ALL

7 So to the God of earth and heaven,
  the Father, Spirit, Son, be given
  praise now, as praise has ever been
  and ever shall be praise. Amen.

Come, worship God

Jesmian 11 10 11 10

Words: from Psalm 95, *Venite*
Michael Perry
Music: G Thalben-Ball (1896–1987)

95B(i)

1 Come, wor-ship God who is wor-thy of hon-our,
en-ter his pre-sence with thanks and a song!
He is the rock of his peo-ple's sal-va-tion,
to whom our ju-bi-lant prais-es be-long.

2 Ruled by his might are the heights of the moun-tains,
held in his hands are the depths of the earth;
his is the sea, his the land, for he made them,
king a-bove all gods, who gave us our birth.

3 We are his peo-ple, the sheep of his pas-ture,
he is our ma-ker and to him we pray;
glad-ly we kneel in o-be-dience be-fore him =
great is the God whom we wor-ship this day!

4 Now let us lis-ten, for God speaks a-mong us,
o-pen our hearts and re-ceive what he says:
peace be to all who re-mem-ber his good-ness,
trust in his word and re-joice in his ways!

95B(ii)

Come, worship God

Epiphany Hymn   11 10 11 10

Words: from Psalm 95, *Venite*
Michael Perry
Music: J F Thrupp (1827–1867)

1 Come, wor-ship God who is wor-thy of hon-our,
2 Ruled by his might are the heights of the moun-tains,
3 We are his peo-ple, the sheep of his pas-ture,
4 Now let us lis-ten, for God speaks a-mong us,

en-ter his pre-sence with thanks and a song!
held in his hands are the depths of the earth;
he is our ma-ker and to him we pray;
o-pen our hearts and re-ceive what he says:

He is the rock of his peo-ple's sal-va-tion,
his is the sea, his the land, for he made them,
glad-ly we kneel in o-be-dience be-fore him —
peace be to all who re-mem-ber his good-ness,—

to whom our ju-bi-lant prais-es be-long.
king a-bove all gods, who gave us our birth.
great is the God whom we wor-ship this day!
trust in his word and re-joice in his ways!

Alternative tune: O quanta qualia, *Hymns for Today's Church* 18

Words: © Michael Perry/Jubilate Hymns †

O come, let us sing out to the Lord

Words: Psalm 95
from *The Liturgical Psalter*
David Frost and others

C V Stanford (1852–1924)

H Lawes (1595–1662)

1 O come, let us sing ' out · to the ' Lord:
   let us shout in triumph to the ' rock of ' our sal'vation.
2 Let us come before his ' face with ' thanksgiving:
   and cry ' out to · him ' joyfully · in ' psalms.

3 For the Lord is a ' great ' God:
   and a great ' king a·bove ' all ' gods.
4 In his hand are the ' depths · of the ' earth:
   and the peaks of the ' mountains · are ' his ' also.

Second part
5 The sea is his and ' he ' made it:
   his hands ' moulded ' dry ' land.

6 Come let us worship and ' bow ' down:
   and kneel be'fore the ' Lord our ' maker.
7 For he is the ' Lord our ' God:
   we are his ' people · and the ' sheep of · his ' pasture.

8 Today if only you would hear his voice
   'Do not harden your ' hearts · as at ' Meribah:
   as on that day at ' Massah ' in the ' wilderness;
9 when your ' fathers ' tested me:
   put me to proof though ' they had ' seen my ' works.

10 'Forty years long I loathed that gener'ation · and ' said:
   "It is a people who err in their hearts,
   for they ' do not ' know my ' ways";
11 of whom I ' swore · in my ' wrath:
   "They ' shall not ' enter · my ' rest."'

   Glory to the Father and ' to the ' Son:
   and ' to the ' Holy ' Spirit;
   as it was in the be'ginning · is ' now:
   and shall be for ' ever. ' A'men.

See also *Venite*, (ASB 1980), *Psalms for Today* 151

96A   Sing a new song of glory

Lord of the years   11 10 11 10

Words: from Psalm 96
Stephen Horsfall
Music: Michael Baughen
arranged David Iliff
Descant: John Barnard

Alternative tune: Strength and stay, *Hymns for Today's Church* 300

earth are blend - ing as all cre -

earth and hea - ven blend - ing as all cre -

- a - tion_____ joins to sing God's grace!

- a - tion joins to sing God's grace!

O sing to the Lord a new song

Words: from Psalm 96
from *The Liturgical Psalter*
David Frost and others
Music: John Barnard

96B

CHOIR O sing to the Lord a new song: sing to the Lord all the earth.__ ALL O sing to the Lord a new song: sing to the Lord all the earth. CHOIR 1 Sing to the Lord and

159

bless his ho - ly name: pro - claim the good news of his sal -

- va - tion from day to day. De - clare his

glo - ry a - mong the na - tions: and his won - ders a - mong all

peo-ples. ALL O sing to the Lord a new song:

Organ   Man.   Ped.

160

sing to the Lord_ all the earth._ CHOIR 2 As for all the gods of the na-

-tions they_ are mere i - dols:_ it is the Lord who made_ the

heavens. Ma - jes - ty_____ and glo - ry are_ be - fore him:

beau - ty_ and power are in_____ his sanc - tu - ary._ ALL O

Organ

161

sing to the Lord a new song: sing to the Lord all the

Man. Ped.

earth.— *mp* CHOIR 3 O wor-ship the Lord— in the beau-ty of——— his

ho - li - ness:— let the whole earth stand——— in awe of him.—

f Say a-mong the na-tions that the Lord——— is king: *mf* he shall

judge the world with right-eous-ness__ and the peo-ples with____ his

truth.

ALL O sing to the Lord a new song:

f

Organ

Man.

Ped.

sing to the Lord all the earth. O sing to the Lord a new song:

Man.

Ped.

sing to the Lord all the earth.

CHOIR O sing a new song!

ff

163

97   The everlasting Lord is king

Neville Court   8 6 8 6 (CM)

Words: from Psalm 97
Timothy Dudley-Smith
Music: Derek Williams

1 The ev - er - last - ing___ Lord is king — let
2 He comes in clouds with___ fire and flame to
3 The sun and moon and___ star - ry sky his
4 De - fend - ed by his___ hand di - vine his

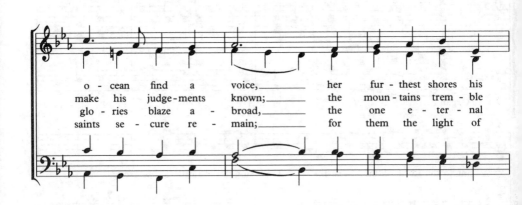

o - cean find a voice,___ her fur - thest shores his
make his judge - ments known;___ the moun - tains trem - ble
glo - ries blaze a - broad,___ the one e - ter - nal
saints se - cure re - main;___ for them the light of

tri - umph sing and___ all the earth re - joice.
at his name and___ melt be - fore his throne.
God most high, the___ true and liv - ing Lord.
life shall shine, the___ King of love shall reign.

Alternative tune: Kilmarnock, *Hymns for Today's Church* 448

Sing to God new songs of worship

Ode to Joy 8 7 8 7 D

Words: from Psalm 98, *Cantate Domino*
Michael Baughen
Music: L van Beethoven (1770–1827)

1 Sing to God new songs of wor-ship– all his deeds are mar-vel-lous;
2 Sing to God new songs of wor-ship– earth has seen his vic-to-ry;
3 Sing to God new songs of wor-ship– let the sea now make a noise;

he has brought sal-va-tion to us with his hand and ho-ly arm.
let the lands of earth be joy-ful prais-ing him with thank-ful-ness.
all on earth and in the wa-ters, sound your prais-es to the Lord.

He has shown to all the na-tions right-eous-ness and sav-ing power;
Sound up-on the harp his prais-es, play to him with me-lo-dy;
Let the hills re-joice to-ge-ther, let the ri-vers clap their hands,

he re-called his truth and mer-cy to his peo-ple Is-ra-el.
let the trum-pets sound his tri-umph, show your joy to God the king!
for with right-eous-ness and jus-tice he will come to judge the earth.

This may be sung in G♭.

98B(i) Sing a new song to the Lord

Onslow Square 7 7 11 8

Words: from Psalm 98, *Cantate Domino*
Timothy Dudley-Smith
Music: David Wilson

UNISON

1 Sing a new song to the Lord, he to whom won-ders be-
2 Now to the ends of the earth see his sal-va-tion is
3 Sing a new song and re-joice, pub-lish his prais-es a-
4 Join with the hills and the sea thun-ders of praise to pro-

-long! Re-joice in his tri-umph and
shown: and still he re-mem-bers his
-broad! Let voi-ces in cho-rus with
-long! In judge-ment and jus-tice he

tell of his power = O sing to the
mer-cy and truth, un-chang-ing in
trum-pet and horn, re-sound for the
comes to the earth = O sing to the

vv 1-3 | v 4

Lord a new song!
love to his own.
joy of the Lord!
Lord a new song!

Sing a new song to the Lord   98B(ii)

Littlebourne 7 7 11 8

Words: from Psalm 98, *Cantate Domino*
Timothy Dudley-Smith
Music: John Barnard

DESCANT

4 Join with the hills and the

1 Sing a new song to the Lord,
2 Now to the ends of the earth
3 Sing a new song and re - joice,
4 Join with the hills and the sea

sea thun - ders of praise to pro-long! In jus - tice he

he to whom won-ders be - long! Re - joice in his tri - umph and
see his sal - va - tion is shown: and still he re-mem-bers his
pub - lish his prais-es a - broad! Let voi - ces in cho - rus, with
thun-ders of praise to pro - long! In judge-ment and jus - tice he

comes to the earth – O sing a new song!

tell of his power – O sing to the Lord a new song!
mer - cy and truth, un - chang - ing in love to his own.
trum - pet and horn, re - sound for the joy of the Lord!
comes to the earth – O sing to the Lord a new song!

98C O sing to the Lord a new song

Words: Psalm 98, *Cantate Domino*
from *The Liturgical Psalter*
David Frost and others
Music: J Goss (1800–1880)

1 O sing to the Lord a ' new ' song:
  for he has ' done ' marvel·lous ' things;
2 his right hand and his ' holy ' arm:
  they have ' got ' him the ' victory.

3 The Lord has made ' known · his sal'vation:
  he has revealed his just de'liverance · in the ' sight of · the ' nations.
4 He has remembered his mercy and faithfulness towards the ' house of ' Israel:
  and all the ends of the earth have seen the sal'vation ' of our ' God.

5 Shout with joy to the Lord ' all the ' earth:
  break into ' singing · and ' make ' melody.
6 Make melody to the Lord up'on the ' harp:
  upon the harp and ' with the ' sounds of ' praise.

7 With trumpets ' and with ' horns:
  cry out in triumph be'fore the ' Lord the ' king.
8 Let the sea roar and ' all that ' fills it:
  the good earth and ' those who ' live up'on it.

9 Let the rivers ' clap their ' hands:
  and let the mountains ring out to'gether · be'fore the ' Lord;
10 for he comes to ' judge the ' earth:
   **he shall judge the world with righteousness
   and the ' peoples ' with ' equity.**

  Glory to the Father and ' to the ' Son:
  and ' to the ' Holy ' Spirit;
  as it was in the be'ginning · is ' now:
  and shall be for ' ever. ' A'men.

God is king – the nations tremble

Goodwyn's Vale 8 8 8 6

Words: from Psalm 99
Michael Saward
Music: Alan Horsey

99A

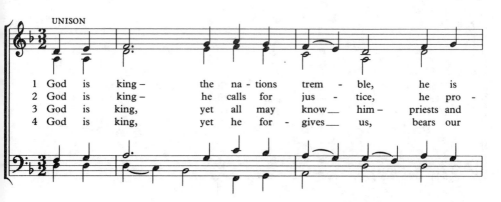

1 God is king – the na-tions trem - ble, he is
2 God is king – he calls for jus - tice, he pro -
3 God is king, yet all may know__ him – priests and
4 God is king, yet he for - gives__ us, bears our

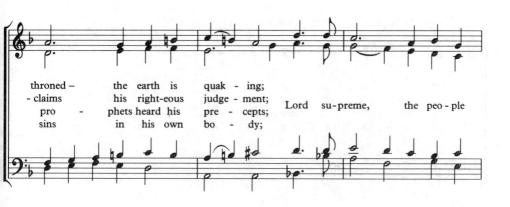

throned – the earth is quak - ing;
- claims his right-eous judge - ment;
pro - phets heard his pre - cepts; Lord su-preme, the peo - ple
sins in his own bo - dy;

praise__ him: Ho - ly, ho - ly, ho - ly!

100A(i) Come, rejoice before your maker

Come rejoice 8 7 8 7

Words: from Psalm 100, *Jubilate Deo*
Michael Baughen
Music: Noël Tredinnick

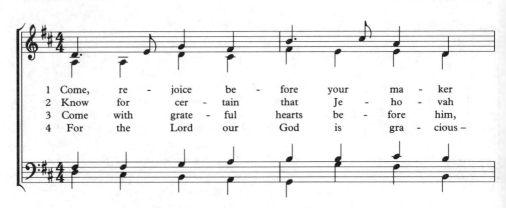

1 Come, re - joice be - fore your ma - ker
2 Know for cer - tain that Je - ho - vah
3 Come with grate - ful hearts be - fore him,
4 For the Lord our God is gra - cious –

all you peo - ples of the earth;__ serve the Lord your
is the true and on - ly God:__ we are his, for
en - ter now his courts with praise;__ show your thank - ful -
ev - er - last - ing in his love;__ and to ev - ery

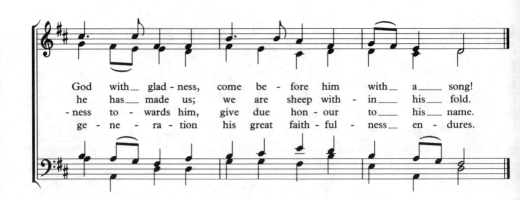

God with__ glad - ness, come be - fore him with__ a__ song!
he has__ made us; we are sheep with - in__ his__ fold.
- ness to - wards him, give due hon - our to__ his__ name.
ge - ne - ra - tion his great faith - ful - ness__ en - dures.

Come, rejoice before your maker 100A(ii)

Gott Will's machen 8 7 8 7

Words: from Psalm 100, *Jubilate Deo*
Michael Baughen
Music: J L Steiner (1668–1761)

1 Come, re - joice___ be - fore your ma - ker
2 Know for cer - tain that Je - ho - vah
3 Come with grate - ful hearts be - fore___ him,
4 For the Lord___ our God is gra - cious –

all you___ peo - ples___ of___ the___ earth;___ serve the Lord your___
is the___ true and___ on - ly God:___ we are his, for___
en - ter___ now his___ courts with___ praise;___ show your thank - ful -
ev - er - last - ing___ in his___ love;___ and to ev - ery___

God with glad - ness,___ come_ be - fore him___ with a___ song!
he has made us;___ we___ are___ sheep with - in his___ fold.
- ness to - wards him,___ give_ due___ hon - our___ to his___ name.
ge - ne - ra - tion___ his___ great_ faith - ful - ness en - dures.

100B   Sing, all creation

Long Crendon   11 11 11 5

Words: from Psalm 100, *Jubilate Deo*
James Quinn SJ
Music: John Barnard

1 Sing, all cre-a-tion, sing to God in glad-ness, joy-ous-ly serve him, sing-ing hymns of hom-age; chant-ing his prais-es, come be-fore his pre-sence: praise the Al-migh-ty!

Alternative tune: Iste Confessor, *Hymns for Today's Church* 391

The Harmony version is harmonically compatible with the Unison setting.

100C

O shout to the Lord in triumph

Words: Psalm 100, *Jubilate Deo*
from *The Liturgical Psalter*
David Frost and others

E Cutler (1831–1916)

T Norris (1741–1790)

1   O shout to the Lord in triumph ' all the ' earth:
    serve the Lord with gladness
    and come before his ' face with ' songs of ' joy.

2   Know that the Lord ' he is ' God:
    it is he who has made us and we are his;
    we are his ' people · and the ' sheep of · his ' pasture.

3   Come into his gates with thanksgiving
    and into his ' courts with ' praise:
    give thanks to him and ' bless his ' holy ' name.

4   For the Lord is good *
    his loving mercy ' is for ' ever:
    his faithfulness through'out all ' gener'ations.

    Glory to the Father and ' to the ' Son:
    and ' to the ' Holy ' Spirit;
    as it was in the be'ginning is ' now:
    and shall be for ' ever. ' A'men.

With joyful shouts acclaim the Lord   100D

Tyrol 8 6 8 6 D (DCM)

Words: from Psalm 100, *Jubilate Deo*
David Preston
Music: Tyrolean melody
arranged David Iliff

1 With joy-ful shouts ac-claim the Lord, all peo-ple ev-ery-where;
3 As you ap-proach his tem-ple steps your thank-ful-ness pro-claim;

bow down to him in glad ac-cord, with songs of joy draw near!
come in with prais-es on your lips and bless his ho-ly name.

2 Ac-know-ledge God the Lord to be the one true God in-deed:
4 Re-joice be-cause the Lord is good, his stead-fast love is sure;

he made us all, his sheep are we, that in his pas-tures feed.
his faith-ful-ness has al-ways stood and shall for ev-er-more.

Alternative tune: Jackson, *Hymns for Today's Church* 572

101   With heart and hands washed clean

Webster 6 6 8 6 (SM)

Words: from Psalm 101
David Mowbray
Music: *Southern Harmony* 1835
arranged David Iliff

1 With heart and hands washed clean____ I'll____
2 For wick - ed - ness must__ pass__ like__
3 Walk with me in God's__ house,__ all__

sing your praise, O Lord— a song of mer - cy,
smoke, and drift__ a - way; de - ceit and pride__ shall
you of up - right heart: for those who keep__ his

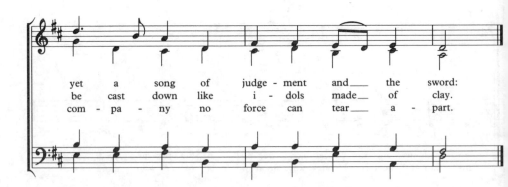

yet a song of judge - ment and__ the sword:
be cast down like i - dols made__ of clay.
com - pa - ny no force can tear__ a - part.

Alternative tunes: Venice, *Psalms for Today* 133A(ii), *Hymns for Today's Church* 34,
Franconia, *Hymns for Today's Church* 110

You laid the foundations of earth 102A(i)

Limburg 8 8 8 8

Words: from Psalm 102
Michael Perry
Music: David Iliff

UNISON

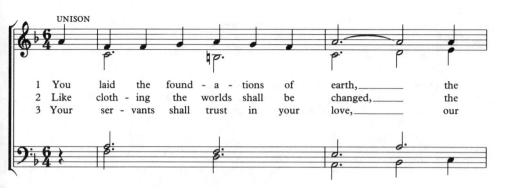

1 You laid the found - a - tions of earth, _____ the
2 Like cloth - ing the worlds shall be changed, _____ the
3 Your ser - vants shall trust in your love, _____ our

hea - vens were wrought by your hands; _____ they pe - rish, but you will re -
skies cast a - way like a veil; _____ but you, Lord, are al - ways the
child - ren shall walk in your ways, _____ till time holds us cap - tive no

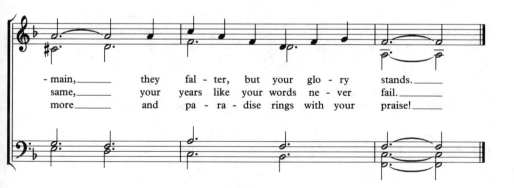

- main, _____ they fal - ter, but your glo - ry stands. _____
same, _____ your years like your words ne - ver fail. _____
more _____ and pa - ra - dise rings with your praise! _____

102A(ii) You laid the foundations of earth

Grendon 8 8 8 8

Words: from Psalm 102
Michael Perry
Music: Paul Edwards

UNISON

1 You laid the found - a - tions of earth, the
2 Like cloth - ing the worlds shall be changed, the
3 Your ser - vants shall trust in your love, our

hea - vens were wrought by your hands; they pe - rish, but you will re -
skies cast a - way like a veil; but you, Lord, are al - ways the
child - ren shall walk in your ways, till time holds us cap - tive no

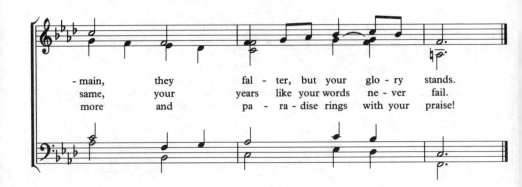

- main, they fal - ter, but your glo - ry stands.
same, your years like your words ne - ver fail.
more and pa - ra - dise rings with your praise!

Praise the Lord and bless his name 103A

Mow Cop 7 7 7 7 7 7

Words: from Psalm 103
Timothy Dudley-Smith
Music: Brian Hoare

1 Praise the Lord and bless his name, life and peace in him are found.
2 High as heaven's furthest star, vaster than the shores of space,
3 Swifter than the winds that pass, fading as the summer flowers,
4 Praise the Lord of earth and heaven, angel hosts about his throne,

All his benefits proclaim, grace with love and mercy crowned:
so he bears our sins afar, so he brings to us his grace.
what though all our days are grass? faith and hope shall still be ours.
sinners by his grace forgiven, saints who his dominion own:

sins forgiven, strength restored! Sing my soul, and praise the Lord!
He who hears his children's prayer ever keeps us in his care.
God's unchanging love is sure and endures for evermore.
God of all, by all adored! Sing, my soul, and praise the Lord!

Alternative tune: England's Lane, *Hymns for Today's Church* 298

Praise the Lord O my soul

Words: Psalm 103
from *The Liturgical Psalter*
David Frost and others
Music: I Atkins (1869–1953)

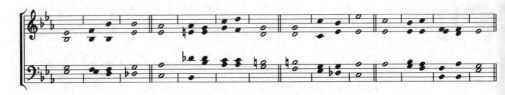

1 Praise the Lord ' O my ' soul:
   and all that is within me ' praise his ' holy ' name.
2 Praise the Lord ' O my ' soul:
   and for'get not ' all his ' benefits,

3 who forgives ' all your ' sin:
   and ' heals ' all · your in'firmities,
4 who redeems your ' life · from the ' Pit:
   and crowns you with ' mercy ' and com'passion;

Second part
5 who satisfies your being with ' good ' things:
   so that your ' youth · is re'newed · like an ' eagle's.

6 The Lord ' works ' righteousness:
   and justice for ' all who ' are op'pressed.
7 He made known his ' ways to ' Moses:
   and his ' works · to the ' children · of ' Israel.

8 The Lord is full of com'passion · and ' mercy:
   slow to anger ' and of ' great ' goodness.
9 He will not ' always · be ' chiding:
   nor will he ' keep his ' anger · for ' ever.

10 He has not dealt with us ac'cording · to our ' sins:
    nor rewarded us ac'cording ' to our ' wickedness.
11 For as the heavens are high a'bove the ' earth:
    so great is his ' mercy · over ' those that ' fear him;

12   as far as the east is ˈ from the ˈ west:
     so far has he ˈ set our ˈ sins ˈ from us.
13   As a father is tender toˈwards his ˈ children:
     so is the Lord ˈ tender · to ˈ those that ˈ fear him.

Second part
14   For he knows of ˈ what · we are ˈ made:
     he reˈmembers · that we ˈ are but ˈ dust.

15   The days of man are ˈ but as ˈ grass:
     he flourishes ˈ like a ˈ flower · of the ˈ field;
16   when the wind goes over it ˈ it is ˈ gone:
     and its ˈ place will ˈ know it · no ˈ more.

17   But the merciful goodness of the Lord
     endures for ever and ever toward ˈ those that ˈ fear him:
     and his righteousness upˈon their ˈ children's ˈ children;
18   upon those who ˈ keep his ˈ covenant:
     and reˈmember · his comˈmandments · to ˈ do them.

19   The Lord has established his ˈ throne in ˈ heaven:
     and his ˈ kingdom ˈ rules · over ˈ all.
20   Praise the Lord all you his angels
     you that exˈcel in ˈ strength:
     you that fulfil his word
     and obey the ˈ voice of ˈ his comˈmandment.

21   Praise the Lord all ˈ you his ˈ hosts:
     his ˈ servants · who ˈ do his ˈ will.
22   Praise the Lord all his works
     in all places of ˈ his doˈminion:
     praise the ˈ Lord ˈ O my ˈ soul!

     Glory to the Father and ˈ to the ˈ Son:
     and ˈ to the ˈ Holy ˈ Spirit;
     as it was in the beˈginning · is ˈ now:
     and shall be for ˈ ever. ˈ Aˈmen.

103C The Lord is full of compassion

Words: from Psalm 103
from *The Liturgical Psalter*
David Frost and others
Music: Philip Moore

SOPRANO
p
The Lord is full of com‑pas‑sion and mer‑cy: slow to anger and of great good‑ness.

He will not al‑ways be chid‑ing: nor will he keep_ his an‑ger for ev‑er.

TENOR & BASS
p
He has not dealt with us ac‑cord‑ing to our sins:____

nor rewarded us according to our wick-ed-ness. For as the heavens are

high a-bove the earth:_ so great is his mer-cy o-ver those that fear him;

as far as the east is from_ the west:_ so far has he

set our sins from us. As a father is tender to-wards his child-ren:

so is the Lord ten - der to those __ that fear him.

SOPRANO

For he knows of what we are made: __ he remembers that we

are __ but dust. The days of man are but as grass: __ he flourishes

like __ a flower of the field; __ when the wind goes over it

TENOR & BASS

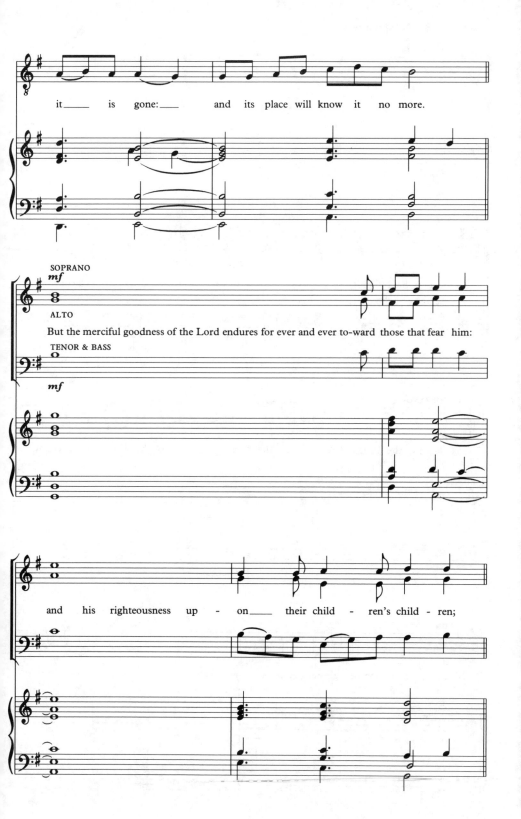

it___ is gone:___ and its place will know it no more.

SOPRANO

mf

ALTO

But the merciful goodness of the Lord endures for ever and ever to-ward those that fear him:

TENOR & BASS

mf

and his righteousness up - on___ their child - ren's child - ren;

SOPRANO
ALTO

upon those who keep his co - ven - ant: and re -

TENOR

BASS

-mem - ber his com - mand - ments to do them.

SOPRANO

p

Glory to the Father and to — the Son: — and to the Ho - ly Spi - rit;

UNISON

ST

p

AB

as it was in the be - gin-ning is now: — and shall be for ev - er. A - men. —

All things I see

Haresfield 8 6 8 6 (CM)

Words: from Psalm 104
Brian Foley
Music: J Dykes Bower (1905–1981)

1 All things I see, Lord, call to me to
2 I see your beau - ty in the dawn, your
3 Your wa - ters ga - ther in the skies and
4 All things that grow, all things that live, and

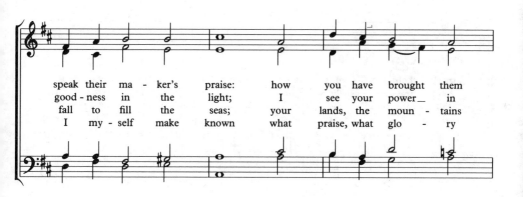

speak their ma - ker's praise: how you have brought them
good - ness in the light; I see your power in
fall to fill the seas; your lands, the moun - tains
I my - self make known what praise, what glo - ry

all to be and guide them in their ways.
winds and storm, your wis - dom in the night.
where they rise, are or - dered as you please.
I must give to you, my God, a - lone.

Music: © Royal School of Church Music,
Addington Palace, Croydon, Surrey CR9 5AD

Words: from the *New Catholic Hymnal*
© 1971 Faber Music Ltd,
3 Queen Square, London WC1N 3AU

104A(ii)   All things I see

Southwell (Irons) 8 6 8 6 (CM)

Words: from Psalm 104
Brian Foley
Music: H S Irons (1834–1905)

1 All things I see, Lord, call to me to
2 I see your beauty in the dawn, your
3 Your waters gather in the skies and
4 All things that grow, all things that live, and

speak their maker's praise: how you have brought them
good - ness in the light; I see your power in
fall to fill the seas; your lands, the mountains
I my - self make known what praise, what glo - ry

all to be and guide them in their ways.
winds and storm, your wis - dom in the night.
where they rise, are or - dered as you please.
I must give to you, my God, a - lone.

Words: from the *New Catholic Hymnal*
© 1971 Faber Music Ltd,
3 Queen Square, London WC1N 3AU

O bless the Lord, my soul

Brightwell Baldwin 8 6 8 6 (CM)

Words: from Psalm 104
Michael Perry
Music: John Barnard

1 'O bless the Lord, my soul!' I sing, and
2 For like a tent you spread the sky, on
MEN 3 You bind the sea, or loose the storm in

wor - ship day and night_____ my God ar - rayed in
cha - riot - clouds you ride;_____ and by the wind, your
light - ning's pri - mal flame;_____ the ris - ing spring and

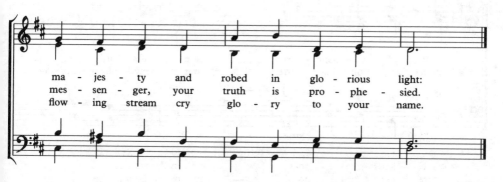

ma - jes - ty and robed in glo - rious light:
mes - sen - ger, your truth is pro - phe - sied.
flow - ing stream cry glo - ry to your name.

ALL
4 O mighty Lord of every land,
    you know our human need,
and all the creatures of the earth
    you guide and tend and feed.

WOMEN
5 The sun and moon appear and set
    controlled by hidden force;
the stars declare your faithfulness,
    consistent in their course.

ALL
6 Yet what you give, O sovereign Lord,
    your power can take away;
our life and death belong to you
    until our dying day.

7 So let me sing your worthy praise,
    your matchless grace extol
till all creation join the hymn:
    'O bless the Lord, my soul!'

Alternative tune: Bishopthorpe, *Psalms for Today* 92A(ii), *Hymns for Today's Church* 379

104C The majesty of mountains

Eythorne 7 6 8 6 8 6

Words: from Psalm 104
Michael Perry
Music: John Barnard

1 The ma-jes-ty of moun-tains, the__ sov-ereign-ty of
skies,__ the__ re-gal rocks that arch a-bove where.
veils__ of va-pour rise,_____ are gifts of God, the
Lord of love, the__ wor-ship-ful, the wise.

2 The run-ning of the ri-ver, the__ surg-ing of the
sea,__ the__ grass that grows high on the hill, the__
flower. and fruit-ing tree,_____ our Sav-iour sends us,
by whose will all__ crea-tures came to be.

106A

Alleluia! Love eternal

South Ormsby 8 7 8 7 and Alleluias

Words: from Psalm 106
Paul Wigmore
Music: Paul Edwards

1 Al - le - lu - ia! Love e - ter - nal flows from
2 Though his peo - ple sinned a - gainst him, wor - shipped
3 Save us, Lord, in your great good - ness, hear us

God's most grac-ious heart. Who can show how great the Lord is? Where the
gods of wood and stone, he de - liv - ered, loved and blessed them! Was such
cal - ling, now as then; as our prais - es rise to greet you, let the

skill and where the art?
mer - cy ev - er shown? Al - le - lu - ia, al - le - lu - ia!
peo - ple say, 'A - men!'

Original key: G

Give God thanks

Cwm Rhondda 8 7 8 7 4 7 extended

Words: from Psalm 107
David Mowbray
Music: J Hughes (1873–1932)

1 'Give God thanks for he___ is___ gra-cious!' now may Is-rael
2 When God's peo - ple walked the___ des - ert, hun - gry, thir - sty,
3 Those who steer their ships_ through trou - ble, ride the storm and
4 Give God thanks for all___ his___ mer - cies: fields are wa - tered,

tru - ly say; through great tri - als he___ has__ brought us
faint of heart; he pre - pared for them_ a___ ci - ty,
plumb the deep, reach at length their pro - mised ha - ven,
crops are sown, sheep and cat - tle fill___ the___ pas - tures,

to the dawn of__ this new day.
gave them hope and_ took their part.
bless that grace which brings them sleep.   All God's child-ren,_ all God's child-ren,
babes in arms have safe - ly grown.

praise the won-ders he has done (he has done), praise the won - ders he has done!

108A

Horsell 8 6 8 6 (CM)

My heart is ready

Words: from Psalm 108
Christopher Idle
Music: Gareth D Green

Moderato

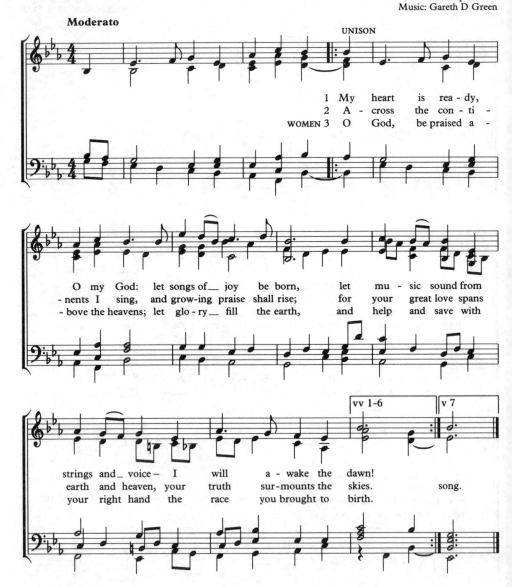

UNISON

1 My heart is rea-dy,
2 A - cross the con - ti -
WOMEN 3 O God, be praised a -

O my God: let songs of— joy be born, let mu - sic sound from
- nents I sing, and grow-ing praise shall rise; for your great love spans
- bove the heavens; let glo - ry— fill the earth, and help and save with

vv 1-6 | v 7

strings and— voice — I will a - wake the dawn!
earth and heaven, your truth sur-mounts the skies.
your right hand the race you brought to birth.

song.

MEN
4 God speaks from his pure sanctuary
  to claim both west and east:
  'The plains and mountains all are mine,
  the greatest and the least.'

WOMEN
5 'My people are my battle-dress,
  my sceptre, helm, and sword;
  while rebel nations have become
  a footstool for the Lord!'

MEN
6 Who else can give us victory
  and break the strongholds down?
  O God, if you reject us now
  we cannot fight alone.

ALL
7 How useless is all human help
  when facing stubborn wrong!
  But we shall triumph in the Lord,
  and God shall be our song.

Alternative tune: St Fulbert, *Hymns for Today's Church* 168

This is the word

110

Pokesdown   8 8 8 8 (LM)

Words: from Psalm 110
Brian Foley
Music: Michael Dawney

UNISON

1 This is the word of God's de - cree, the
2 'That Ci - ty built for me of old, his
3 'A King to rule – my oath, my word! – a
4 'A Judge when earth - ly king - doms fall, to

voice of God who ev - er is: 'I send my Son, true
throne makes strong - er, ho - lier still; the Reign of Jus - tice,
great - er King than kings be - fore; a Priest to pray – and
speak his ver - dict on their ways; and then my Son, the

Son to me, to make all king - doms ev - er his!
long fore - told, this Son of mine will there ful - fil!
will be heard! – of high - est Priest - hood ev - er - more;
King of all, will bring to me his King - dom's praise!'

Alternative tune: Splendour, *Psalms for Today* 70, *Hymns for Today's Church* 118

111A God's holy ways are just and true

Easter Song 8 8 4 4 8 8 and Alleluias

Words: from Psalm 111
Barbara Woollett
Music: *Geistliche Kirchengesang* Cologne 1623
adapted David Iliff

1 God's ho - ly ways are just and true, his
2 Bring back to mind his grace and love, our
3 Tell once a - gain his deeds of old, the

pro - mis - es are ev - er___ new, O___ praise_ him, al - le -
needs pro - vid - ed from a - bove; O___ praise_ him, al - le -
sto - ry of our migh - ty___ God, O___ praise_ him, al - le -

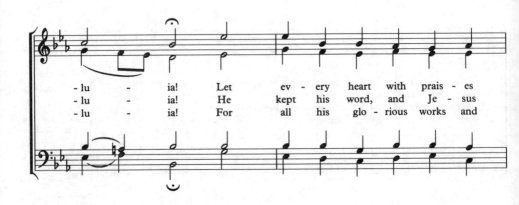

- lu - ia! Let ev - ery heart with prais - es
- lu - ia! He kept his word, and Je - sus
- lu - ia! For all his glo - rious works and

sing_____ and make this house with voi - ces
came_____ to make a peo - ple for his
ways_____ we shall re - joice through end - less

ring;___ O___ praise_ him, O___ praise_ him! Al - le -
name;___
days;___

-lu - ia,___ al - le - lu - ia, al - le - lu - ia!

112(i) How blessed are those who live by faith

Cross Deep 8 8 8 8 (LM)

Words: from Psalm 112
Michael Perry
Music: Barry Rose

UNISON

1 How blessed are those who live by faith, de -
2 How hap - py those who free - ly give, who
3 How joy - ful those who, strong for truth, re -
4 Then praise the Lord – let joy - ful praise to

- light - ing in God's sure com - mand; for rich in grace will
just - ly deal and kind - ly care; for in their dark - ness
- ly up - on the Lord most high; un - like the wick - ed
Fa - ther, Spi - rit, Son be given; to God who loved us,

be their homes, their child - ren migh - ty in the land:
light shall dawn, and long shall be their me - mory here:
they shall live, and lift their heads up to the sky!
came to save and fills our hearts with grace from heaven!

How blessed are those who live by faith 112(ii)

Morning Hymn 8 8 8 8 (LM)

Words: from Psalm 112
Michael Perry
Music: melody by F H Barthélémon (1741–1808)

1 How__ blessed are those who__ live by faith, de-
2 How__ hap - py those who__ free - ly give, who
3 How__ joy - ful those who, __ strong for truth, re-
4 Then__ praise the Lord – let__ joy - ful praise to

-light - ing in__ God's sure com - mand; for__ rich in__ grace will__
just - ly deal__ and__ kind - ly care; for__ in their__ dark - ness__
-ly up - on__ the__ Lord most high; un - like the__ wick - ed__
Fa - ther, Spi - rit,__ Son be given; to__ God who__ loved us,__

be their homes, their child - ren migh - ty__ in the land:
light shall dawn, and long shall be__ their__ me - mory here:
they shall live, and lift their heads__ up__ to the sky!
came to save and fills our hearts__ with__ grace from heaven!

113A Servants of the living Lord

Slovenia 7 7 7 7 7 7

Words: from Psalm 113
Timothy Dudley-Smith
Music: Colin Evans

UNISON

1 Ser - vants of the liv - ing Lord, bend in awe be - fore his throne,_____ tell his ma - jes - ty a - broad,
2 Age to age, his name be blessed, An - cient of e - ter - nal days._____ Fur - thest bounds of east and west
3 Who like him in glo - ry reigns high - er than the heavens are high?_____ he who world on world sus - tains,
4 Lord of grace! In him we trust; by his love the lost are found,_____ low - ly lift - ed from the dust,

Alternative tune: St Petersburg, *Psalms for Today* 25A

200

know and name him God a - lone.
e - cho his per - pet - ual praise:
sun and stars and sea and sky:
hap - py homes with child - ren crowned.

Join to praise the
ev - er - liv - ing
he it is who,
All who stand be -

Lord of grace,
Lord of grace,
Lord of grace,
- fore his face,

all who stand be - fore his
throned be - yond all time and
hears from heaven, his dwell - ing -
praise, O praise, the Lord of

vv 1-3

face.
space.
- place.

v 4

grace!

201

114   When Israel broke their cruel chains

Dundee 8 6 8 6 (CM)

Words: from Psalm 114
David Mowbray
Music: *Scottish Psalter* Edinburgh 1615

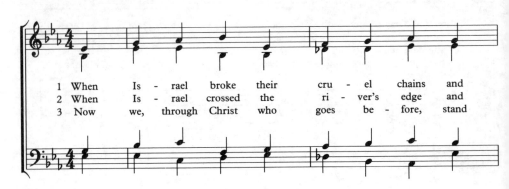

1 When Is - rael broke their cru - el chains and
2 When Is - rael crossed the ri - ver's edge and
3 Now we, through Christ who goes be - fore, stand

E - gypt lost the day, the Lord's own peo - ple
reached the pro - mised land, they felt in their de -
firm on so - lid ground; we sing God's praise, and

sang for joy and laughed up - on their way.
- liv - er - ance the touch of____ God's good hand.
all the earth shall trem - ble____ at the sound.

Not to us be glory given 115

Lux Eoi 8 7 8 7 D

Words: from Psalm 115
Timothy Dudley-Smith
Music: A Sullivan (1842–1900)

1 Not to us be glo - ry giv - en but to him who reigns a - bove.
2 Not what hu - man fin - gers fash - ion, gold and sil - ver, deaf and blind,
3 Not in them is hope of bless - ing— hope is in the liv - ing Lord!
4 Not the dead, but we the liv - ing praise the Lord with all our powers;

Glo - ry to the God of hea - ven for his faith - ful - ness and love!
dead to know-ledge and com - pas - sion, hav - ing nei - ther— heart nor mind –
High and low, his name con - fess - ing, find in him their shield and sword;
of his good-ness free - ly giv - ing— his is hea - ven; earth is ours.

What though un - be - liev - ing voi - ces hear no word and— see no sign,
life - less gods, some yet a - dore them, nerve-less hands and— feet of clay;
hope of all whose hearts re - vere him, God of Is - rael,— still the same!
Not to us be glo - ry giv - en but to him who— reigns a - bove.

still in God my heart re - joic - es, work-ing out his will di - vine.
all be - come, who bow be - fore them, lost in - deed, and dead as they.
God of Aa - ron! Those who fear him, he re - mem - bers them by name.
Glo - ry to the God of hea - ven, for his faith - ful - ness and love!

Alternative tune: Alleluia, *Psalms for Today* 34A, *Hymns for Today's Church* 428

203

116A(i) I love the Lord, he heard my voice

Carter Knowle 8 8 8 8 8 8

Words: from Psalm 116
Barbara Woollett
Music: Derek Williams

Refrain

Let love to love re-spond and_ say, 'O praise the Lord with me to-day!'

Verses

1 I love the Lord, he heard my voice,   he list-ened when I called his name;
2 When dark des-pair en-tan-gled me,   in depths of grief I called his name;
3 I cried with sor-row ma-ny tears –   in guil-ty dread I called his name;

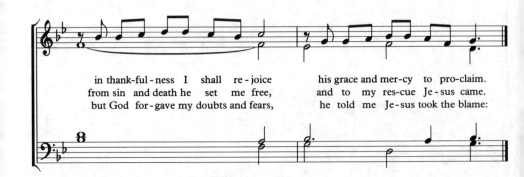

in thank-ful-ness I shall re-joice   his grace and mer-cy to pro-claim.
from sin and death he set me free,   and to my res-cue Je-sus came.
but God for-gave my doubts and fears,   he told me Je-sus took the blame:

4 Now that I know he answers prayer,
    with child-like trust I'll call his name;
    when there is no one else to care
    his steadfast love will stay the same.
        Let love to love . . .

5 Turn to the Lord, his word obey,
    lift up your voice and call his name;
    ask him to lead you in his way –
    his promised love is yours to claim:
        Let love to love . . .

The refrain can be sung in 4-part harmony.

I love the Lord, he heard my voice   116A(ii)

St Matthias   8 8 8 8 8 8

Words: from Psalm 116
Barbara Woollett
Music: W H Monk (1823–1889)

1 I love the Lord, he heard my voice, he list-ened when I called his name; in thank-ful-ness I shall re-joice his grace and mer-cy to pro-claim.

2 When dark des-pair en-tan-gled me, in depths of grief I called his name; from sin and death he set me free, and to my res-cue Je-sus came. Let love to love re-spond and say, 'O praise the Lord with me to-day!'

3 I cried with sor-row ma-ny tears – in guil-ty dread I called his name; but God for-gave my doubts and fears, he told me Je-sus took the blame:

4 Now that I know he answers prayer,
with child-like trust I'll call his name;
when there is no one else to care
his steadfast love will stay the same.
Let love to love . . .

5 Turn to the Lord, his word obey,
lift up your voice and call his name;
ask him to lead you in his way –
his promised love is yours to claim:
Let love to love . . .

Words: Barbara Woollett/Jubilate Hymns †

116B   How can I repay the Lord

Words: Psalm 116
adapted from *The Liturgical Psalter*
David Frost and others
Music: Stephen Dean and John Barnard

How can I repay the Lord
for all the goodness he shows to me?

1 I love the Lord because he ' heard my ' voice:
   the ' voice of · my ' suppli'cation;
2 because he in'clined his ' ear to me:
   in the ' day ' that I ' called to him.
   How can I repay ...

3 The cords of death encompassed me
   the snares of the ' grave took ' hold on me:
   I ' was in ' anguish · and ' sorrow.
4 Then I called upon the ' name · of the ' Lord:
   'O ' Lord · I be'seech you · de'liver me!'
   How can I repay ...

5 Gracious and righteous ' is the ' Lord:
   full of com'passion ' is our ' God.
6 The Lord pre'serves the ' simple:
   when ' I was · brought ' low he ' saved me.
   How can I repay ...

7 Return O my ' soul · to your ' rest:
   for the ' Lord ' has re'warded you.
8 For you O Lord have delivered my ' soul from ' death:
   my eyes from ' tears · and my ' feet from ' falling.
   How can I repay ...

There should be no pause between the end of the verses
and the start of the introduction to the Refrain.

Praise the Lord, all nations, praise 117A

Veni Sancte Spiritus 7 7 7 D

Words: from Psalm 117
Christopher Idle
Music: later form of melody by
S Webbe the elder (1740–1816)

Praise the Lord, all na - tions, praise; wor - ship God, all hu - man-kind:

Al - le - lu - ia, praise the Lord! Migh-ty is your love_ for us,

firm for ev - er is your truth: Al - le - lu - ia, praise the Lord!

117B   Praise him, you nations

Laudate Dominum

Words: from Psalm 117
Taizé
Words and music: Jacques Berthier

na - tions, praise him, you peo - ples; praise him, praise him,

praise_ the Lord; praise him, you na - tions, praise him, you

peo - ples; praise him, praise him, praise_ the Lord;

The Refrain is intended to act as an accompaniment to the Verses:
A and B indicate coinciding points in Verse and Refrain.

118A(i) Open the gates of righteousness

Sennen Cove 8 6 8 6 (CM)

Words: from Psalm 118
David Mowbray
Music: W H Harris (1883–1973)

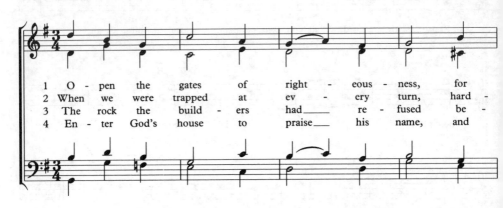

1 O - pen the gates of right - eous - ness, for
2 When we were trapped at ev - ery turn, hard -
3 The rock the build - ers had re - fused be -
4 En - ter God's house to praise his name, and

we have come to pray; to of - fer thanks for
- pressed on ev - ery side, the Lord our God came
- came the cor - ner - stone: who can de - ny this
all his tri - umphs tell; sal - ute the peo - ple

all God's gifts with - in his house to - day.
to our help and all our bonds un - tied.
is a thing the Lord him - self has done?
of the Lord = Be - loved, we wish you well!

Open the gates of righteousness 118A(ii)

Chorus Angelorum 8 6 8 6 (CM)

Words: from Psalm 118
David Mowbray
Music: A Somervell (1863–1937)

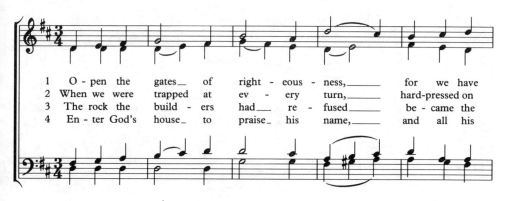

1 O - pen the gates__ of right - eous - ness,____ for we have
2 When we were trapped at ev - ery turn,____ hard-pressed on
3 The rock the build - ers had__ re - fused____ be - came the
4 En - ter God's house__ to praise__ his name,____ and all his

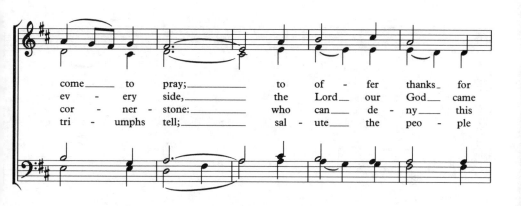

come____ to pray;_____ to of - fer thanks_ for
ev - ery side,_____ the Lord__ our God__ came
cor - ner - stone:_____ who can__ de - ny____ this
tri - umphs tell;_____ sal - ute__ the peo - ple

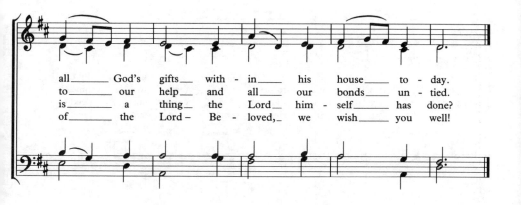

all____ God's gifts__ with - in____ his house____ to - day.
to____ our help__ and all____ our bonds____ un - tied.
is____ a thing__ the Lord__ him - self____ has done?
of____ the Lord – Be - loved,_ we wish____ you well!

The will of God

University 8 6 8 6 (CM)

Words: from Psalm 119
Timothy Dudley-Smith
Music: C Collignon (1725–1785)

1 The will of God to mark my way, the
2 Your eyes of mer - cy keep me still, your
3 With or - dered step se - cure and strong, from
4 So set my heart to love your word and

word of God for light; e - ter - nal jus - tice
gra - cious love be mine; so work in me your
sin's op - pres - sion freed, re - deemed from ev - ery
ev - ery pro - mise prove, to walk with truth be -

to o - bey in ev - er - last - ing right.
per - fect will and cause your face to shine.
kind of wrong in thought and word and deed –
- fore the Lord in right - eous - ness and love.

212

With all my heart I seek   119B

Ibstone 6 6 6 6

Words: from Psalm 119
David Mowbray
Music: M Tiddeman (1837–1915)

1 With all my heart I seek the true and liv-ing— way!
2 Let me not wa-ver now from sim-ple hon-es— ty,
3 Your laws and your com-mands re-main my great de-light;
4 Through youth and through old age, Lord, may I not for-get

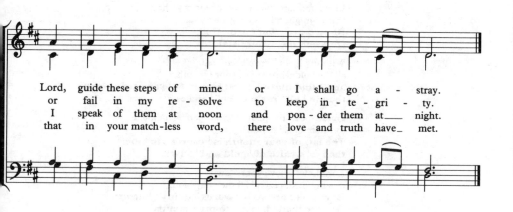

Lord, guide these steps of mine or I shall go a-stray.
or fail in my re-solve to keep in-te-gri-ty.
I speak of them at noon and pon-der them at— night.
that in your match-less word, there love and truth have— met.

119C Blessed are those whose way is blameless

Words: from Psalm 119
from *The Liturgical Psalter*
David Frost and others
Music: E J Hopkins (1818–1901)

Blessed are those whose ' way is ' blameless:
who ' walk · in the ' law · of the ' Lord.
Blessed are those who ' keep · his com'mands:
and seek him ' with their ' whole ' heart.

I have treasured your ' words · in my ' heart:
that I ' might not ' sin a'gainst you.
Blessed are ' you Lord ' God:
O ' teach me ' your ' statutes.

With my lips I ' have been ' telling:
all the ' judgements ' of your ' mouth;
and I find more joy in the way of ' your com'mands:
than in ' all ' manner · of ' riches.

Guide me in the path of ' your com'mandments:
for there'in is ' my de'light.
The law of your mouth is ' dearer · to ' me:
than a ' wealth of ' gold and ' silver.

Lord how I ' love your ' law:
it is my medi'tation ' all the · day ' long.
How sweet are your ' words · to my ' tongue:
sweeter than ' honey ' to my ' mouth.

Your word is a lantern ' to my ' feet:
and a ' light ' to my ' path.
Your commands are my in'heritance · for ' ever:
they ' are the ' joy of · my ' heart.

Glory to the Father and ' to the ' Son:
and ' to the ' Holy ' Spirit;
as it was in the be'ginning · is ' now:
and shall be for ' ever. 'A'men.

I see the mountains far away

Eureka 8 8 8 8 (LM)

Words: from Psalm 121
Brian Foley
Music: from *The Good Old Songs* 1913
arranged David Iliff

121A

1 I see the moun - tains far a - way, the____
2 I look be - yond fa - mil - iar things, be -
3 Yet God is pre - sent where I am, a____
4 My place in his - tory and my name, my____

bor - ders of the____ world I know, where____ God, it seems, must____
- yond the li - mits____ set for me,____ to____ where, it seems, God____
hid - den God, though____ ev - er near,____ not____ one who lives and____
years, my days, and____ all they bring - in____ these I see God's____

live a - lone in____ pla - ces where I may not go!
hides him - self, too____ far, too deep, in se - cre - cy!
loves a - lone, but____ God, my God, who loves me here.
will for me, his____ love for me, in ev - ery - thing.

Alternative tune: Angels' Song, *Hymns for Today's Church* 306

215

I lift my eyes

Davos 9 8 9 7

Words: from Psalm 121
Timothy Dudley-Smith
Music: Michael Baughen and Elisabeth Crocker
arranged John Barnard

1 I lift my eyes to the qui-et hills in the
2 I lift my eyes to the qui-et hills to a
4 I lift my eyes to the qui-et hills and my

press of a bu-sy day; as green hills stand se-cure and still
calm that is mine to share;
heart to the Fa-ther's throne; in all my ways

in a dus-ty land so God is my strength and stay.
in the Fa-ther's will and kept by the Fa-ther's care.
to the end of days the Lord will pre-serve his own.

3 I lift my eyes_____ to the qui - et hills with a

3 I lift my eyes to the qui - et____ hills with a

3 I lift my eyes_____ to the qui - et hills with a

3 I lift my eyes to the qui - et hills with a

prayer as I turn to sleep; by day, by night,____

prayer as I turn to sleep;_ by day, by night,

prayer as I turn to sleep; by____ day, by night,_____

prayer as I turn to sleep;_ by day, by night, through the

through the dark and light my Shep - herd will guard his sheep.

through the dark and light my Shep - herd will guard his sheep.

through the____ dark and light my Shep - herd will guard his sheep.

dark and light my Shep - herd will guard his sheep.

The Harmony version is harmonically compatible with the Unison setting.

121C   I will lift up my eyes to the hills

From Psalm 121
Words and music: Mark Pallant
and Steven Brazier

The accompaniment for verse 1 is also suitable for verses 2 and 3.

The accompaniment may be sung in harmony (alto, tenor and bass) to *Ah*.

218

slum - ber;___ he who watch - es o - ver

Is - ra - el will nei - ther slum - ber_ nor sleep.

2 The Lord, he is your___ guard - ian,___ the
Lord is your de-fence at your right hand;___ the sun will not harm. you_ by
day_____ nor the moon_____ by night.

3 The Lord will pro - tect you from all dan - ger,___
he will watch o - ver_ your life;___ the Lord will guard your com-ing and your
go - ing,___ both now_____ and for ev - er - more._

Refrain after verse 3 overleaf

219

121c I will lift up my eyes to the hills

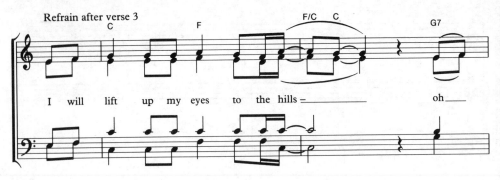

Refrain after verse 3

I will lift up my eyes to the hills — oh —

where — shall I find — my help? — My — help will come — from the

Lord, — the ma - ker of hea - ven, — the

the — ma - ker

ma - ker of hea - ven, — the ma - ker of hea - ven — and earth.

I lift up my eyes to the hills

121D

Words: Psalm 121
from *The Liturgical Psalter*
David Frost and others
Music: Barry Rose

1 I lift up my ' eyes · to the ' hills:
  but ' where · shall I ' find ' help?
2 My help ' comes · from the ' Lord:
  who has ' made ' heaven · and ' earth.

3 He will not suffer your ' foot to ' stumble:
  and he who watches ' over · you ' will not ' sleep.
4 Be sure he who has ' charge of ' Israel:
  will ' neither ' slumber · nor ' sleep.

5 The Lord him'self is · your ' keeper:
  the Lord is your defence up'on your ' right ' hand;
6 the sun shall not ' strike you · by ' day:
  nor ' shall the ' moon by ' night.

7 The Lord will defend you from ' all ' evil:
  it is ' he · who will ' guard your ' life.
8 The Lord will defend your going out and your ' coming ' in:
  from this time ' forward · for ' ever'more.

Glory to the Father and ' to the ' Son:
and ' to the ' Holy ' Spirit;
as it was in the be'ginning · is ' now:
and shall be for ' ever. ' A'men.

Set for Her Majesty the Queen's Jubilee Service in St Paul's Cathedral, 7th June 1977.
Original key: F

122A I rejoiced to hear them say

St George's, Windsor 7 7 7 7 D

Words: from Psalm 122
Basil Bridge
Music: G J Elvey (1816–1893)

1 I re-joiced to hear them say, 'Come and wor - ship God to - day!
2 Here in gra - ti - tude we bring all we are to serve our King;
3 God, the Lord of peace, is near – come in faith, and meet him here;

Come, with heart and mind and soul, seek the peace that makes us whole;
his for - give - ness we en - treat in whom love and jus - tice meet:
let each rest - less soul be still, glad to know and do his will:

see dis - or - dered lives re - stored in the pre - sence of the Lord:
bring our needs to him in prayer, ask his help, and trust his care;
as a ci - ty's walls and towers of - fered safe - ty – God is ours!

from your bur - dens find re - lease; in his pre - sence there is peace.'
join with all, in ev - ery place, who have sought and known his grace.
There - fore we re - joice, and say, 'Come and wor - ship God to - day!'

Jerusalem! How glad I was

122B

Durrow 8 6 8 6 D (DCM)

Words: from Psalm 122
Christopher Idle
Music: Irish traditional melody
arranged John Barnard

1 Je - ru - sa - lem! How glad I was when they in - vit - ed me
2 Je - ru - sa - lem! A ci - ty built com - pact and walled a - round;
3 Je - ru - sa - lem! May you have peace, your peo - ple long en - dure;

to climb with them the mount of prayer, the place of ma - jes - ty:
the sa - cred tribes as - cend - ed here and made their psalms re - sound.
may all your ci - ti - zens be safe, your towers and streets se - cure.

Je - ru - sa - lem! With - in your gates our will - ing feet have stood,
Let us, like Is - ra - el, go up to pay the Lord our dues,
For bro - thers, sis - ters, friends, I pray let peace re - turn a - gain:

and there we raised our voic - es high to fill the house of God.
to hear the judge - ments of the law, the joy of God's good news.
O Lord our God, meet us in grace, in glo - ry come to reign!

Alternative tune: Kingsfold, *Hymns for Today's Church* 457

123A(i) I lift my eyes to you

West Wickham 6 6 8 6 (SM)

Words: from Psalm 123
Christopher Idle
Music: Alan Ridout

1 I lift my eyes to you, to heaven your
2 Have mer - cy, Lord, we pray, and hear your
3 The proud have mocked us long, their scorn we

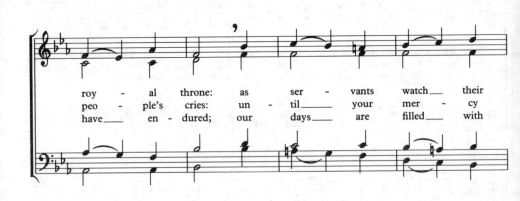

roy - al throne: as ser - vants watch their
peo - ple's cries: un - til your mer - cy
have en - dured; our days are filled with

mas - ter's hand we look to you a - lone.
reach - es us on you we fix our eyes.
their con - tempt: we look to you, O Lord.

I lift my eyes to you

St Michael 6 6 8 6 (SM)

Words: from Psalm 123
Christopher Idle
Music: *Genevan Psalter* 1551
adapted W Crotch (1775–1847)

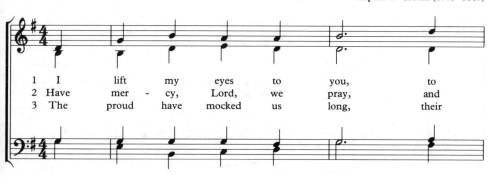

1 I lift my eyes to you, to
2 Have mer - cy, Lord, we pray, and
3 The proud have mocked us long, their

heaven your roy - al throne: as ser - vants watch their
hear your peo - ple's cries: un - til your mer - cy
scorn we have en - dured; our days are filled with

mas - ter's hand we look___ to you a - lone.
reach - es us on you___ we fix our eyes.
their con - tempt: we look___ to you, O Lord.

123B Master, we lift our eyes

Little Venice 4 5 4 5 D

Words: from Psalm 123
David Mowbray
Music: G H Knight (1908–1979)

1 Mas - ter, we lift_____ our eyes, ex - pect - ing__ your pro-mised gift,_____
2 Tri - ni - ty strong,____ source of all bless - ing:__ joy - ful our song,____

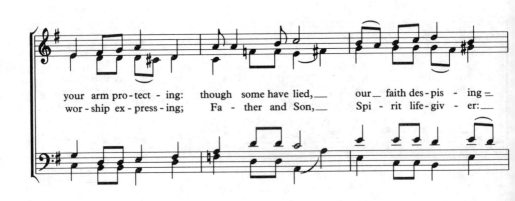

your arm pro-tect - ing: though some have lied,___ our__ faith des-pis - ing =
wor - ship ex - press - ing; Fa - ther and Son,___ Spi - rit life-giv - er:

you are our guide,___ rest - ing and ris - ing.
your will be done,___ now and for ev - er.

Words: © David Mowbray/Jubilate Hymns †

If the Lord had not been near 124A(i)

Anderson 7 7 7 5

Words: from Psalm 124
Paul Wigmore
Music: Jane Marshall

1 If____ the Lord had not been near,
2 If____ the Lord had not come in,
3 If____ the Lord who set us free
4 Swift____ and cer - tain to our aid

at____ our side and quick to hear, who__ would then have
strong to save from dead - ly sin, who__ would then have
did____ not hear us, could not see, who__ would then our
comes the one by whom were made star - ry hea - vens,

calmed our fear?
helped_ us win?   Let us praise the Lord!____
sav - iour be?
wood - land glade.

Original key: D♭

124A(ii) If the Lord had not been near

Capetown 7 7 7 5

Words: from Psalm 124
Paul Wigmore
Music: F Filitz (1804–1876)

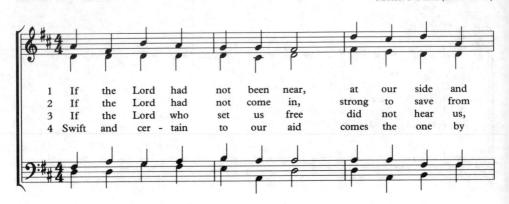

1 If the Lord had not been near, at our side and
2 If the Lord had not come in, strong to save from
3 If the Lord who set us free did not hear us,
4 Swift and cer - tain to our aid comes the one by

quick___ to hear,___ who would then have
dead - ly sin,___ who would then have
could___ not see,___ who would then our
whom___ were made___ star - ry hea - vens,

calmed our fear?___
helped us win?___ Let us praise the Lord!
sav - iour be?___
wood - land glade.___

Those who rely on the Lord

Was lebet   12 10 12 10

Words: from Psalm 125
Christopher Idle
Music: melody from manuscript
by J H Rheinhardt, Üttingen (1754)

1 Those who— re - ly on the Lord are un - shake - ab - le,
2 E - vil— shall not al - ways rule o - ver right - eous-ness,

firm— as mount Zi - on, su - preme - ly as - sured;
God's— time will come when op - press - ion shall cease:

just as— the moun - tains en - cir - cle Je - ru - sa - lem,
Lord, bless— the right - eous, re - strain the im - pe - ni - tent,

round us for ev - er is stand - ing the Lord.
grant to your peo - ple the gift of your peace.

126A

Laughter and song

Vossem 10 10

Words: from Psalm 126
David Mowbray
Music: David Iliff

UNISON

1 Laugh - ter and song! The Lord has done great things: his
peo - ple once were freed from ty - rant kings.

HARMONY

2 Yet now we wait in___ sad cap - ti - vi - ty: rise
3 Tears turn to joy! The___ weep - ing farm - er sows and,

up, re - deem - ing Lord, to set___ us free!
slow - ly through the storms, the har - vest grows.

The Unison and Harmony versions are not harmonically compatible.

Alternative tune: Song 46, *Psalms for Today* 68A, *Hymns for Today's Church* 149

When the Lord turned again 126B

Words: Psalm 126
from *The Liturgical Psalter*
David Frost and others

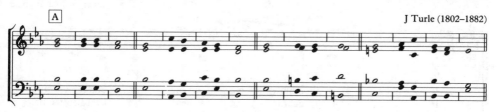

J Turle (1802–1882)

T A Walmisley (1814–1856)

1 When the Lord turned again the ' fortunes · of ' Zion:
   then were we like ' men re'stored to ' life.

2 Then was our mouth ' filled with ' laughter:
   and ' our ' tongue with ' singing.

3 Then said they a'mong the ' heathen:
   'The Lord has ' done great ' things for ' them.'

4 Truly the Lord has done great ' things for ' us:
   and ' therefore ' we re'joiced.

5 Turn again our ' fortunes · O ' Lord:
   as the streams re'turn · to the ' dry ' south.

6 Those that ' sow in ' tears:
   shall ' reap with ' songs of ' joy.

Second part
7 He who goes out weeping ' bearing · the ' seed:
   shall come again in gladness '
   bringing · his ' sheaves ' with him.

Glory to the Father and ' to the ' Son:
and ' to the ' Holy ' Spirit;
as it was in the be'ginning · is ' now:
and shall be for ' ever. ' A'men.

127A(i) If God is building when we build

Land of Rest 8 6 8 6 (CM)

Words: from Psalms 127 and 124
Brian Foley
Music: American folk melody
arranged John Barnard

1 If God is build - ing when we build, the
2 If God is guard - ing when we guard, he
3 If God is work - ing when we work to

house we raise will stand; if God de - signs when
keeps the watch we keep, pro - tects our ways, pro -
make the things we make; he gives ap - pro - val

we de - sign, his skill is in our hand:
- vides our days the har - vest that we reap:
and suc - cess to la - bour for his sake:

4 If God is speaking when we speak,
   our words become his word,
   and in the speech of everyday,
   eternal things are heard:

5 If God is building when we build,
   we call each work our own,
   but not for us to praise ourselves –
   our praise is God alone!

If God is building when we build   127A(ii)

McKee   8 6 8 6 (CM)

Words: from Psalms 127 and 124
Brian Foley
Music: American melody
arranged H T Burleigh (1866–1949)

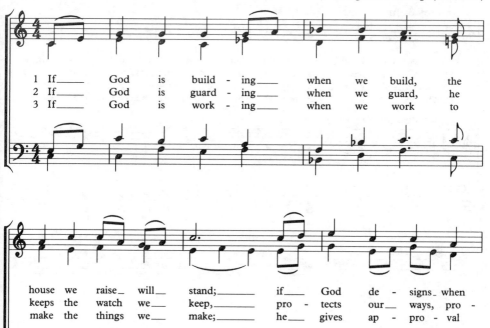

1 If____ God is build - ing____ when we build, the
2 If____ God is guard - ing____ when we guard, he
3 If____ God is work - ing____ when we work to

house we raise_ will_ stand;_____ if_ God de - signs_ when
keeps the watch we_ keep,_____ pro - tects our_ ways, pro -
make the things we_ make;_____ he_ gives ap - pro - val

we_ de - sign, his_ skill_ is in_ our hand:
-vides_ our_ days the_ har - vest that_ we reap:
and_ suc - cess to_ la - bour for_ his sake:

4   If God is speaking when we speak,
    our words become his word,
    and in the speech of everyday,
    eternal things are heard:

5   If God is building when we build,
    we call each work our own,
    but not for us to praise ourselves –
    our praise is God alone!

127B Unless the Lord has built the house

Hemsby 8 6 8 6 (CM)

Words: from Psalm 127
David Mowbray
Music: Mervyn Horder

UNISON OR HIGH VOICES

1 Un - less the Lord has built the house it must be built a - gain;
2 What va - lue has a life of haste, of end - less, an - xious toil?
3 A - mong God's gifts, a hap - py home a bless - ing rich in - deed;
4 That home, that house, as years go by must wea - ther storm and strain:

LOW VOICES (OPTIONAL)

ex - cept the Lord de - fends a town its watch - men wake in vain.
God has for those who keep his law a gar - land none can spoil:
a joy - ful, lov - ing part - ner - ship, a strength to those in need.
un - less the Lord has built the house it must be built a - gain.

Alternative tune: Albano, *Hymns for Today's Church* 135

Blessed are those who fear the Lord 128A

Innocents 7 7 7 7

Words: from Psalm 128
Christopher Idle
Music: *The Parish Choir* 1850

1 Blessed are those who fear the Lord, walk - ing
2 Bless - ings greet the hus - band, wife, par - ents,
3 Bless us, Lord! Your king - dom come; child - ren's

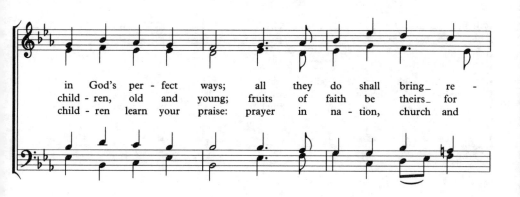

in God's per - fect ways; all they do shall bring re -
child - ren, old and young; fruits of faith be theirs for
child - ren learn your praise: prayer in na - tion, church and

- ward, love en - rich - es all their days.
life, joy in songs to - ge - ther sung.
home, peace in Christ to crown our days.

128B   Bless all who trust in God

Doncaster 6 6 8 6 (SM)

Words: from Psalm 128
David Mowbray
Music: S Wesley (1766–1837)

1 Bless all who trust in God and
2 Let mar - riag - es be strong and
3 And since we may not boast such

walk with - in God's_ ways; bless ev - ery soul whose
spar - kle bright as_ wine; let part - ners and let
joys are ours by_ right, teach us, good Lord, to

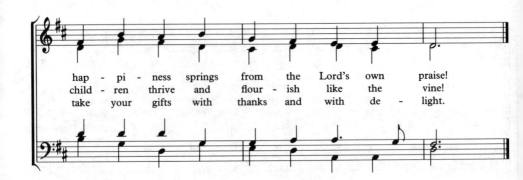

hap - pi - ness springs from the Lord's own praise!
child - ren thrive and flour - ish like the vine!
take your gifts with thanks and with de - light.

Alternative tune: Sandys, *Hymns for Today's Church* 493

Out of our failure to create

130A

Billing 8 6 8 6 (CM)

Words: from Psalm 130
Fred Kaan
Music: R R Terry (1865–1938)

1 Out of our fail - ure to＿＿ cre - ate a
2 Out of the dark - ness of＿＿ our time, of
3 Out of the depths we cry＿＿ to him whose
4 Hope in the Lord whose time - less love gives

world＿ of love＿ and care; out of＿＿ the＿ depths of
days＿ for ev - er gone, our souls＿ are＿ long - ing
will＿ is strong＿ and just; all hu - man＿ hole - and -
laugh - ter where＿ we wept; the 'Fa - ther, who＿ at

hu - man life＿＿ we cry＿＿ to God＿ in prayer.
for＿＿ the light, like watch - men for＿＿ the dawn.
- cor - ner ways＿ are by＿＿ his light＿ ex - posed.
ev - ery point＿ his word＿ has given＿ and kept.

Alternative tune: Gerontius, *Hymns for Today's Church* 140

130B   Up from the depths I cry to God

Macpherson's Farewell   8 6 8 6 D (DCM)

Words: from Psalm 130
Christopher Idle
Music: Scottish traditional melody
arranged David Iliff

1 Up from the depths I___ cry_ to_ God: O___ lis - ten, Lord, to me;___
2 If you, my God, should mea - sure guilt who then could ev - er stand?
3 O Is - rael, set your hope on_ God whose mer - cy is su - preme:

O_ hear my_ voice in__ this_ dis - tress, this_ mire of mi - se - ry.
But_ those who fear your name will find for - give-ness from your hand.
the_ na - tion mourn-ing_ for_ its_ sin he_ sure - ly will_ re - deem.

I___ wait for God with all my heart, my_ hope is in__ his__ word;___

and_ more than watch-men for the dawn I'm_ long-ing for_ the_ Lord.

Alternative tune: Kingsfold, *Hymns for Today's Church* 457

Out of the depths I cry

130C

Words: from Psalm 130
David Mowbray
Music: Robin Sheldon

Growing 6 6 6 6

1 Out of the depths I cry: O God, re-mem-ber me! What earth-ly help have I if you watch si-lent-ly?

2 If you watch si-lent-ly and mark things done a-miss, to whom then may I fly at such a time as this?

3 At such a time as this my soul waits for the Lord; no joy is there, no bliss with-out his sav-ing word.

4 With-out his sav-ing word, all hope for ev-er dies: speak now, most migh-ty Lord, and from the depths I rise!

vv 1-3   v 4

Alternative tune: Eccles, *Hymns for Today's Church* 409

131A   Before the Lord my soul is bowed

Herongate   8 8 8 8 (LM)

Words: from Psalm 131
Stephen Horsfall
Music: English traditional melody
collected R Vaughan Williams (1872–1958)
arranged David Iliff

1 Be - fore＿ the Lord＿ my soul＿ is bowed in
2 But I＿ have made＿ my spi - rit calm; my
3 Let grate - ful voi - ces tell＿ a - broad the

trust and quiet hu - mi - li - ty; I do＿ not let＿ my
soul is like a＿ child＿ at＿ rest who knows that it＿ is
migh - ty name that＿ we＿ a - dore: O Is - rael, hope＿ in

heart＿ grow proud or pon - der things too great＿ for me.
safe＿ from harm and sleeps up - on＿ its mo - ther's breast.
God＿ the Lord, your glo - ry now＿ and ev - er - more!

Lord, this thing I ask you

Belgravia 6 5 6 5

Words: from Psalm 131
David Mowbray
Music: Gareth D Green

1 Lord, this thing I ask you:
2 All God's sons and daugh - ters

hold in check my pride,
to his heart are dear:

as a child o - be - dient
let them now and al - ways

at its mo - ther's side.
trust, and ne - ver fear.

Alternative tune: North Coates, *Psalms for Today* 162B(ii), *Hymns for Today's Church* 384

132   As David took no rest

Elmore 8 6 8 6 (CM)

Words: from Psalm 132
David Mowbray
Music: Anthony Greening

1 As Da - vid took no rest un - til he housed the ark se - cure,
2 As Da - vid trust - ed God to set an heir up - on his throne,
3 A - rise, O Lord, and come to - day in your great power and might;·

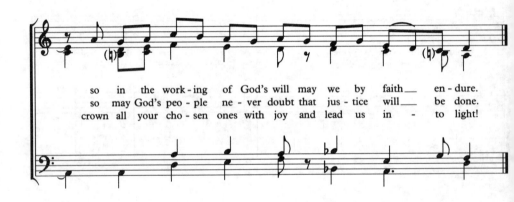

so in the work - ing of God's will may we by faith＿ en - dure.
so may God's peo - ple ne - ver doubt that jus - tice will＿ be done.
crown all your cho - sen ones with joy and lead us in - to light!

Alternative tune: Irish, *Hymns for Today's Church* 363

How good a thing it is

Steeple Ashton 6 6 8 6 (SM)

Words: from Psalm 133
J E Seddon (1915–1983)
Music: John Barnard

133A(i)

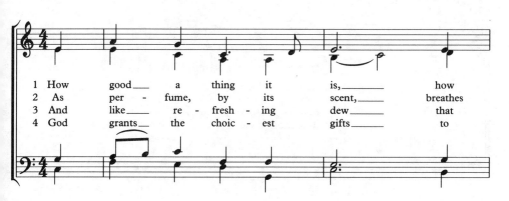

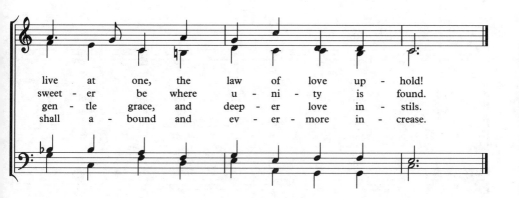

1 How good a thing it is, how
2 As perfume, by its scent, breathes
3 And like refreshing dew that
4 God grants the choicest gifts to

plea - sant to be - hold, when all God's peo - ple
fra - grance all a - round, so life it - self will
falls up - on the hills, true un - ion sheds its
those who live in peace; to them such bless - ings

live at one, the law of love up - hold!
sweet - er be where u - ni - ty is found.
gen - tle grace, and deep - er love in - stils.
shall a - bound and ev - er - more in - crease.

133A(ii)
How good a thing it is

Venice 6 6 8 6 (SM)

Words: from Psalm 133
J E Seddon (1915–1983)
Music: W Amps (1824–1910)

1 How good a thing it is, how
2 As per - fume, by its scent, breathes
3 And like re - fresh - ing dew that
4 God grants the choic - est gifts to

plea - sant to be - hold, when all God's peo - ple
fra - grance all a - round, so life it - self will
falls up - on the hills, true u - nion sheds its
those who live in peace; to them such bless - ings

live at one, the law of love up - hold!
sweet - er be where u - ni - ty is found.
gen - tle grace, and deep - er love in - stils.
shall a - bound and ev - er - more in - crease.

Behold how pleasant

Cornwall 8 8 6 8 8 6

Words: from Psalm 133
Keith Landis
Music: S S Wesley (1810–1876)

133B

1 Be - hold how____ plea - sant it shall____ be for____
those who dwell in u - ni - ty as____ child - ren of the____
Lord; though not by na - ture so in - clined, they
have in Christ one heart and____ mind, mi - ra - cu - lous ac - cord!

2 Like pre - cious____ oil poured on each____ head, like____
dew up - on mount Zi - on shed, his____ mer - cies free - ly____
flow; and ev - en more, the Lord com - mands the
fair - est bles - sing of his____ hands - e - ter - nal life to____ know!

134A

Bless the Lord as day departs

Asthall 7 8 7 8

Words: from Psalm 134,
Come bless the Lord
Timothy Dudley-Smith
Music: John Barnard

DESCANT

3 So may we who watch or rest bless the Lord of

1 Bless the Lord as day de-parts; let your lamps be
2 As with-in the dark-ened shrine, faith-ful to their
3 So may we who watch or rest bless the Lord of

earth and hea-ven; and by him our-selves be blessed,

bright-ly burn-ing, lift-ing ho-ly hands and hearts
sa-cred call-ing, sons and priests of Le-vi's line
earth and hea-ven; and by him our-selves be blessed,

grace and peace and mer-cy giv - en.

to the Lord, till day's re-turn-ing.
blessed the Lord as night was fall-ing:
grace and peace and mer-cy giv-en.

Come, praise the Lord

134B

Les Commandemens 9 8 9 8

Words: from Psalm 134,
Come bless the Lord
Christopher Idle
Music: L Bourgeois (c1510–c1561)
arranged mainly by C Goudimel (c1514–1572)

1 Come, praise the Lord, all you his ser - vants who stand with - in his
2 Come, bless the Lord, all those who love him, who serve with - in the

house by night; come lift your hands and hearts in
ho - ly place; may God who made both earth and

wor - ship, God be your praise and your de - light.
hea - ven grant us the bless - ings of his grace.

Alternative tune: Spiritus Vitae, *Hymns for Today's Church* 43

Come bless the Lord

134C

Words: from Psalm 134
Come bless the Lord
from *The Liturgical Psalter*
David Frost and others

J Stainer (1840–1901)

J Jones (1728–1796)

1 Come bless the Lord all you ' servants · of the ' Lord:
you that by night ' stand · in the ' house of · our ' God.

2 Lift up your hands toward the holy place and ' bless the ' Lord:
may the Lord bless you from Zion
the ' Lord who · made ' heaven · and ' earth.

Glory to the Father and ' to the ' Son:
and ' to the ' Holy ' Spirit;
as it was in the be'ginning · is ' now:
and shall be for ' ever. ' A'men.

Give thanks to God

Lyminge 8 8 7 D

Words: from Psalm 136
Paul Wigmore
Music: John Barnard

1 Give thanks to God, the Lord of all cre - a - tion's won - ders,
2 And to the joy of hu - man eye be - yond the earth he
3 And from op - press-ion's e - vil spell he led his peo - ple
4 Give thanks to God, the God of all, for he is good, he

great and small, whose
set the sky – his
Is - ra - el – his
hears our call, his

love en - dures for ev - er:_____

he gave the splen-dour of the earth, the birth of spring, the
he blessed the dark - ness with the light, the sun by day, the
through sea and de - sert, pain and fear their strength was his, for
our God is from e - ter - ni - ty, he lifts and feeds us,

Organ

win - ter's death –
stars by night – his_ love en - dures for ev - er.
he was near –
sets us free –

137A

By rivers of sorrow

Streets of Laredo   12 11 12 11

Words: from Psalms 137 and 138
Michael Perry
Music: American traditional melody
arranged Noël Tredinnick
Descant: David Iliff

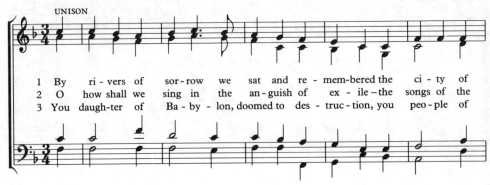

UNISON

1 By ri - vers of sor - row we sat and re - mem-bered the ci - ty of
2 O how shall we sing in the an - guish of ex - ile – the songs of the
3 You daugh-ter of Ba - by - lon, doomed to de - struc - tion, you peo - ple of

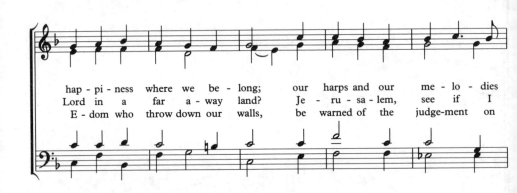

hap - pi - ness where we be - long; our harps and our me - lo - dies
Lord in a far a - way land? Je - ru - sa - lem, see if I
E - dom who throw down our walls, be warned of the judge-ment on

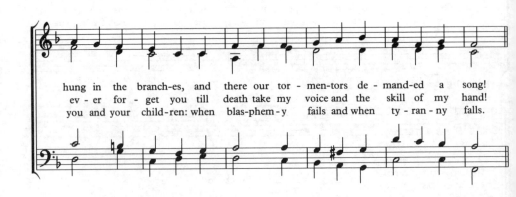

hung in the branch-es, and there our tor - men-tors de - mand-ed a song!
ev - er for - get you till death take my voice and the skill of my hand!
you and your child - ren: when blas-phem - y fails and when ty - ran - ny falls.

DESCANT

4 And then shall strings and harp yield their mu - sic, and then shall the

4 And then shall the strings of the harp yield their mu - sic, and then shall the

tune of our song be re - stored; and then shall the kings of the

tune of our song be re - stored; and then shall the kings of the

earth see God's pur - pose, the strong, un - quench-a - ble, love of the Lord.

earth see God's pur - pose, the strong, the un - quench - a - ble, love of the Lord.

138A   I'll praise you, Lord

Highwood   11 10 11 10

Words: from Psalm 138
Michael Perry
Music: R R Terry (1865–1938)

1 I'll praise you, Lord, with heart content and joyful,
   before the world I'll tell your righteous ways;
   I will bow down towards your holy temple,
   and breathe your name and sing your worthy praise.

2 Beyond the skies you set your timeless kingdom
   your word shall last, your throne shall never fall;
   the lords of earth will marvel at your wisdom
   and kneel before the mighty Lord of all.

3 Though set on high, you look upon the lowly
   the proud you know with sorrow from afar;
   in all my trouble you are swift to save me,
   and with your arm restrain the threat of war.

4 For ever you will keep your face towards us,
   your truth, your faithful love – they will not cease:
   then come in power, fulfil your mighty purpose,
   and grant to your creation perfect peace.

There is no moment

Maisemore   8 6 8 6 (CM)

Words: from Psalm 139
Brian Foley
Music: J Dykes Bower (1905–1981)

1 There is no mo - ment of___ my life,
2 Be - fore I speak,___ my words___ are known,
3 If I should close___ my eyes___ to him,
4 He knew my days___ be - fore___ all days,

no place where I___ may go, no___ ac - tion___ which___ God
and all that I___ de - cide. To___ come___ or___ go?___ God
he comes to give___ me sight; if___ I___ should go___ where
be - fore I came___ to be; he___ keeps___ me,___ loves___ me,

does___ not see,___ no thought he does not___ know.
knows___ my choice, and makes___ him - self my___ guide.
all___ is dark,___ he makes___ my dark - ness___ light.
in___ my ways =___ no lov - er such as___ he.

Alternative tune: Albano, *Hymns for Today's Church* 135

139B Lord all-knowing

Berkswell 8 7 8 7

Words: from Psalm 139
Christopher Idle
Music: English traditional melody
arranged David Iliff

1 Lord all-know-ing, you have found me; ev-ery se-cret
2 Lord al-migh-ty, you have made me, fash-ioned me to
3 Lord all-ho-ly, you have judged me by a stan-dard

thought and word,___ all my ac-tions,
keep your laws;___ your de-sign and
true and right;___ all the best I

all my long-ings you have__ seen and you have__ heard.
your cre-a-tion, ev-ery__ part of me is__ yours.
have to of-fer wi-thers__ in your burn-ing__ light.

4 Lord all-loving, you have saved me
in supreme and mighty grace;
by your Son's triumphant mercy,
suffering, dying in my place.

5 Lord all-glorious, you receive me
where your ransomed servants sing;
you have spoken, rescued, conquered –
Christ, our prophet, priest, and king!

Alternative tune: Cross of Jesus, *Hymns for Today's Church* 52

O Lord, come quickly

Bugeilio'r Gwenith Gwyn 8 7 8 7 D

Words: from Psalm 141
Michael Perry
Music: Welsh traditional melody
arranged John Barnard

141

1 O Lord, come quick-ly when I call; re - ceive my prayer with fa - vour,_ fair
2 O Lord, I'll seek your dis - ci - pline – but streng-then me__ to choose it;__ your

as the even - ing sac - ri - fice, as in-cense sweet_ to sa - vour.__ Keep
oil of grace a - noints my head – my head will not__ re - fuse it.___ My

watch up - on my mouth, O Lord, and guard my lips from e - vil;___ so
eyes are fixed on you, O Lord, though dan-gers yet sur - round me;___ in

turn my heart from wick-ed ways that I may shame the de - vil.__
life your love_ will be my rock, and death shall not con - found me.__

Alternative tune: Dominus regit me, *Hymns for Today's Church* 44

142A You are my refuge

Words: from Psalm 142
Michael Perry
Music: John Barnard

1 When I lift up my voice, and I
2 When I see no-one cares, and I
3 When he comes to my side_ and he

cry to the Lord, and I pour out my trou-bles_ be - fore_ him: I say_
walk all a - lone,. and my spi - rit grows wear-y__ with - in__ me:
an-swers my prayers, and he sets my soul free from. its pri - son:

CODA

You are my re - fuge,_

I will praise your name; you are good to me, O_____ Lord!

rall.

257

143A   Hear me, O Lord, in my distress

The Truth from above 8 8 8 8 (LM)

Words: from Psalm 143
David Preston
Music: English traditional melody
arranged R Vaughan Williams (1872–1958)

1 Hear me, O Lord, in my dis-tress, give
2 I claim no fav-our as of right; you
3 My fierce op-press-or hunts me down = I

ear to my des-pair-ing plea! In faith-ful-ness, in
are the God I serve and trust, yet judge me not: for
shrink in dark-ness, like the dead; my spi-rit fails = all

right-eous-ness, oh, hear my prayer and ans-wer me.
in your sight no liv-ing soul is count-ed just.
hope is gone, my heart is o - ver-whelmed with dread.

4 Days long since vanished I review,
   I see the wonders of your hands,
   and I stretch out my hands to you,
   for you I thirst like desert sands.

5 Lord, answer me without delay!
   I perish if you hide your face;
   in you I trust: let this new day
   bring word of your unfailing grace.

6 For your name's sake, Lord, hear my plea:
   your servant's stricken life preserve!
   From all oppression set me free
   to live and love the God I serve.

To God our great salvation

Crüger 7 6 7 6 D

Words: from Psalm 145
Timothy Dudley-Smith
Music: J Crüger (1598–1662)

1 To God our great sal - va - tion a tri-umph-song we raise,
2 De - clare in song and sto - ry the won-ders we con - fess,
3 His king-dom knows no end - ing, en - throned in light sub - lime,
4 The King of all cre - a - tion is near to those who call;

with hymns of a - dor - a - tion and ev - er - last - ing praise.
who hail the King of Glo - ry the Lord our Right-eous - ness.
his sov-ereign power ex - tend - ing be - yond all space and time.
the God of our sal - va - tion has stooped to save us all.

That name be - yond all nam - ing, from age to age a - dored,
In lov - ing - kind-ness car - ing his mer - cies stand dis - played,
To us and all things liv - ing he comes in word and deed,
Lift high your hearts and voic - es, his prais - es sound a - gain;

we lift on high, pro - claim - ing the great-ness of the Lord.
for - giv - ing and for - bear - ing to all his hand has made.
for - bear - ing and for - giv - ing, to meet us in our need.
in God his earth re - joic - es for ev - er - more. A - men!

I will exalt you O God

Words: from Psalm 145
from *The Liturgical Psalter*
David Frost and others
Music: T W Hanforth (1867–1948)

I will exalt you O ' God my ' king:
I will bless your ' name for ' ever · and ' ever.
Every ' day · will I ' bless you:
and praise your ' name for ' ever · and ' ever.

Great is the Lord *
and wonderfully ' worthy · to be ' praised:
his greatness is ' past ' searching ' out.
One generation shall praise your ' works · to an'other:
and de'clare your ' mighty ' acts.

Your kingdom is an ever'lasting ' kingdom:
and your dominion en'dures through ' all · gener'ations.
The Lord upholds all ' those who ' stumble:
and raises up ' those · that are ' bowed ' down.

The eyes of all look to ' you in ' hope:
and you give them their ' food in ' due ' season;
you open ' wide your ' hand:
and fill all things ' living · with your ' bounte·ous ' gift.

The Lord is just in ' all his ' ways:
and ' faithful · in ' all his ' dealings.
The Lord is near to all who ' call up'on him:
to all who ' call up'on him · in ' truth.

He will fulfil the desire of ' those that ' fear him:
he will ' hear their ' cry and ' save them.
The Lord preserves all ' those that ' love him:
but the wicked ' he will ' utterly · de'stroy.

Second part
My mouth shall speak the ' praises · of the ' Lord:
and let all flesh bless his holy ' name for ' ever · and ' ever.

Glory to the Father and ' to the ' Son:
and ' to the ' Holy ' Spirit;
as it was in the be'ginning · is ' now:
and shall be for ' ever. ' A'men.

Praise the God of our salvation

146

Canterbury Cathedral 8 7 8 7

Words: from Psalm 146
Timothy Dudley-Smith
Music: Alan Ridout

1 Praise the___ God___ of our sal - va - tion, all life long your___
2 Turn to___ him,___ his help en - treat - ing; on - ly in his___
3 Thank - ful___ hearts his praise have sound - ed down the a - ges___

voi - ces raise! Stir your hearts to
mer - cy trust: hu - man pomp and
long gone by: hap - py they whose

a - dor - a - tion, set your souls to___ sing his___ praise!
power are fleet - ing; mor - tal flesh is___ born for___ dust.
hopes are found - ed in the God of___ earth and___ sky!

4 Faithful Lord of all things living –
   by his bounty all are blessed,
   bread to hungry bodies giving,
   justice to the long-oppressed.

5 For the strength of our salvation,
   light and life and length of days,
   praise the King of all creation,
   set your souls to sing his praise!

Alternative tune: Marching, *Hymns for Today's Church* 360

147A Fill your hearts with joy and gladness

Regent Square   8 7 8 7 8 7

Words: from Psalm 147
Timothy Dudley-Smith
Music: H T Smart (1813–1879)
verse 4 arranged with descant John Barnard

1 Fill your hearts with joy and glad-ness, sing and praise your God and mine!
2 Praise the Lord, his peo - ple, praise him! Wound-ed souls his com - fort know.
3 Praise the Lord for times and sea - sons, cloud and sun - shine, wind and rain;

Great the Lord in_ love and wis-dom, might and ma - jes - ty di - vine!
Those who fear him_ find his mer-cies, peace for pain and_ joy for woe;
spring to melt the_ snows of win - ter till the wa - ters_ flow a - gain;

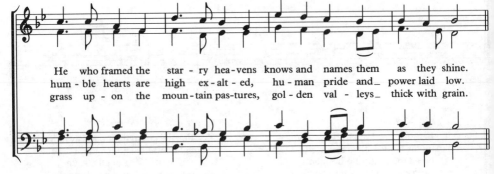

He who framed the star - ry hea-vens knows and names them as they shine.
hum - ble hearts are high ex - alt - ed, hu - man pride and_ power laid low.
grass up - on the moun-tain pas-tures, gol - den val - leys_ thick with grain.

DESCANT

4 Fill your hearts with joy__ and glad-ness, peace and plen-ty crown your days;

4 Fill your hearts with joy and glad-ness, peace and plen-ty crown your days;

love his laws, de - clare his judge-ments, walk in all__ his__ words and ways;

love his laws, de - clare his judge-ments, walk in all his__ words and ways;

he the Lord and we his child - ren – praise the Lord, all__ peo - ple, praise!

he the Lord and we his child-ren – praise the Lord, all peo - ple, praise!

263

147B(i)

O let the Church rejoice

Burgate 6 6 6 6 8 8

Words: from Psalm 147
Barbara Woollett
Music: Alan Ridout

1 O let the Church re - joice _____ in God our sav - iour's
2 Our God com-mands the storm _____ and sends the warm - ing
3 He makes the mea - dow flower, _____ the clouds, the wind and

grace, _____ for it is good to voice his all - de - serv - ing _____ praise:
breeze; _____ he can with-in _____ us form a life _ of joy _____ and _____ peace.
rain; _____ the hum-ble, by _ his power he'll lov - ing - ly _____ sus - tain.

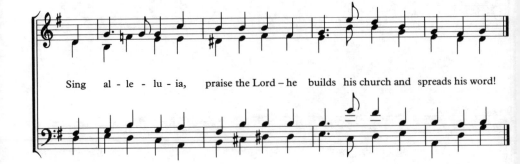

Sing al - le - lu - ia, praise the Lord – he builds his church and spreads his word!

4 The broken-hearted sigh –
   he bears their guilt and shame;
   like numbered stars on high
   he knows them all by name.
      Sing alleluia . . .

5 Hope in the Lord above –
   he will provide our needs;
   trust his unfailing love
   praise all his gracious deeds!
      Sing alleluia . . .

O let the Church rejoice

Christchurch 6 6 6 6 8 8

Words: from Psalm 147
Barbara Woollett
Music: C Steggall (1826–1905)

1 O let the Church re - joice in God our sav - iour's grace,
2 Our God com-mands the storm and sends the warm - ing breeze;
3 He makes the mea - dow flower, the clouds, the wind and rain;

for it is good to voice his all - de - serv - ing praise:
he can with - in us form a life of joy and peace.
the hum - ble, by his power he'll lov - ing - ly sus - tain.

Sing al - le - lu - ia, praise the Lord – he builds his church and spreads his word!

4 The broken-hearted sigh –
  he bears their guilt and shame;
  like numbered stars on high
  he knows them all by name.
    Sing alleluia . . .

5 Hope in the Lord above –
  he will provide our needs;
  trust his unfailing love,
  praise all his gracious deeds!
    Sing alleluia . . .

148A

Praise the Lord of heaven

Camberwell 6 5 6 5 D

Words: from Psalm 148
Timothy Dudley-Smith
Music: Michael Brierley

1 Praise the Lord of hea - ven, praise him in the height;
2 Earth and o - cean praise him; moun-tains, hills and trees;
3 Now by prince and peo - ple let his praise be told;

praise him, all his an - gels, praise him, hosts of light.
fire and hail and tem-pest, wind and storm and seas.
praise him, men and maid-ens, praise him, young and old.

Sun and moon to - ge-ther, shin-ing stars a - flame, pla - nets in their
Praise him, fields and for-ests, birds on flash-ing wings, praise him, beasts and
He, the Lord of glo-ry! We, his praise pro - claim! High a - bove all

Fine after vv 1 and 2

cours-es, mag-ni - fy his name!
cat - tle, all cre - a - ted things.
hea-vens mag-ni - fy his name!

Alternative tune: Evelyns, *Hymns for Today's Church* 172

1 Praise the Lord of hea-ven, praise him in the height;____
2 Earth and o-cean praise him; moun-tains, hills and trees;____
3 Now by prince and peo-ple let his praise be told;____

praise him, all his an-gels,__ praise him, hosts____ of__ light.
fire and hail and tem-pest,__ wind and storm____ and__ seas.
praise him, men and maid-ens,__ praise him, young____ and__ old.

Sun and moon to-ge-ther,__ shin - ing stars a - flame,____
Praise him, fields and for-ests,__ birds on flash-ing wings,____
He, the Lord of glo-ry!__ We, his praise pro - claim!____

Fine after vv 1 and 2

Organ interlude

pla-nets in their cours-es, mag-ni - fy his name!
praise him, beasts and cat-tle, all cre - a - ted things.
High a - bove all hea-vens mag-ni - fy his name!

The Unison and Harmony versions are harmonically compatible.

267

148B Praise him, praise him, praise him

St Helens 12 13 13 10

Words: from Psalm 148
Michael Perry
Music: Kenneth W Coates
Descant: David Iliff

DESCANT

3 Praise him, praise him, praise him, saints of God who

1 Praise him, praise him, praise him, powers and do-mi-
2 Praise him, praise him, praise him, o-cean depths and
3 Praise him, praise him, praise him, saints of God who

fear him! To the high-est

-na- tions! Praise his name in
wa- ters! E-le-ments of
fear him! To the high-est

name of all, con-cert-ed an-thems

glor-ious light, you crea-tures of the
earth and heaven, your sev-eral prais-es
name of all, con-cert-ed an-thems

Alternative tune: Nicaea (adapted), *Hymns for Today's Church* 7

raise, all you seed of Is - rael,

day!_____ Moon and stars,_ ring prais - es____
blend!_____ Birds and beasts and cat - tle,___
raise,_____ all you seed_ of Is - rael,___

ho - ly peo - ple near_ him___ whom he ex - alts, ex -

through the_ con - stel - la - tions:___ Lord___ God, whose
A - dam's sons_ and daugh - ters,___ wor - ship the
ho - ly_ peo - ple near_ him___ whom__ he ex -

- alts and crowns, and_ crowns with praise!

word___ shall_ ne - ver pass_ a - way!
king___ whose_ reign_ shall ne - ver end!
- alts___ and_ crowns with end - less praise!

148c   All things that are, praise God

Upton Scudamore 10 10 10 10

Words: from Psalm 148
Brian Foley
Music: John Barnard

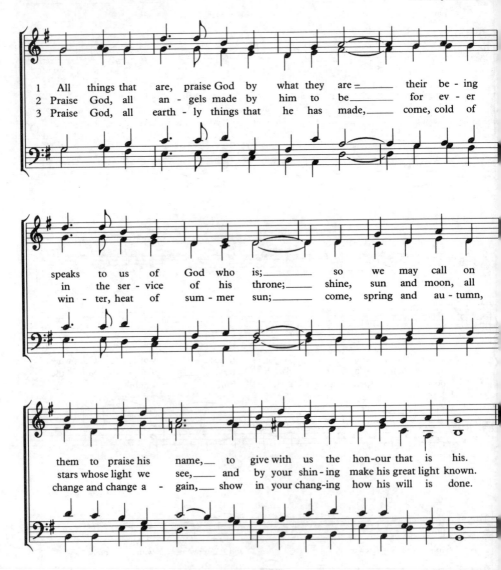

1 All things that are, praise God by what they are — their be-ing
2 Praise God, all an - gels made by him to be — for ev - er
3 Praise God, all earth - ly things that he has made, — come, cold of

speaks to us of God who is; — so we may call on
in the ser - vice of his throne; — shine, sun and moon, all
win - ter, heat of sum - mer sun; — come, spring and au - tumn,

them to praise his name, — to give with us the hon-our that is his.
stars whose light we see, — and by your shin - ing make his great light known.
change and change a - gain, — show in your chang-ing how his will is done.

4 Praise God, all lands and seas, all living things,
   all trees and plants that he has made to grow;
   all birds and beasts, praise, each in your own way,
   his greatness, which all things created show.

5 Praise God, all men and women, young and old –
   creation's highest praise is yours to sing;
   to honour God, to praise with every praise
   his Being, everywhere, in everything.

Alternative tune: Woodlands, *Hymns for Today's Church* 42

Words: from the *New Catholic Hymn*
© 1971 Faber Music Lt
3 Queen Square, London WC1N 3A

Music: © John Barnard/Jubilee Hymns †

Bring to the Lord a glad new song

Jerusalem 8 8 8 8 D (DLM)

Words: from Psalms 149 and 150
Michael Perry
Music: C H H Parry (1848–1918)

149A

Slow but with animation

Bring to the Lord a glad new song, child-ren of grace ex-tol your

king: your love and praise to God be - long – to in-stru-ments of mu - sic,

sing!   Let those be warned   who spurn God's name,   let rul - ers

poco cresc.

all   o - bey God's word,   for jus - tice shall   bring ty - rants

f

poco rit.   *a tempo*

shame –   let ev-ery crea-ture praise the   Lord!

Sing praise with - in these hal - lowed walls, wor-ship be - neath the dome of heaven; by cym-bals' sounds and trum - pets' calls let prais - es fit for God be

Praise the Lord with joyful cry

150A

Orientis partibus 7 7 7 7

Words: from Psalm 150
Fred Kaan
Music: P de Corbeil (died 1222)

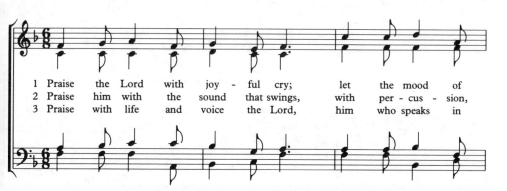

1 Praise the Lord with joy - ful cry; let the mood of
2 Praise him with the sound that swings, with per - cus - sion,
3 Praise with life and voice the Lord, him who speaks in

praise run high. Praise him who with migh - ty deeds
brass and strings. Let the world at ev - ery chance
deed and word, who to life the world or - dained —

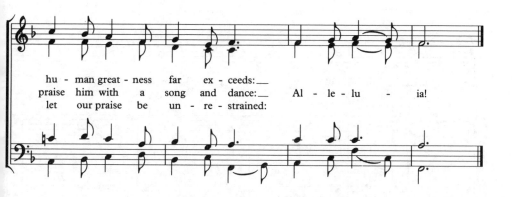

hu - man great - ness far ex - ceeds:___
praise him with a song and dance:___ Al - le - lu - ia!
let our praise be un - re - strained:

Words: © Stainer & Bell Ltd,
82 High Road, London N2 9PW

150B   Let everything that has breath

Words: from Psalm 150
from *The Liturgical Psalter*
David Frost and others
Music: John Barnard

CHOIR Let ev-ery-thing that__ has breath praise__ the Lord: ALL Let ev-ery-thing that__ has breath praise__ the Lord! CHOIR O praise God in his sanc-tu-ary,

Words: From *The Psalms : A New Translation for Worship*
© English text 1976, 1977 David L Frost, John A Emerton,
Andrew A Macintosh, all rights reserved

praise him in the fir-ma-ment of his power; praise him for his migh-ty acts,___ praise him ac-cord-ing to his a-bund-ant good-ness:_____ ALL Let ev-ery-thing that___ has breath_ praise_____ the Lord!

CHOIR Praise him in the blast of the ram's horn, praise him on the lute and harp, praise him with the tim-brels and dan-ces, praise him on the strings and pipe:_____ ALL Let ev-ery-thing that__ has breath praise_____ the Lord!

CHOIR Praise him on the high-sound-ing cym-bals, praise him on the loud___

cym-bals; let ev-ery-thing that___ has breath praise___ the

Lord:___ ALL Let ev-ery-thing that___ has

breath___ praise___ the Lord! CHOIR praise___ the Lord!

150C

O praise God in his sanctuary

Words: from Psalm 150
from *The Liturgical Psalter*
David Frost and others
Music: C V Stanford (1852–1924)

UNISON

f

1 O praise God in his sanctua-ry: praise him in the firma-ment of his power.

2 Praise him for his migh-ty acts: praise him according to his a - bun-dant goodness.

HARMONY

3 Praise him in the blast of the ram's horn: praise him up - on the lute and harp.

4 Praise him with the timbrel and dan-ces: praise him up - on the strings and pipe.

TENORS AND BASSES

ff

5 Praise him on the high sounding cym-bals: praise him up - on the loud cymbals.

ALL VOICES   HARMONY

ff

6 Let everything that has breath praise the Lord: O praise the Lord.

UNISON

Glory to the Father and to the Son: and to the Ho - ly Spirit;

HARMONY

as it was in the be-ginning is now: and shall be for ev-er. A men.

151   O come let us sing out to the Lord

Words: from Psalms 95 and 96, *Venite*
from *The Liturgical Psalter*
David Frost and others

C V Stanford (1852–1924)

H Lawes (1595–1662)

1   O come let us sing ˈ out · to the ˈ Lord:
     let us shout in triumph to the ˈ rock of ˈ our salˈvation.

2   Let us come before his ˈ face with ˈ thanksgiving:
     and cry ˈ out to · him ˈ joyfully · in ˈ psalms.

3   For the Lord is a ˈ great ˈ God:
     and a great ˈ king a·bove ˈ all ˈ gods.

4   In his hand are the ˈ depths · of the ˈ earth:
     and the peaks of the ˈ mountains · are ˈ his ˈ also.

Second part

5   The sea is his and ˈ he ˈ made it:
     his hands ˈ moulded ˈ dry ˈ land.

6   Come let us worship and ˈ bow ˈ down:
     and kneel beˈfore the ˈ Lord our ˈ maker.

7   For he is the ˈ Lord our ˈ God:
     we are his ˈ people · and the ˈ sheep of · his ˈ pasture.

8   If only you would hear his ˈ voice toˈday:
     for he ˈ comes to ˈ judge the ˈ earth.

9   He shall judge the ˈ world with ˈ righteousness:
     and the ˈ peoples ˈ with his ˈ truth.

     Glory to the Father and ˈ to the ˈ Son:
     and ˈ to the ˈ Holy ˈ Spirit;
     as it was in the beˈginning · is ˈ now:
     and shall be for ˈ ever. ˈ Aˈmen.

Now lives the Lamb of God

Darwall's 148th   6 6 6 6 8 8

Words: from 1 Corinthians 5 and 15,
and Romans 6, *The Easter Anthems*
David Mowbray
Music: J Darwall (1731–1789)

152A

1 Now lives the Lamb of God, our Pass - ov - er, the
2 Now ris - en from the dead Christ ne - ver dies a -
3 In A - dam all must die, for - lorn and un - for -
4 Give praise to God a - lone who life from death can

Christ, who once with nails and wood for us was
- gain; in us, with Christ as head, sin ne - ver -
- given; in Christ we come a - live, the sec - ond
bring; whose migh - ty power can turn our win - ter

sac - ri - ficed:
- more shall reign: Come, keep the feast, the
Man from heaven.
in - to spring:

an - them sing that Christ in - deed is Lord and king!

Alternative tune: Harewood, *Hymns for Today's Church* 564

152B   Christ our passover

Words: from 1 Corinthians 5 and 15,
and Romans 6, *The Easter Anthems*
after *The Book of Common Prayer*
in *The Alternative Service Book 1980*

J Goss (1800–1880)

H Skeats (died 1831)

1 Christ our passover has been ' sacri·ficed ' for us:
   so let us ' cele'brate the ' feast,
2 not with the old leaven of cor'ruption · and ' wickedness:
   but with the unleavened ' bread of · sin'cerity · and ' truth.

3 Christ once raised from the dead ' dies no ' more:
   death has no ' more do'minion ' over him.
4 In dying he died to sin ' once for ' all:
   in ' living · he ' lives to ' God.

5 See yourselves therefore as ' dead to ' sin:
   and alive to God in ' Jesus ' Christ our ' Lord.
6 Christ has been ' raised · from the ' dead:
   the ' firstfruits · of ' those who ' sleep.

7 For as by ' man came ' death:
   by man has come also the resur'rection ' of the ' dead;
8 for as in ' Adam · all ' die:
   even so in Christ shall ' all be ' made a'live.

Glory to the Father and ' to the ' Son:
and ' to the ' Holy ' Spirit;
as it was in the be'ginning · is ' now:
and shall be for ' ever. ' A'men.

O bless the God of Israel

Morning Light 7 6 7 6 D

Words: from Luke 1,
The Song of Zechariah/Benedictus
Michael Perry
Music: G J Webb (1803–1887)

1 O bless the God of Is - rael, who comes to set us free,
2 Now from the house of Da - vid a child of grace is given;
3 Where once were fear and dark - ness the sun be - gins to rise –

who vi - sits and re - deems us and grants us li - ber - ty.
a Sav - iour comes a - mong us to raise us up to heaven.
the dawn - ing of for - give - ness up - on the sin - ner's eyes,

The pro - phets spoke of mer - cy, of res - cue and re - lease;
Be - fore him goes the her - ald – fore - run - ner in the way,
to guide the feet of pil - grims a - long the paths of peace:

God shall ful - fil the pro - mise to bring our peo - ple peace.
the pro - phet of sal - va - tion, the mes - sen - ger of Day.
O bless our God and Sav - iour, with songs that ne - ver cease!

Alternative tune: Roewen, *Songs from the Psalms* 153A

153B(i) O praise our great and faithful God

Covenanters 8 6 8 6 (CM)

Words: from Luke 1,
The Song of Zechariah/Benedictus
Michael Hewlett
Music: American traditional melody

1 O praise our great and faithful God, the
2 The oath he swore to save us all he
3 O children's children, you in turn shall

God our parents knew, for in his Name the
kept, and it was done: protection, pardon,
go before his face, to give the knowledge

prophets spoke, and we have found them true.
peace and hope, we have them in his Son.
of his love and to prepare his ways.

4 Tell them the Dayspring from on high
has dawned for our release:
benighted, lost, in fear of death,
the world can know our peace.

5 To Father, Son and Spirit, praise!
To God whom we adore
be worship, glory, power and love,
both now and evermore!

O praise our great and faithful God 153B(ii)

Wiltshire 8 6 8 6 (CM)

Words: from Luke 1,
The Song of Zechariah/Benedictus
Michael Hewlett
Music: G T Smart (1776–1867)

1 O praise our great__ and faith - ful God,__ the
2 The oath he swore__ to save__ us all__ he
3 O child - ren's child - ren, you__ in turn__ shall

God__ our par - ents__ knew,__ for in__ his Name__ the
kept,__ and it__ was__ done:__ pro - tec - tion, par - don,
go__ be - fore__ his__ face,__ to give__ the know - ledge

pro - phets spoke, and__ we__ have found__ them true.
peace__ and__ hope,__ we__ have__ them in__ his__ Son.
of__ his__ love__ and__ to__ pre - pare__ his__ ways.

4 Tell them the Dayspring from on high
  has dawned for our release:
  benighted, lost, in fear of death,
  the world can know our peace.

5 To Father, Son and Spirit, praise!
  To God whom we adore
  be worship, glory, power and love,
  both now and evermore!

153C   Blessed be the Lord the God of Israel

Words: from Luke 1,
The Song of Zechariah/Benedictus
in *The Alternative Service Book 1980*
International Consultation on English Texts

J Turle (1802–1882)

G C Martin (1844–1916)

1   Blessed be the Lord the ' God of ' Israel:
     for he has come to his ' people · and ' set them ' free.

2   He has raised up for us a ' mighty ' saviour:
     born of the ' house · of his ' servant ' David.

3   Through his holy prophets he ' promised · of ' old:
     that he would save us from our enemies
     from the ' hands of ' all that ' hate us.

4   He promised to show ' mercy · to our ' fathers:
     and to re'member · his ' holy ' covenant.

5   This was the oath he swore to our ' father ' Abraham:
     to set us ' free · from the ' hands of · our ' enemies,

6   free to worship him with'out ' fear:
     holy and righteous in his sight ' all the ' days of · our ' life.

7   You my child shall be called the prophet of the ' Most ' High:
     for you will go before the ' Lord · to pre'pare his ' way,

8   to give his people knowledge ' of sal'vation:
     by the for'giveness · of ' all their ' sins.

9   In the tender compassion ' of our ' God:
     the dawn from on ' high shall ' break up'on us,

10   to shine on those who dwell in darkness and the ' shadow · of ' death:
     and to guide our feet ' into · the ' way of ' peace.

     Glory to the Father and ' to the ' Son:
     and ' to the ' Holy ' Spirit;
     as it was in the be'ginning · is ' now:
     and shall be for ' ever. ' A'men.

Bless the Lord, created things

154A

Antiphoner 7 7 7 6

Words: from *A Song of Creation/Benedicite*
Judy Davies
Music: Gradual, Paris 1685
arranged David Iliff

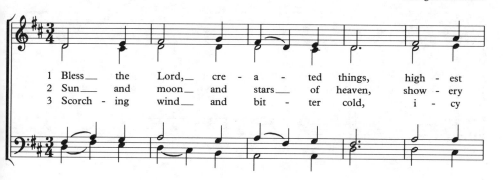

1 Bless the Lord, cre - a - ted things, high - est
2 Sun and moon and stars of heaven, show - ery
3 Scorch - ing wind and bit - ter cold, i - cy

hea - vens, an - gel host; bless the Fa - ther,
wa - ters, rain and dew, stor - my gale and
bliz - zard, morn - ing mist, light and dark - ness,

Spi - rit, Son:
fi - ery heat: wor - ship, all cre - a - tion.
nights and days:

4 Frosty air and falling snow,
clouds and lightnings, dales and hills,
all that grows upon the earth:
worship, all creation.

5 Springs and rivers, ocean deeps,
whales and fishes of the sea,
prowling beasts and soaring birds:
worship, all creation.

6 All on earth who serve our God,
priests and people of the Lord,
upright, holy, humble hearts:
worship, all creation.

154B   Angels, praise him

Little Barrington

Words: from *A Song of Creation/Benedicite*
Michael Perry
Music: John Barnard

1 An-gels, praise him, hea-vens, praise him, wa-ters, praise him, Al - le -
2 Sun, praise him, moon, praise him, stars, praise him, Al - le -

-lu - ia! crea-tures of the Lord, all praise him for
-lu - ia! showers, praise him, dews, praise him for

ev - er - more: ev - er - more:

3 Wind, praise him, fire, praise him, heat, praise him, Al - le -
5 Earth, praise him, moun-tains, praise him, hills, praise him, Al - le -

Alternative tunes: Song of Creation or Angels, praise him, *Songs from the Psalms* 154B(i), 154B(ii)

-lu - ia! win - ter, praise him, sum-mer, praise him for ___ ev - er -
-lu - ia! green things, praise him, wells, ___ praise him for ___ ev - er -

- more: 4 Nights, praise him, days, praise him, light, praise him, Al - le -
- more: 6 Seas, praise him, ri - vers, praise him, fish, praise him, Al - le -

-lu - ia! light-nings, praise him, clouds, praise him for ___ ev - er - more:
-lu - ia! birds, ___ praise him, beasts, praise him for ___ ev - er - more:

7 Na - tions, praise him, church-es, praise him, saints, praise him, Al - le -

-lu - ia! all his peo - ple, join to praise him for ___ ev - er - more!

154c   Bless the Lord all created things

Words: from *A Song of Creation/Benedicite*
after *The Book of Common Prayer*
in *The Alternative Service Book 1980*

P Whitlock (1903–1946)

C F South (1850–1916)

1 Bless the Lord all cre'ated ' things:
  sing his ' praise · and ex'alt him · for ' ever.

2 Bless the ' Lord you ' heavens:
  sing his ' praise · and ex'alt him · for ' ever.

3 Bless the Lord you ' angels · of the ' Lord:
  bless the ' Lord all ' you his ' hosts;

4 bless the Lord all ' men · on the ' earth:
  sing his ' praise · and ex'alt him · for ' ever.

5 O people of God ' bless the ' Lord:
  bless the ' Lord you ' priests · of the ' Lord;

6 bless the Lord you ' servants · of the ' Lord:
  sing his ' praise · and ex'alt him · for ' ever.

7 Bless the Lord all men of ' upright ' spirit:
  bless the Lord you that are ' holy · and ' humble · in ' heart.
  Bless the Father the Son and the ' Holy ' Spirit:
  sing his ' praise · and ex'alt him · for ' ever.

Great and wonderful your deeds

Württemberg 7 7 7 7 6

Words: from *Great and wonderful*
Christopher Idle
Music: *Hundert Arien* Dresden 1694

1 Great and won - der - ful your deeds, God from whom all
2 King of na - tions, take your crown! Ev - ery race shall
3 To the one al - migh - ty God, to the Lamb who

power pro - ceeds; true and right are all your ways –
soon bow down. Ho - ly God and Lord a - lone,
shed his blood, to the Spi - rit now be given

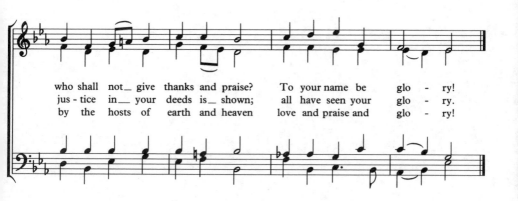

who shall not＿ give thanks and praise? To your name be glo - ry!
jus - tice in＿ your deeds is＿ shown; all have seen your glo - ry.
by the hosts of earth and heaven love and praise and glo - ry!

155B   Wonderful your deeds, Lord

Erlestoke   6 5 6 5

Words: from *Great and wonderful*
David Mowbray
Music: John Barnard

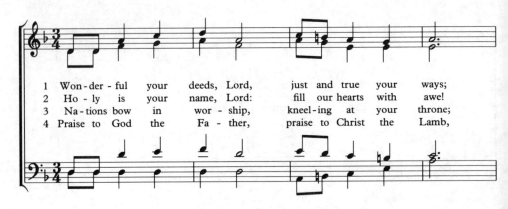

1 Won-der-ful your deeds, Lord,   just and true your ways;
2 Ho-ly is your name, Lord: fill our hearts with awe!
3 Na-tions bow in wor-ship,   kneel-ing at your throne;
4 Praise to God the Fa-ther,   praise to Christ the Lamb,

you are God al-migh-ty,   king be-yond all praise.
Who shall not re-vere you   now and ev-er-more?
faith-ful are your deal-ings,   all your judge-ments known.
and to God the Spi-rit   ev-er and a-men!

Alternative tune: North Coates, *Psalms for Today* 162B(ii), *Hymns for Today's Church* 384

Great and wonderful

Words: from *Great and wonderful*
derived from the Daily Office
of the Joint Liturgical Group

J Nares (1715–1783)

G J Elvey (1816–1893)

1 Great and wonderful are your deeds Lord ˈ God · the Alˈmighty:
   just and true are your ˈ ways O ˈ King · of the ˈ nations.

2 Who shall not revere and praise your ˈ name O ˈ Lord?
   for ˈ you aˈlone are ˈ holy.

3 All nations shall come and worship ˈ in your ˈ presence:
   for your just ˈ dealings · have ˈ been reˈvealed.

   **To him who sits on the throne ˈ and · to the ˈ Lamb:
   be praise and honour   glory and might
   for ever and ˈ ever. ˈ Aˈmen.**

156A God of gods, we sound his praises

God of gods 8 7 8 7 8 8 8 7

Words: from *Te Deum*
Timothy Dudley-Smith
Music: Christian Strover

1 God of gods, we sound his praises, high-est heaven its ho-mage brings;
2 Christ-ians in their hearts en-throne him, tell his prais-es wide a-broad;
3 Hail the Christ, the King of glo-ry, he whose praise the an-gels cry;
4 Lord, we look for your re-turn-ing; teach us so to walk your ways,

earth and all cre-a-tion rais-es glo-ry to the King of kings:
pro-phets, priests, a-pos-tles own him mar-tyrs' crown and saints' re-ward.
born to share our hu-man sto-ry, love and la-bour, grieve and die:
hearts and minds your will dis-cern-ing, lives a-light with joy and praise:

ho-ly, ho-ly, ho-ly, name him, Lord of all his hosts pro-claim him;
Three-in-One his glo-ry shar-ing, earth and heaven his praise de-clar-ing,
by his cross his work com-plet-ed, sin-ners ran-somed, death de-feat-ed;
in your love and care en-fold us, by your con-stan-cy up-hold us;

to the ev-er-last-ing Fa-ther ev-ery tongue in tri-umph sings.
praise the high ma-jes-tic Fa-ther, praise the ev-er-last-ing Lord!
in the glo-ry of the Fa-ther Christ a-scend-ed reigns on high.
may your mer-cy, Lord and Fa-ther, keep us now and all our days!

God, we praise you

156B

Rustington 8 7 8 7 D

Words: from *Te Deum*
Christopher Idle
Music: C H H Parry (1848–1918)

1 God, we praise you! God, we bless you! God, we name you sove-reign Lord!
2 True a - pos - tles, faith-ful pro-phets, saints who set their world a - blaze,
3 Je - sus Christ, the king of glo - ry, ev - er - last - ing Son of God,
4 Christ, at God's right hand vic - tor - ious, you will judge the world you made;

Migh-ty King whom an - gels wor-ship, Fa - ther, by your church a - dored:
mar-tyrs, once un-known, un - heed-ed, join one grow-ing song of_ praise,
hum-ble was your vir - gin mo-ther, hard the lone - ly path you_ trod:
Lord, in mer - cy help your ser-vants for whose free-dom you have paid:

all cre - a - tion shows your glo - ry, heaven and earth draw near your throne
while your church on earth con - fess-es one ma - jes - tic Tri - ni - ty:_
by your cross is sin de - feat-ed, hell con - front - ed face to face,_
raise us up from dust to glo - ry, guard us from all sin to - day;_

sing-ing 'Ho - ly, ho - ly, ho - ly, Lord of hosts, and_ God a - lone!'
Fa - ther, Son, and Ho - ly Spi - rit, God, our hope e - ter - nal - ly.
hea - ven o-pened to be - liev-ers, sin-ners jus - ti - fied by grace.
King en - throned a - bove all prais-es, save your peo - ple, God, we pray.

Alternative tune: Lux Eoi, *Psalms for Today* 115, *Hymns for Today's Church* 151

156C   You are God and we praise you

Words: *Te Deum*
in *The Alternative Service Book 1980*
International Consultation on English Texts

1 You are ' God · and we ' praise you:
   you are the ' Lord and ' we ac'claim you;
2 you are the e'ternal ' Father:
   all cre'ation ' worships ' you.

3 To you all angels *
   all the ' powers of ' heaven:
   cherubim and seraphim ' sing in ' endless ' praise,
4 Holy holy holy Lord *
   God of ' power and ' might:
   heaven and ' earth are ' full of · your ' glory.

5 The glorious company of a'postles ' praise you:
   the noble fellowship of prophets praise you
   the white-robed ' army · of ' martyrs ' praise you.
6 Throughout the world the holy ' Church ac'claims you:
   Father of ' majes'ty un'bounded;

Second part
7 your true and only Son *
   worthy of ' all ' worship:
   and the Holy ' Spirit ' advocate · and ' guide.

Verses *14–18* may be omitted.

8   You Christ are the ' King of ' glory:
     the e'ternal ' Son · of the ' Father.

9   When you became man to ' set us ' free:
     you did not ab'hor the ' Virgin's ' womb.

10   You overcame the ' sting of ' death:
     and opened the kingdom of ' heaven · to ' all be'lievers.

11   You are seated at God's right ' hand in ' glory:
     we believe that you will ' come and ' be our ' judge.

12   Come then Lord and ' help your ' people:
     bought with the ' price of ' your own ' blood;

13   and bring us ' with your ' saints:
     to ' glory ' ever'lasting.

14   Save your people Lord and ' bless · your in'heritance:
     govern and up'hold them ' now and ' always.

15   Day by ' day we ' bless you:
     we ' praise your ' name for ' ever.

16   Keep us today Lord from ' all ' sin:
     have mercy ' on us ' Lord have ' mercy.

17   Lord show us your ' love and ' mercy:
     for we ' put our ' trust in ' you.

Second part

18   In you Lord ' is our ' hope:
     let us not be con'founded ' at the ' last.

156D(i)   Great is the Lord we now acclaim

Acclamation   8 8 8 8 (LM)

Words: from *Te Deum*
David Mowbray
Music: Andrew Maries

1 Great is the Lord we now ac-claim — God ev-er-last-ing is
2 Let pro-phets and a-pos-tles join with mar-tyrs in tri-um-
3 We praise God's true and on-ly Son, for ev-er with the Fa-

his name: let heaven and earth with mu-sic ring,
-phant line to e-cho the an-gel-ic cry
-ther one; we praise the Spi - rit at their side,

and 'Ho-ly, ho-ly, ho-ly' sing!
and ce-le-brate God's mys-te-ry.
the Chur-ch's ad-vo-cate and guide.

This simpler rhythm may be substituted for bars 3 and 4:

God ev-er-last-ing is his name: let

4 When once the time had fully come
  Christ did not scorn the Virgin's womb;
  our Lord the sting of death defied
  and flung the gate of heaven wide!

5 He shed his blood to pay sin's price,
  the full and perfect sacrifice;
  as Saviour, reigns eternally,
  as Judge of all, presides on high.

6 Lord God, protect us all from sin,
  our hearts to love and goodness win;
  that we yet firm in faith, shall stay
  unshaken in the last great day.

Great is the Lord we now acclaim 156D(ii)

Old 100th 8 8 8 8 (LM)

Words: from *Te Deum*
David Mowbray
Music: melody from *Genevan Psalter* 1551

1 Great is the Lord we now ac - claim — God
2 Let pro - phets and a - pos - tles join with
3 We praise God's true and on - ly Son, for

ev - er - last - ing is his name: let heaven and earth with
mar - tyrs in tri - umph - ant line to e - cho the an -
ev - er with the Fa - ther one; we praise the Spi - rit

mu - sic ring, and 'Ho - ly, ho - ly, ho - ly' sing!
- gel - ic cry and ce - le - brate God's mys - te - ry.
at their side, the Chur-ch's ad - vo - cate___ and guide.

4 When once the time had fully come
Christ did not scorn the Virgin's womb;
our Lord the sting of death defied
and flung the gate of heaven wide!

5 He shed his blood to pay sin's price,
the full and perfect sacrifice;
as Saviour, reigns eternally,
as Judge of all, presides on high.

6 Lord God, protect us all from sin,
our hearts to love and goodness win;
that we yet firm in faith, shall stay
unshaken in the last great day.

157A   All glory be to God

Nicolaus 8 6 8 8 6

Words: from *Gloria in excels*
Timothy Dudley-Smit
Music: Nicolaus Herman (c1485–156)
arranged J S Bach (1685–175()

1 All glo - ry__ be__ to God on__ high, his peace on earth pro -
2 In songs of__ thank-ful - ness__ and praise our hearts their hom - age
3 O Christ, the__ Fa - ther's on - ly__ Son, O Lamb en - throned on
4 Most high and__ ho - ly is__ the__ Lord, most high his hea - venly

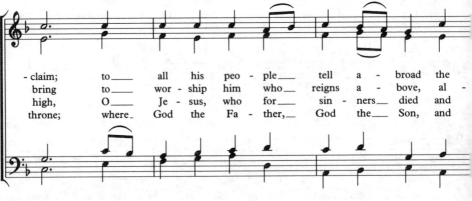

- claim;   to__ all his peo - ple__ tell a - broad the
bring   to__ wor - ship him who__ reigns a - bove, al -
high,   O__ Je - sus, who for__ sin - ners__ died and
throne;   where__ God the Fa - ther,__ God the__ Son, and

grace and__ glo - ry of__ the__ Lord, and bless his__ ho - ly__ name.
- migh - ty__ Fa - ther, Lord of__ love, our God and__ hea - venly King.
reigns at__ God the Fa - ther's side, in mer - cy__ hear our__ cry.
God the__ Spi - rit, ev - er__ One, in glo - ry__ reigns a - lone.

Glory to God in the highest 157B

Words: from *Gloria in excelsis*
in *The Alternative Service Book 1980*
International Consultation on English Texts

F A G Ouseley (1825–1889)

W H Havergal (1793–1870)

1 Glory to ' God · in the ' highest:
and ' peace · to his ' people · on ' earth.

2 Lord God ' heaven·ly ' King:
al'mighty ' God and ' Father,

3 we worship you we ' give you ' thanks:
we ' praise you ' for your ' glory.

4 Lord Jesus Christ only ' Son · of the ' Father:
Lord ' God ' Lamb of ' God,

5 you take away the ' sin · of the ' world:
have ' mercy ' on ' us;

6 you are seated at the right hand ' of the ' Father:
re'ceive ' our ' prayer.

7 For you a'lone · are the ' Holy One:
you a'lone ' are the ' Lord,

8 you alone are the Most High
Jesus Christ with the ' Holy ' Spirit:
in the glory of God the ' Father. ' A'men.

158A(i) Saviour Christ, in mercy come

Salvator mundi 7 7 7 7

Words: from *Saviour of the world*
David Mowbray and Michael Perry
Music: David Llewellyn Green

1 Sav - iour Christ, in__ mer - cy come! By your cross__ and
2 Come in power and__ loose our chains, come in peace, for -
3 Come to live a - mong us, Lord – come to save__ us

life__ laid down__ set__ your__ wait - ing__
-give__ our sins,__ come__ in__ truth__ to__
by__ your word;__ come__ to - day__ and

peo - ple__ free =__ come a - mong us,__ Lord, to - day:
make us__ wise,__ come and__ fill__ our__ hearts with praise:
make us__ one,__ Sav - iour__ Christ, in__ mer - cy__ come!

Saviour Christ, in mercy come 158A(ii)

Culbach 7 7 7 7

Words: from *Saviour of the world*
David Mowbray and Michael Perry
Music: adapted from a chorale in J Scheffler's
Heilige Seelenlust Breslau 1657

1 Sav - iour Christ, in mer - cy come! By your cross and
2 Come in power and loose our chains, come in peace, for -
3 Come to live a - mong us, Lord – come to save us

life laid___ down set your wait - ing
- give our___ sins, come in truth to
by your___ word; come to - day and

peo - ple free – come a - mong us, Lord, to - day:
make us wise, come and fill our hearts with__ praise:
make us one, Sav - iour Christ, in mer - cy___ come!

158B   Jesus, Saviour of the world

St Albinus 7 8 7 8 4

Words: from *Saviour of the world*
Christopher Idle
Music: H J Gauntlett (1805–1876)

1 Je - sus, Sav - iour of the world, you have bought your
2 Christ, who once on Ga - li - lee came to your dis -
3 Lord, make known your pro - mised power; show your - self our
4 When you come, Lord Je - sus Christ, fill - ing earth and

peo - ple's_ free - dom by your cross, your life laid_ down:
- ci - ples'_ res - cue: we, like them, cry out for_ help –
strong de - liv - erer: so our prayer shall turn to_ praise –
heaven with_ won - der, come to make us one with_ you –

now bring in your glo - rious king - dom. Come to help us!
free us from our sins, we ask you. Come to save us!
hear us, stay with us for ev - er. Come to rule us!
heirs of life, to reign in splen - dour. Al - le - lu - ia!

Saviour of the world

Words: *Saviour of the world*
derived from the Daily Office
of the Joint Liturgical Group

Roger Lowman

P C Buck (1871–1947)

1 Jesus saviour of the world *
  come to us ˈ in your ˈ mercy:
  we look to ˈ you to ˈ save and ˈ help us.
2 By your cross and your life laid down
  you set your ˈ people ˈ free:
  we look to ˈ you to ˈ save and ˈ help us.

3 When they were ready to perish you ˈ saved · your disˈciples:
  we look to ˈ you to ˈ come to · our ˈ help.
4 In the greatness of your mercy loose us ˈ from our ˈ chains:
  forgive the ˈ sins of ˈ all your ˈ people.

5 Make yourself known as our saviour and ˈ mighty · deˈliverer:
  save and ˈ help us · that ˈ we may ˈ praise you.
6 Come now and dwell with us ˈ Lord Christ ˈ Jesus:
  hear our ˈ prayer · and be ˈ with us ˈ always.

Second part
7 And when you ˈ come in · your ˈ glory:
  make us to be one with you *
  and to ˈ share the ˈ life of · your ˈ kingdom.

159A   Light of gladness, Lord of glory

Quem pastores laudavere 8 8 8 7

Words: from *Phos hilaron*
Christopher Idle
Music: fourteenth-century German melody
arranged John Barnard

1 Light_ of glad - ness, Lord_ of glo - ry, Je - sus
2 Let_ us sing_ at sun's_ de - scend - ing as_ we
3 Son_ of God,_ through all_ the a - ges wor - thy

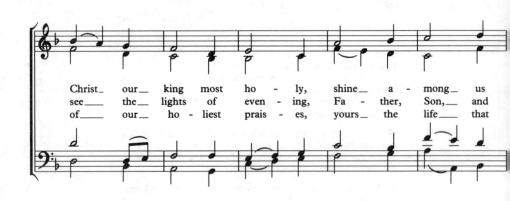

Christ_ our_ king most ho - ly, shine_ a - mong_ us
see_ the_ lights of even - ing, Fa - ther, Son,_ and
of_ our_ ho - liest prais - es, yours_ the life_ that

in_ your mer - cy: earth_ and hea - ven join_ their hymn.
Spi - rit prais - ing with_ the ho - ly se - ra - phim.
ne - ver ceas - es, light_ which ne - ver shall_ grow dim.

Light of gladness, shining radiance 159B

Light of gladness 8 7 8 7

Words: from *Phos hilaron*
Words and music: Paul Inwood

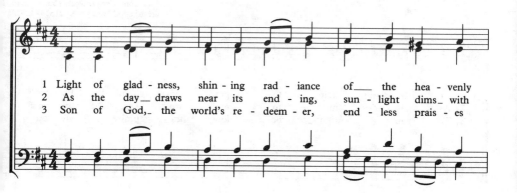

1 Light of glad - ness, shin - ing rad - iance of___ the hea - venly
2 As the day___ draws near its end - ing, sun - light dims___ with
3 Son of God,___ the world's re - deem - er, end - less prais - es

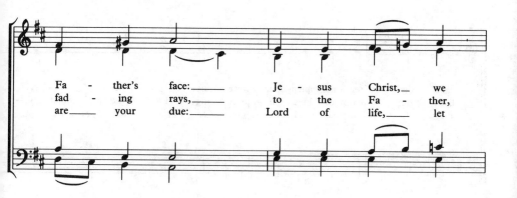

Fa - ther's face:_____ Je - sus Christ,___ we
fad - ing rays,_____ to the Fa - ther,
are___ your due:_____ Lord of life,___ let

greet you, bless___ you, ho - ly Lord of sav - ing grace.
Son and Spi - rit now___ we sing our song___ of praise.
all cre - a - tion bring___ its joy - ful thanks to you.

Alternative tunes: Shipston, Halton Holgate, *Hymns for Today's Church* 282, 370

159C · O gladdening light

Nunc dimittis 6 6 7 D

Words: from *Phos hilaron*
R S Bridges (1844–1930)
in this version Word & Music
Music: from *The Genevan Psalter* 1549
arranged C Goudimel (c1514–1572)

1 O glad-dening light,___ O grace of God the Fa-ther's
2 As day fades in - to night we see the eve - ning
3 To you of right___ be - longs the praise of all our

face, the e - ter - nal splen-dour wear - ing: ce - les - tial, ho - ly,
light, our hymn of love out - pour - ing; Fa - ther of might un -
songs, O Son of God, life - giv - er; you, there-fore, Lord most

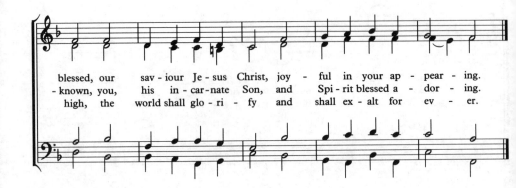

blessed, our sav - iour Je - sus Christ, joy - ful in your ap - pear - ing.
-known, you, his in - car-nate Son, and Spi - rit blessed a - dor - ing.
high, the world shall glo - ri - fy and shall ex - alt for ev - er.

Alternative tune: *Songs from the Psalms* 159C

My soul proclaims the greatness of the Lord 160A

Andrew Mark

Words: from Luke 1,
The Song of Mary/Magnificat
Christopher Idle
Music: Norman Warren

UNISON

1 My soul pro-claims the great-ness of the Lord, and my
2 In ev - ery age, for those who fear the Lord come his
3 To Is - ra - el his ser - vant he brings help, and the

spi - rit sings for joy to my sav - iour God! His
mer - cy, and the strength of his migh - ty arm; he
pro - mise to our fa - thers is now ful - filled: for

low - ly slave he looked up - on in love: they will call me hap-py now, for
routs the proud, throws mon-archs off their thrones, while he lifts the low-ly high, fills
Christ has come ac - cord-ing to his word, and the mer-cy that he showed to

migh - ty are the works he has done, and ho - ly is his name!
hun-gry souls with food, and the rich sends emp - ty a - way.
A - bra-ham is now for his child - ren's child-ren ev - er - more.

160B   With Mary let my soul rejoice

St Stephen   8 6 8 6 (CM)

Words: from Luke 1,
The Song of Mary/Magnificat
David Mowbray
Music: W Jones (1726–1800)

1 With Ma - ry let my____ soul re - joice, and____
2 How strong his arm, how____ great his power! The____
3 The rich our God will____ send a - way and____

praise God's____ ho - ly name – his sav - ing love from
proud he____ will dis - own; the meek and hum - ble
feed the____ hun - gry poor; the arms of love re -

first____ to____ last, from age to____ age, the____ same!
he____ ex - alts to share his____ glo - rious____ throne.
- main____ out - stretched at mer - cy's____ o - pen____ door.

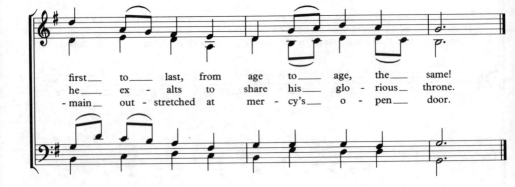

4 So shall God's promise be fulfilled,
to Israel firmly made:
a child is born, a Son is given
whose crown will never fade.

5 All glory to the Father, Son
and Spirit now proclaim;
with Mary let the world rejoice
and praise God's holy name!

My soul proclaims

Words: from Luke 1,
The Song of Mary/Magnificat
in *The Alternative Service Book 1980*
International Consultation on English Texts

E J Hopkins (1818–1901)

Andrew Millington

1 My soul proclaims the ⸍ greatness · of the ⸍ Lord:
   my spirit re⸍joices · in ⸍ God my ⸍ saviour;
2 for he has looked with favour on his ⸍ lowly ⸍ servant:
   from this day all gener⸍ations · will ⸍ call me ⸍ blessed;

Second part

3 the Almighty has done ⸍ great things ⸍ for me:
   and ⸍ holy ⸍ is his ⸍ name.

4 He has mercy on ⸍ those who ⸍ fear him:
   in ⸍ every ⸍ gener⸍ation.

5 He has shown the ⸍ strength · of his ⸍ arm:
   he has scattered the ⸍ proud in ⸍ their con⸍ceit.

6 He has cast down the mighty ⸍ from their ⸍ thrones:
   and has ⸍ lifted ⸍ up the ⸍ lowly.

7 He has filled the hungry with ⸍ good ⸍ things:
   and the rich he has ⸍ sent a⸍way ⸍ empty.

8 He has come to the help of his ⸍ servant ⸍ Israel:
   for he has re⸍membered · his ⸍ promise · of ⸍ mercy,
9 the promise he ⸍ made · to our ⸍ fathers:
   to Abraham ⸍ and his ⸍ children · for ⸍ ever.

Glory to the Father and ⸍ to the ⸍ Son:
and ⸍ to the ⸍ Holy ⸍ Spirit;
as it was in the be⸍ginning · is ⸍ now:
and shall be for ⸍ ever. ⸍ A⸍men.

161A   Bless the Lord, our fathers' God

Orientis partibus   7 7 7 7

Words: from *Bless the Lord*
Christopher Idle
Music: P de Corbeil (died 1222)

1 Bless the Lord, our fa - thers' God,
2 Bless the Lord who reigns on high
3 Bless the Lord for ev - er - more,

bless the name of____ hea - ven's king; bless him in his
throned a - bove the____ che - ru - bim; bless the Lord who
bless the Ho - ly____ Tri - ni - ty; bless the Fa - ther,

ho - ly____ place, tell his praise, his glo - ries sing.
knows the____ depths, show his praise and wor - ship him.
Spi - rit,____ Son, sing his praise e - ter - nal - ly!

Bless the Lord the God of our fathers 161B(i)

Words: *Bless the Lord*
derived from the Daily Office
of the Joint Liturgical Group
Music: John Barnard

CHOIR
1 Bless the Lord the God of our fa - thers: **sing his**

praise and ex - alt him for ev - er. CHOIR 2 Bless his ho - ly and

glo - ri - ous name: **sing his praise and ex - alt him for ev - er.**

CHOIR
3 Bless him in his ho - ly and glo - ri - ous tem - ple: **sing his**

This setting may be sung in harmony or in unison, with or without accompaniment.

ALL
sing___ his praise and ex - alt him for ev - er.

CHOIR
7 Bless___ him in___ the heights of hea - ven: ALL sing___ his

praise and ex - alt him for ev - er. CHOIR 8 Bless___ the

Fa - ther, the Son and the Ho - ly Spi - rit:

poco rall.

ALL
sing___ his praise and ex - alt him for ev - er.

161B(ii) Bless the Lord the God of our fathers

Words: *Bless the Lord*
derived from the Daily Office
of the Joint Liturgical Group
Music: Norman Warren

Alternative tune: *Songs from the Psalms* 161B

ALL
sing his praise and ex - alt him for ev - er. 4 Bless him who be -

LEADER

- holds the __ depths: sing his praise and ex - alt him for ev - er.

ALL

5 Bless him who sits be -

LEADER

- tween the __ che - ru - bim: sing his praise and ex - alt him for ev - er.

ALL

LEADER
6 Bless him on the___ throne of his king-dom:

ALL
sing his praise and ex -

-alt him for ev - er.

LEADER
7 Bless him in the heights of hea - ven:

ALL
sing his praise and ex - alt him for ev - er.

Slower

LEADER
8 Bless the Fa - ther, the Son and the Ho - ly Spi - rit:

ALL
sing his praise and ex - alt him for ev - er.

Bless the Lord the God of our fathers 161c

Words: *Bless the Lord*
derived from the Daily Office
of the Joint Liturgical Group

G C Martin (1844–1916)

George Guest

1 Bless the Lord the ˈ God of · our ˈ fathers:
   sing his ˈ praise · and exˈalt him · for ˈ ever.
2 Bless his holy and ˈ glori·ous ˈ name:
   sing his ˈ praise · and exˈalt him · for ˈ ever.

3 Bless him in his holy and ˈ glori·ous ˈ temple:
   sing his ˈ praise · and exˈalt him · for ˈ ever.
4 Bless him who beˈholds the ˈ depths:
   sing his ˈ praise · and exˈalt him · for ˈ ever.

5 Bless him who sits beˈtween the ˈ cherubim:
   sing his ˈ praise · and exˈalt him · for ˈ ever.
6 Bless him on the ˈ throne of · his ˈ kingdom:
   sing his ˈ praise · and exˈalt him · for ˈ ever.

7 Bless him in the ˈ heights of ˈ heaven:
   sing his ˈ praise · and exˈalt him · for ˈ ever.
8 Bless the Father the Son and the ˈ Holy ˈ Spirit:
   sing his ˈ praise · and exˈalt him · for ˈ ever.

Words: © Joint Liturgical Group

Faithful vigil ended

Faithful vigil 6 5 6 5

Words: from Luke 2,
The Song of Simeon/Nunc dimittis
Timothy Dudley-Smith
Music: David Wilson
arranged John Barnard

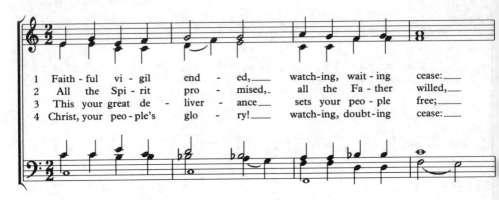

1 Faith - ful vi - gil end - ed,___ watch-ing, wait - ing cease:___
2 All the Spi - rit pro - mised,_ all the Fa - ther willed,___
3 This your great de - liver - ance___ sets your peo - ple free;___
4 Christ, your peo - ple's glo - ry!___ watch-ing, doubt-ing cease:___

Mas - ter, grant your ser - vant___ his dis-charge in peace.___
now these eyes be - hold___ it___ per - fect - ly ful - filled.___
Christ their light up - lift - ed___ all the na - tions see.___
grant to us your ser - vants___ our dis-charge in peace.___

Alternative tune: Caswall, *Hymns for Today's Church* 126

Lord, now let your servant

Oakmount 6 5 6 5

Words: from Luke 2,
The Song of Simeon/Nunc dimittis
J E Seddon (1915–1983)
Music: Hugh Benham

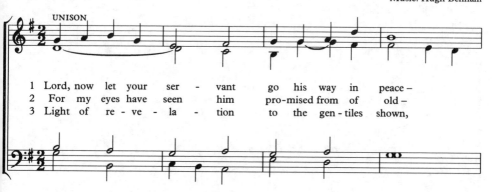

1 Lord, now let your ser - vant go his way in peace –
2 For my eyes have seen him pro-mised from of old –
3 Light of re - ve - la - tion to the gen - tiles shown,

your great love has brought me joy that will not cease:
sav - iour of all peo - ple, shep - herd of one fold:
light of Is - rael's glo - ry to the world made known.

162B(ii)   Lord, now let your servant

North Coates 6 5 6 5

Words: from Luke 2,
The Song of Simeon/Nunc dimittis
J E Seddon (1915–1983)
Music: T R Matthews (1826–1910)

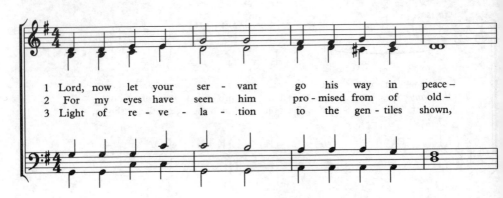

1 Lord, now let your ser - vant go his way in peace –
2 For my eyes have seen him pro - mised from of old –
3 Light of re - ve - la - tion to the gen - tiles shown,

your great love has brought me joy that will not cease:
sav - iour of all peo - ple, shep - herd of one fold:
light of Is - rael's glo - ry to the world made known.

Lord now you let your servant

C

Words: from Luke 2,
The Song of Simeon/Nunc dimittis
in *The Alternative Service Book 1980*
International Consultation on English Texts

G A Macfarren (1813–1887)

J Battishill (1738–1801)

1 Lord now you let your servant | go in | peace:
   your | word has | been ful|filled.

2 My own eyes have | seen the · sal|vation:
   which you have prepared in the | sight of | every | people;

3 a light to re|veal you · to the | nations:
   and the | glory · of your | people | Israel.

Glory to the Father and | to the | Son:
and | to the | Holy | Spirit;
as it was in the be|ginning · is | now:
and shall be for | ever. | A|men.

162D
Now at last

Bertem 3 8 3 6

Words: from Luke 2
The Song of Simeon/Nunc dimitti.
Michael Saward
Music: David Iliff

UNISON

1 Now at last your ser - vant can de - part in peace,
2 My own eyes have wit - nessed your sal - va - tion, Lord,
3 Light for all, re - veal - ing you to ev - ery land;
4 Prais - es be to God the Fa - ther, Spi - rit, Son —

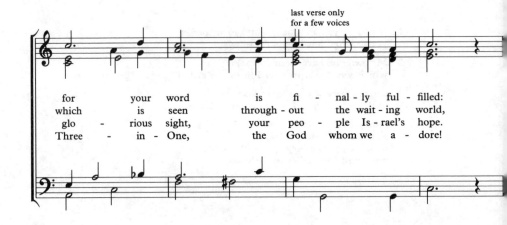

last verse only
for a few voices

for your word is fi - nal - ly ful - filled:
which is seen through - out the wait - ing world,
glo - rious sight, your peo - ple Is - rael's hope.
Three - in - One, the God whom we a - dore!

All praise to Christ

Engelberg 10 10 10 4

Words: from Philippians 2,
The Song of Christ's Glory
F B Tucker (1895–1984)
Music: C V Stanford (1852–1924)

1 All praise to Christ, our Lord and king di-vine,_____ yield-ing your
2 You came to us in low-li-ness of thought;_____ by you the
3 The mind of Christ is as our mind should be = _____ he was a

glo - ry in your love's de-sign,_____ that in our dark-ened hearts your
out - cast and the poor were sought,_____ and by your death was our re-
ser - vant, that we might be free;_____ humb-ling him-self to death on

vv 1-4

grace might shine:_____
- demp - tion bought:_____ Al - le - lu - ia!
Cal - va - ry:_____

v 5   HARMONY

all a-dored:_____ Al - le - lu - ia! A - men.

4 And so we see in God's great purpose, how
Christ has been raised above all creatures now;
and at his name shall every nation bow:
Alleluia!

5 Let every tongue confess with one accord,
in heaven and earth, that Jesus Christ is Lord,
and God the Father be by all adored:
Alleluia! (Amen.)

Alternative tune: Creation, *Hymns for Today's Church* 204

163B   Before the heaven and earth

Narenza 6 6 8 6 (SM)

Words: from Philippians 2, *The Song of Christ's Glory*
Brian Black and Word & Music
Music: from J Leisentritt, *Catholicum Hymnologium* 1584
arranged W H Havergal (1793–1870)
verse 6 arranged with descant John Barnard

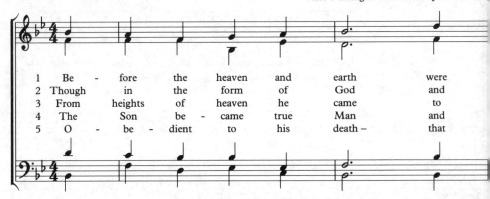

1 Be - fore the heaven and earth were
2 Though in the form of God and
3 From heights of heaven he came to
4 The Son be - came true Man and
5 O - be - dient to his death – that

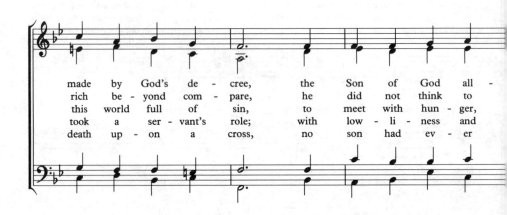

made by God's de - cree, the Son of God all -
rich be - yond com - pare, he did not think to
this world full of sin, to meet with hun - ger,
took a ser - vant's role; with low - li - ness and
death up - on a cross, no son had ev - er

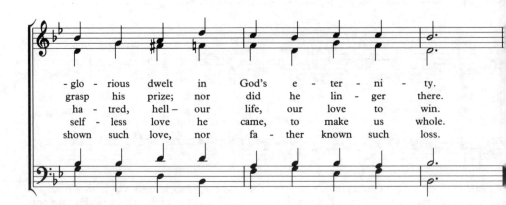

- glo - rious dwelt in God's e - ter - ni - ty.
grasp his prize; nor did he lin - ger there.
ha - tred, hell – our life, our love to win.
self - less love he came, to make us whole.
shown such love, nor fa - ther known such loss.

Alternative tune: *Songs from the Psalms* 163B

6 To him en-throned on high, by

6 To him en - throned on high, by

an - gel hosts a - dored,____ all knees shall bow, and

an - gel hosts a - dored, all knees shall bow, and

tongues con - fess that____ Je - sus Christ is Lord.

tongues con - fess that Je - sus Christ is Lord.

163c   Christ Jesus was in the form of God

Words: from Philippians
The Song of Christ's Glor
Liturgy of the Church of South Afri

E J Hopkins (1818–190

John Barnar

1   Christ Jesus was in the ǀ form of ǀ God:
   but he did not ǀ cling · to eǀquality · with ǀ God.
2   He emptied himself *
   taking the ǀ form · of a ǀ servant:
   and was ǀ born · in the ǀ likeness · of ǀ men.

3   Being found in human form he ǀ humbled · himǀself:
   and became obedient unto death ǀ even ǀ death · on a ǀ cross.
4   Therefore God has ǀ highly · exǀalted him:
   and bestowed on him the ǀ name a·bove ǀ every ǀ name,

5   that at the name of Jesus every ǀ knee should ǀ bow:
   in heaven and on ǀ earth and ǀ under · the ǀ earth;
6   and every tongue confess that Jesus ǀ Christ is ǀ Lord:
   to the ǀ glory · of ǀ God the ǀ Father.

   Glory to the Father and ǀ to the ǀ Son:
   and ǀ to the ǀ Holy ǀ Spirit;
   as it was in the beǀginning · is ǀ now:
   and shall be for ǀ ever. ǀ Aǀmen.

A setting for choir is available in *Church Family Worship* 800.

Though Christ put on our frail humanity 163D

Sursum Corda   10 10 10 10

Words: from Philippians 2,
The Song of Christ's Glory
Stephen Horsfall
Music: A M Smith (1879–1971)

UNISON

1 Though Christ put on our frail hu - man - i - ty, he
2 As God and man he chose the way to death, bear -
3 Since for our sake he glad - ly went to die, tak -
4 So at the name of Je - sus, ev - ery knee in

was in ve - ry truth our God and king; and yet he did not
- ing our sins up - on the cru - el cross; he blessed his kil - lers
- ing up - on him - self our ra - ce's shame, God raised him, and ex -
heaven, on earth and in the depths, should bow; and ev - ery tongue con -

claim e - qual - i - ty, but trod the path of hum - ble suf - fer - ing.
with his dy - ing breath, his a - go - ny re - deemed our griev - ous loss.
- alt - ed him on high, gave him the high - est place and ho - liest name:
- fess that on - ly he is Lord. Come, let us praise his glo - ry now!

164A   Heavenly hosts in ceaseless worship

Blaenwern 8 7 8 7 D

Words: from Revelation 4, 5
Glory and honou
Timothy Dudley-Smith
Music: W P Rowlands (1860–1937

1 Hea - venly hosts in cease - less wor - ship
2 All cre - a - tion, all_____ re - demp - tion,

'Ho - ly, ho - ly, ho - ly!' cry;
join_____ to sing the sav - iour's worth;

'He who is, who was_____ and will be,
Lamb of God whose blood_____ has bought us,

God al - migh - ty, Lord most_ high.'
kings and priests,_____ to reign on_ earth.

Alternative tune: Gott Will's machen, *Psalms for Today* 100A(ii), *Hymns for Today's Church* 360

Praise and hon - our, power___ and glo - ry,
Wealth and wis - dom, power___ and glo - ry,

be to him___ who reigns___ a - lone!
hon - our, might,___ do - min - ion,___ praise,

We, with all his hands___ have fash - ioned,
now be his from all___ his crea - tures

fall___ be - fore___ the Fa - ther's___ throne.
and___ to ev - er - last - ing___ days!

164B
Glory and honour

Schönster Herr Jesu 5 5 9 5 5 8

Words: from Revelation 4, 5
Glory and honour
Michael Perry
Music: *Silesian Folk Songs* Leipzig 184...

1 Glo - ry and hon - our, wis - dom and splen - dour,
2 Once was the ran - som paid for our free - dom—

Lord of cre - a - tion, are yours a - lone:
from ev - ery na - tion with you we reign:

all of earth's crea - tures in ex - ul - ta - tion
yours be the prais - es, high ve - ne - ra - tion,

sing to the Lamb up - on the throne.
wor - ship for ev - er - more. A - men.

Glory and honour

Words: from Revelation 4, 5,
Glory and honour
derived from the Daily Office
of the Joint Liturgical Group

G R Woodward (1848–1934)

J Hindle (1761–1796)

1 Glory and ˈ honour · and ˈ power:
   are yours by ˈ right O ˈ Lord our ˈ God:

2 for you creˈated ˈ all things:
   and by your ˈ will they ˈ have their ˈ being.

3 Glory and ˈ honour · and ˈ power:
   are yours by ˈ right O ˈ Lamb · who was ˈ slain;

4 for by your blood you ransomed ˈ us for ˈ God:
   from every race and language *
   from ˈ every ˈ people · and ˈ nation,

5 to make us a ˈ kingdom · of ˈ priests:
   to stand and ˈ serve beˈfore our ˈ God.

   To him who sits on the throne ˈ and · to the ˈ Lamb:
   be praise and honour glory and might *
   for ever and ˈ ever. ˈ Aˈmen.

165A(i) Before the ending of the day

Alicia 8 8 8 8 (LM)

Words: from *Te Lucis ante terminum*
(Before the ending of the day)
in this version Jubilate Hymns
Music: Andrew Maries

Gently rocking like a lullaby

1 Be-fore the end - ing of the day,
2 Bless us in sleep, that we may find
3 O Fa-ther, may your will be done

Cre - a - tor of the world, we pray: pro - tect us by your migh-ty grace,
no ter-rors to dis - turb. our mind; our cun - ning e - ne - my re-strain –
through Je - sus Christ your on - ly Son; whom with. the Spi - rit we a-dore,

grant us your mer - cy and your peace:
guard us from sin and all its stain.
one God, both now and ev - er - more.

(Fine)

Words: © in this version Jubilate Hymns

Before the ending of the day   165A(ii)

Tallis' Canon   8 8 8 8 (LM)

Words: from *Te Lucis ante terminum*
(Before the ending of the day)
in this version Jubilate Hymns
Music: T Tallis (c1505–1585)

1 Be - fore the end - ing of the day, Cre -
2 Bless us in sleep, that we may find no
3 O Fa - ther, may your will be done through

- a - tor of the world, we pray: pro - tect us by your
ter - rors to dis - turb our mind; our cun - ning e - ne -
Je - sus Christ your on - ly Son; whom with the Spi - rit

migh - ty grace, grant us your mer - cy and your peace:
- my re - strain – guard us from sin and all its stain.
we a - dore, one God, both now and ev - er - more.

165B(i)

Now evening comes

Charnwood 8 6 8 6 (CM)

Words: from *Te Lucis ante terminum*
(Before the ending of the day)
Michael Perry
Music: Peter White

1 Now even-ing comes to close the day, and soon the
2 In-to your hands, e-ter-nal Friend, we give our-
3 In wak-ing, lift our thoughts a-bove, in sleep-ing,
4 To Fa-ther, Son and Spi-rit-praise, all mor-tal

si-lent hours shall ban-ish all our fears a-
-selves a-gain, and to your watch-ful care com-
guard us still, that we may rise to know your
praise be given, till sleep at last shall end our

-way, and sleep re-new our powers.
-mend all those in grief or pain.
love and prove your per-fect will.
days and we shall wake in heaven!

Now evening comes

Stracathro 8 6 8 6 (CM)

Words: from *Te Lucis ante terminum*
(Before the ending of the day)
Michael Perry
Music: C Hutcheson (1792–1860)
arranged David Iliff

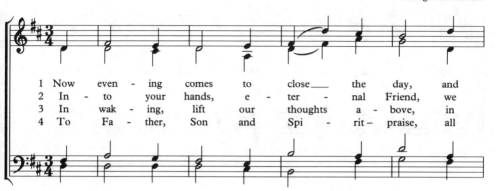

1 Now even - ing comes to close___ the day, and
2 In - to your hands, e - ter - nal Friend, we
3 In wak - ing, lift our thoughts a - bove, in
4 To Fa - ther, Son and Spi - rit - praise, all

soon___ the si - lent hours shall ban - ish___ all___ our
give___ our - selves a - gain, and to___ your___ watch - ful
sleep - ing, guard us still, that we___ may___ rise___ to
mor - tal praise be given, till sleep___ at___ last shall

fears___ a - way, and sleep___ re - new our powers.
care___ com - mend all those___ in grief or pain.
know___ your love and prove___ your per - fect will.
end___ our days and we___ shall wake in heaven!

166(i) Exult, creation round God's throne

Fenny Stratford 8 8 8 8 (LM)

Words: from *Exsultet* (Easter song of praise)
Christopher Idle
Music: Paul Edwards

1 Ex - ult, cre - a - tion round God's throne! All heaven, re-

-joice! All an - gels, sing! Sal - va - tion's trum - pet

sound a - loud for Je - sus Christ, our ris - en king.

HARMONY

2 Ex - ult, O earth, in ra - diant hope; in Christ's ma -
3 Ex - ult, all Christ - ians, one in praise with our Je -

- jes - tic splen - dour shine! The Lord is here, the
- ru - sa - lem a - bove! This roof shall ring with

vic - tory won, the dark-ness drowned in light di - vine.
Eas - ter songs that e - cho Christ's re - deem - ing love.

OPTIONAL VERSE
Exult in God, pure well of truth;
in Christ, fresh fountainhead of grace;
in Spirit, flowing stream of life –
eternal Joy our hearts embrace.

This version is compatible with the Unison setting.
Original key: A
If the piece is sung by choir alone the original key is preferable.

166(ii)   Exult, creation round God's throne

Agincourt 8 8 8 8 (LM)

Words: from *Exsultet* (Easter song of praise)
Christopher Idle
Music: English traditional melody
arranged John Barnard

1 Ex - ult, cre - a - tion round God's throne! All
2 Ex - ult, O earth, in ra - diant hope; in
3 Ex - ult, all Christ - ians, one in praise with

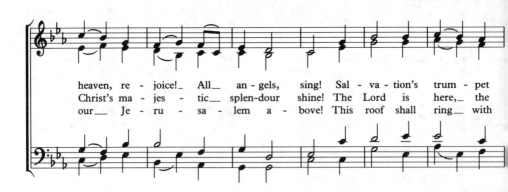

heaven, re - joice! All an - gels, sing! Sal - va - tion's trum - pet
Christ's ma - jes - tic splen-dour shine! The Lord is here, the
our Je - ru - sa - lem a - bove! This roof shall ring with

sound a - loud for Je - sus Christ, our ris - en king.
vic - tory won, the dark - ness drowned in light di - vine.
Eas - ter songs that e - cho Christ's re - deem - ing love.

OPTIONAL VERSE
Exult in God, pure well of truth;
in Christ, fresh fountainhead of grace;
in Spirit, flowing stream of life –
eternal Joy our hearts embrace.

I will sing the Lord's high triumph 167(i)

Tyddyn Llwyn 8 7 8 7 8 7 7

Words: from Exodus 15, *The Easter Liturgy*
Christopher Idle
Music: E Morgan (1846–1920)

1 I will sing the Lord's high triumph, rul-ing earth and sky and sea; God, my strength, my song, my glo-ry, my sal- -va-tion now is he. Through the wa-ters, through the wa-ters, God has brought us li-ber-ty, God has brought us li-ber-ty.

2 By the storm and at the moun-tain grace and judge-ment both are shown; all who planned his peo-ple's ru-in power di- -vine has o-ver-thrown. Na-tions trem-ble, na-tions trem-ble; God has made his mer-cy known, God has made his mer-cy known.

3 Who is like the God of Is-rael, faith-ful, ho-ly, throned a- -bove? Stretch-ing out the arm of an-ger, yet he guides us by his love. To our home-land, to our home-land, God will see us safe-ly move, God will see us safe-ly move.

4 Praise our God, who in his thun-der led a na-tion through the sea; praise the one whose blood re-leased us from our deep-er sla-ve-ry. Al-le-lu-ia, al-le-lu-ia, Christ is ris-en: we are free; Christ is ris-en: we are free!

167(ii) I will sing the Lord's high triumph

Westminster Abbey 8 7 8 7 8 7

Words: from Exodus 15, *The Easter Liturgy*
Christopher Idle
Music: H Purcell (1659–1695)

1 I will sing the Lord's high triumph, rul-ing earth and
2 By the storm and at the moun-tain grace and judge-ment
3 Who is like the God of Is-rael, faith-ful, ho-ly,
4 Praise our God, who in his thun-der led a na-tion

sky and sea; God, my strength, my song, my glo-ry,
both are shown; all who planned his peo-ple's ru-in
throned a-bove? Stretch-ing out the arm of an-ger,
through the sea; praise the one whose blood re-leased us

my sal-va-tion now is he. Through the wa-ters,
power di-vine has o-ver-thrown. Na-tions trem-ble,
yet he guides us by his love. To our home-land,
from our deep-er sla-ve-ry. Al-le-lu-ia,

through the wa-ters, God has brought us li-ber-ty.
na-tions trem-ble; God has made his mer-cy known.
to our home-land, God will see us safe-ly move.
al-le-lu-ia, Christ is ris-en: we are free!

LITURGICAL
PSALMS

8L Psalm 8.1–9

O Lord, our Lord:
how great is your name in all the world!
A **Your glory fills the skies.**
B **Your praise is sung by children.**
C **You silence your enemies.**

I look at the sky your hands have made, the
moon and stars you put in place:
ALL **Who are we that you care for us?**

You made us less than gods:
ALL **to crown us with glory and honour.**

You put us in charge of creation:
A **the beasts of the field.**
B **the birds of the air.**
C **the fish of the sea.**

O Lord, our Lord:
ALL **how great is your name in all the world!**

Glory to the Father, and to the Son,
and to the Holy Spirit:
as it was in the beginning, is now,
and shall be for ever. Amen.

The congregation may divide at A, B *and* C.

24L Psalm 24.1–10

The earth is the Lord's, and everything in it:
the world, and all who live here.

He founded it upon the seas:
and established it upon the waters.

E Who has the right to go up the Lord's hill;
who may enter his holy temple?
Those who have clean hands
 and a pure heart,
who do not worship idols
or swear by what is false.

They receive blessing continually from the
Lord:
and righteousness
from the God of their salvation.

Such are the people who seek for God:
who enter the presence of the God of Jacob.

D Fling wide the gates, open the ancient doors:
that the king of glory may come in.

E Who is the king of glory?
The Lord, strong and mighty,
the Lord mighty in battle.

D Fling wide the gates, open the ancient doors:
that the king of glory may come in.

E Who is he, this king of glory?
The Lord almighty,
he is the king of glory.

Glory to the Father, and to the Son,
and to the Holy Spirit:

as it was in the beginning, is now,
and shall be for ever. Amen.

E – *enquirer,* D – *director, or these lines may also be said*
by the minister.

33L Psalm 33.1–22

Sing joyfully to the Lord, you righteous:
it is right that his people should praise him.

Praise the Lord with the harp:
A **make music to him on the strings.**

Sing to the Lord a new song:
B **play skilfully, and shout for joy.**

For the word of the Lord is right and true:
ALL **and all his work is faithfulness.**

The Lord loves righteousness and justice:
A **his endless love fills the earth.**

By the word of the Lord the skies were
formed:
B **his breath created moon and stars.**

Let all the earth fear the Lord:
ALL **the people of the world revere him.**

For he spoke, and it came to be:
A **he commanded, and all was made.**

The Lord holds back the nations:
B **he thwarts their evil intent.**

God's purposes are sure:
ALL **his plans endure for ever.**

Happy is the nation whose God is the Lord:
A **happy the people he makes his own.**

The eyes of the Lord are on those who fear
him:
B **who trust in his unfailing love.**

We wait in hope for the Lord:
A **he is our help and shield.**

In him our hearts rejoice:
B **we trust his holy name.**

May your constant love be with us, Lord:
ALL **as we put our hope in you. Amen.**

The congregation – and ministers – may divide at A
and B.

36L Psalm 36.5–9

Your love, O Lord, reaches the heavens:
A **your faithfulness extends to the skies.**

Your righteousness is towering like the
mountains:
B **your justice is like the great deep.**

How precious is your love, O God:
A **we find shelter beneath your wings!**

We feast on the food you provide:
B we drink from the river of your goodness:

For with you is the fountain of life:
ALL **in your light we see light. Amen.**

The congregation – and ministers – may divide at A *and* B.

40L(i) Psalm 40.1–3

I waited patiently for the Lord:
he turned and heard my cry.

He pulled me out of the slimy pit:
out of the mud and mire.

He set my feet upon a rock:
and made my step secure.

He put a new song in my mouth:
a hymn of praise to God.

Many will see it and fear;
and put their trust in the Lord. Amen.

40L(ii) Psalm 40.4–16

Happy are those who trust in God:
who do not worship idols.

Sacrifice and offering you do not desire:
A **but you want my ears to be open.**

So I said, 'Lord I come:
B **obedient to your word.'**

I delight to do your will, O God:
A **and keep your teaching in my heart.**

I'll tell the world your saving news:
B **you know my lips will not be sealed.**

I have not hid your righteousness:
A **but speak of all your salvation, Lord.**

I do not hide your faithful love:
B **but share your mercy with them all.**

May all who come to you be glad; may all who
know your saving power for ever say:
ALL **How great is the Lord! Amen.**

The congregation – and ministers – may divide at A *and* B.

46L Psalm 46.1–11

God is our refuge and strength:
an ever-present help in trouble.

Therefore we will not fear:
A **though the earth should shake,**
B **though the mountains fall into the sea,**
A **though the waters surge and foam,**
B **though the mountains shake and roar.**

The Lord almighty is with us:
ALL **the God of Jacob is our fortress.**

There is a river whose streams make glad the
city of God: the holy place where the Most
High dwells.
A **God is within her, she will not fall:**
B **God will help her at break of day.**

Nations are in uproar, kingdoms fall:
A **God lifts his voice –**
B **the earth melts away.**

The Lord Almighty is with us:
ALL **the God of Jacob is our fortress.**

Come and see what God has done:
ALL **his devastation on the earth!**

He stops the wars throughout the world:
A **he breaks the bow and shatters the spear –**
B **he sets the shield on fire.**

V Be still, and know that I am God: I will be
exalted over the nations, I will be exalted over
the earth.

The Lord Almighty is with us:
ALL **the God of Jacob is our fortress. Amen.**

The congregation may divide at A *and* B; V *can be a distant voice, or said by the minister.*

47L Psalm 47.1–9

Clap your hands, all you nations:
shout to God with cries of joy.

How awesome is the Lord most high:
A **the King who rules the whole wide earth!**

God has ascended to his throne:
B **with shouts of joy and sound of trumpets.**

Sing praises to our God, sing praises:
A **sing praises to our King, sing praises.**

For God is King of all the earth:
B **sing to him a psalm of praise.**

God is seated on his throne:
A **he rules the nations of the world.**

The leaders of the nations come:
B **as subjects of our holy God.**

The lords of earth belong to God:
ALL **he reigns supreme. Amen.**

The congregation may divide at A *and* B.

51L Psalm 51.6–12, and Psalm 143.6–10

O Lord, I spread my hands out to you:
A **I thirst for you like dry ground.**

Teach me to do your will, for you are my God:
B **let your good Spirit lead me in safety.**

You require sincerity and truth in me:
A **fill my mind with your wisdom.**

Create in me a pure heart, O God:
B **renew a faithful spirit in me.**

Do not cast me from your presence:
A **or take your Holy Spirit from me.**

Give me again the joy of your salvation:
B **and make me willing to obey.**

Glory to the Father, and to the Son,
and to the Holy Spirit:
as it was in the beginning, is now,
and shall be for ever. Amen.

The congregation may divide at A *and* B, *in which case the Gloria should be used. Psalms 51 and 143 have been grouped together to provide for an occasion when the person and work of the Holy Spirit is being considered.*

65L Psalm 65.1–13

O God, it is right for us to praise you, because you answer our prayers:

You care for the land and water it:
A **and make it rich and fertile.**

You fill the running streams with water:
B **and irrigate the land.**

You soften the ground with showers:
A **and make the young crops grow.**

You crown the year with goodness:
B **and give us a plentiful harvest.**

The pastures are filled with flocks:
A **the hillsides are clothed with joy.**

The fields are covered with grain:
ALL **they shout for joy and sing.**

Glory to the Father, and to the Son,
and to the Holy Spirit:
as it was in the beginning, is now,
and shall be for ever. Amen.

The congregation may divide at A *and* B.

66L Psalm 66.1–20

Praise your God with shouts of joy:
all the earth, sing praise to him.

Sing the glory of his name:
A **offer him your highest praise.**

Say to him: How great you are:
B **wonderful the things you do!**

All your enemies bow down:
C **all the earth sings praise to you.**

Come and see what God has done:
A **causing mortal men to fear –**
B **for he turned the sea to land,**
C **let his people safely through.**

We rejoice at what he does –
A **ruling through eternity,**
B **watching over all the world,**
C **keeping every rebel down.**

Praise our God, you nations, praise:
A **let the sound of praise be heard!**
B **God sustains our very lives:**
C **keeps our feet upon the way.**

Once, you tested us, O God –
A **silver purified by fire –**

Let us fall into a trap,
B **placed hard burdens on our backs –**

Sent us through the flame and flood:
C **now you bring us safely home.**

I will come to worship you:
A **bring to you my offering,**
B **give you what I said I would,**
C **when the troubles threatened me.**

All who love and honour God:
A **come and listen, while I tell**
B **what great things he did for me**
C **when I cried to him for help,**
A **when I praised him with my songs.**
B **When my heart was free from sin,**
C **then he listened to my prayer.**

Praise the Lord who heard my cry:
ALL **God has shown his love to me! Amen.**

The congregation may divide at A, B *and* C.

67L Psalm 67.1–7

May God be gracious to us and bless us:
A **and make his face to shine upon us.**

Let your ways be known upon earth:
B **your saving grace to every nation.**

Let the peoples praise you, O God:
ALL **let the peoples praise you.**

Let the nations be glad:
A **and sing aloud for joy.**

Because you judge the peoples justly:
B **and guide the nations of the earth.**

Let the peoples praise you, O God:
ALL **let all the peoples praise you.**

Then the land will yield its harvest:
A **and God, our God, will bless us.**

God will bless us:
B **and people will fear him**
ALL **to the ends of the earth. Amen.**

Glory to the Father, and to the Son,
and to the Holy Spirit:
as it was in the beginning, is now,
and shall be for ever. Amen.

The congregation may divide at A *and* B.

80L Psalm 80.1–19

ᴬ Hear us, O Shepherd of Israel, leader of your flock.

ᴮ Hear us from your throne above the cherubim.

ᶜ Shine forth, awaken your strength, and come to save us.
**Bring us back, O God, and save us,
make your face to shine upon us.**

ᴬ O Lord God almighty, how long will you be angry with your people's prayers?

ᴮ You have given us sorrow to eat and tears to drink.

ᶜ You have made us a source of contention to our neighbours, and our enemies insult us.
**Bring us back, O God, and save us,
make your face to shine upon us.**

ᴬ Return to us, O God Almighty, look down from heaven and see.

ᴮ Look on this vine that you planted with your own hand, this child you raised for yourself.

ᶜ Let your hand rest upon the people you have chosen, then we will not turn away from you; revive us, and we shall praise your name.
**Bring us back, O God, and save us,
make your face to shine upon us.**

**Glory to the Father, and to the Son,
and to the Holy Spirit:
as it was in the beginning, is now,
and shall be for ever. Amen.**

Ministers/leaders may divide at A, B *and* C.

93L Psalm 93.1–5

The Lord reigns, robed in majesty:
ᴬ **he arms himself with power.**

The earth is firmly set in place:
ᴮ **it never can be moved.**

Your throne was founded long ago:
ᴬ **before all time began.**

The oceans raise their voice, O Lord:
ᴮ **and lift their roaring waves.**

The Lord is mightier than the sea:
ᴬ **he rules supreme on high.**

His laws stand firm through endless days:
ᴮ **his praise for evermore.**
ᴬᴸᴸ **Amen.**

**Glory to the Father, and to the Son,
and to the Holy Spirit:
as it was in the beginning, is now,
and shall be for ever. Amen.**

The congregation may divide at A *and* B.

95L Psalm 95.1–7

ᴹ Come, let's joyfully praise our God, acclaiming the Rock of our salvation.

ᴺ Come before him with thanksgiving, and greet him with melody.

ᴬ **Our God is a great God –**
ᴮ **a king above all other gods.**

ᴬ **The depths of the earth are in his hands –**
ᴮ **the mountain peaks belong to him.**

ᴬ **The sea is his – he made it!**
ᴮ **His own hands prepared the land.**

ᴹ Come, bow down to worship him;
ᴺ kneel before the Lord who made us.

ᴬ&ᴮ **We are his people,
the sheep of his flock.**

ᴹ&ᴺ **You shall know his power today –**
ᴺ **if you listen to his voice.**

**Glory to the Father, and to the Son,
and to the Holy Spirit:
as it was in the beginning, is now,
and shall be for ever. Amen.**

The congregation may divide at A *and* B, *the ministers at* M *and* N.

96L Psalm 96.1–13

Sing to the Lord a new song:
ᴬ **sing to the Lord, all the earth.**

Sing to the Lord, praise his name:
ᴮ **proclaim his salvation each day.**

Declare his glory among the nations:
ᴬ **his marvellous deeds among the peoples.**

Great is the Lord, and worthy of praise:
ᴮ **honour him above all gods.**

Splendour and majesty surround him:
ᴬ **power and beauty fill his temple.**

Praise the Lord all people on earth:
ᴮ **praise his glory and might.**

Give him the glory due to his name:
ᴬ **bring an offering into his temple.**

Worship the Lord in his beauty and holiness:
ᴮ **tremble before him all the earth.**

Say to the nations:
ᴬᴸᴸ **The Lord is king!**

Let the heavens rejoice and the earth be glad:
ᴬ **let all creation sing for joy.**

For God shall come to judge the world:
ᴮ **and rule the people with his truth.**
ᴬᴸᴸ **Amen.**

The congregation may divide at A *and* B.

97L   Psalm 97.1–12

The Lord is king:
the Lord is king!

Let the whole wide earth rejoice:
A **let the islands all be glad.**

Thunder-clouds encircle him:
B **truth and justice are his throne.**

Fire shall go before the Lord:
C **burning up his enemies.**

Lightning strikes the darkened world:
A **all the people see and fear.**

Mountains melt before our God:
B **he is Lord of all the earth.**

Skies proclaim his righteousness:
C **nations see his glory now.**

Idol-worshippers are shamed:
A **gods bow down before the Lord.**

Let Jerusalem rejoice:
B **in your faithful judgements, Lord!**

Sovereign of the universe:
C **mightier still than all the gods!**

Yet you help your saints, O Lord:
A **saving them from wicked men.**

Light will shine upon the good:
B **gladness fill the righteous heart.**

Now recall what God has done:
C **thank him,**
B **praise him,**
ALL **and rejoice!**

Glory to the Father, and to the Son,
and to the Holy Spirit:
as it was in the beginning, is now,
and shall be for ever. Amen.

The congregation may divide at A, B *and* C.

98L   Psalm 98.1–9

Sing to the Lord a new song:
for he has done marvellous things.

His right hand and his holy arm:
have brought a great triumph to us.

A **He lets his salvation be known:**
B **his righteousness seen by the world.**
A **To us he continues his love:**
B **his glory is witnessed by all.**

Shout for joy to the Lord, all the earth:
ALL **and burst into jubilant song.**

A **Make music to God with the harp:**
B **with songs and the sound of your praise.**
A **With trumpets and blast of the horn:**
B **sing praises to God as your king.**

Let rivers and streams clap their hands:
ALL **the mountains together sing praise.**

The Lord comes to judge the whole earth:
in righteousness God rules the world. Amen.

The congregation may divide at A *and* B.

99L   Psalm 99.1–9

The Lord reigns:
A **let the nations tremble!**

He sits enthroned on high:
B **let the earth shake!**

Great is the Lord our God:
ALL **exalted over all the world.**

Let the nations praise his awesome name, and say:
A **God is holy!**

Praise the Lord our God, and worship at his feet:
B **God is holy!**

Exalt the Lord our God, and worship on his holy mountain:
ALL **The Lord our God is holy!**

Glory to the Father, and to the Son,
and to the Holy Spirit:
as it was in the beginning, is now,
and shall be for ever. Amen.

The congregation may divide at A *and* B.

100L   Psalm 100.1–5

Rejoice in the Lord, all the earth:
worship the Lord with gladness.

Remember the Lord is our God:
A **we are his flock and he made us.**

Come to his temple with praise:
B **enter his gates with thanksgiving.**

The love of the Lord will not fail:
God will be faithful for ever. Amen.

The congregation may divide at A *and* B.

103L   Psalm 103.1–22

Praise the Lord, my soul:
A **all my being, praise his holy name!**

Praise the Lord, my soul:
B **and do not forget how generous he is.**

A **He forgives all my sins:**
B **and heals all my diseases.**
A **He keeps me from the grave:**
B **and blesses me with love and mercy.**

The Lord is gracious and compassionate:
A **slow to become angry,**
B **and full of constant love.**

He does not keep on rebuking:
A **he is not angry for ever.**

He does not punish us as we deserve:
B **or repay us for our wrongs.**

As far as the east is from the west:
A **so far does he remove our sins from us.**

As kind as a Father to his children:
B **so kind is the Lord to those who honour him.**

Praise the Lord, all his creation:
ALL **praise the Lord, my soul! Amen.**

The congregation may divide at A *and* B.

104L Psalm 104.1–4, 29–30

O Lord our God, you are very great:
you are clothed with splendour and majesty.

You make winds your messengers:
A **and flashes of fire your servants.**

How many are your works:
B **the earth is full of your creatures!**

When you hide your face, they are afraid:
A **when you take away their breath, they die.**

When you send your Spirit they are created:
B **and you renew the face of the earth.**

**Glory to the Father, and to the Son,
and to the Holy Spirit:
as it was in the beginning, is now,
and shall be for ever. Amen.**

The congregation may divide at A *and* B, *in which case the* Gloria *should be used.*

105L Psalm 105.1–45

Give thanks to the Lord, praise his name:
A **tell the nations what he has done.**

Sing to him, sing praise to him:
B **tell of all his wonderful deeds.**

Glory in his holy name:
C **let all who worship him rejoice.**

Go to the Lord for help:
A **and worship him for ever.**

Remember the wonders he does:
B **the miracles he performs.**

He is the Lord our God:
C **he judges the whole wide earth.**

He keeps his word and covenant:
A **for a thousand generations.**

The covenant he made with Abraham:
B **the oath he swore to Israel.**

He brought them out of Egypt:
C **and none of them was lost.**

He gave a cloud for covering:
A **a pillar of fire by night.**

He gave them bread from heaven:
B **and water from the rock.**

He brought his people out rejoicing:
C **his chosen ones with shouts of joy.**

ALL **Praise the Lord!**

**Glory to the Father, and to the Son,
and to the Holy Spirit:
as it was in the beginning, is now,
and shall be for ever. Amen.**

The congregation – and ministers/leaders – may divide at A, B *and* C.

107L Psalm 107.1–31

Give thanks to the Lord, for he is good:
his love endures for ever.

Repeat these words in praise to the Lord:
all those he has redeemed.

Some sailed the ocean in ships:
A **they earned their way on the seas.**

They saw what the Lord can do:
B **his wonderful deeds in the deep.**

For he spoke and stirred up a storm:
A **and lifted high the waves.**

Their ships were thrown in the air:
B **and plunged into the depths.**

Their courage melted away:
A **they reeled like drunken men.**

They came to the end of themselves:
B **and cried to the Lord in their trouble.**

He brought them out of distress:
A **and stilled the raging storm.**

They were glad because of the calm:
B **he brought them safely to harbour.**

Let them give thanks to the Lord:
ALL **for his unfailing love.**

**Glory to the Father, and to the Son,
and to the Holy Spirit:
as it was in the beginning, is now,
and shall be for ever. Amen.**

The congregation may divide at A *and* B.

111L Psalm 111.1–10

Praise the Lord:
praise the Lord!

With my whole heart I will thank the Lord: in
the company of his people. Great are the works
of the Lord:
A **those who wonder, seek them.**

Glorious and majestic are his deeds:
B **his goodness lasts for ever.**

He reminds us of his works of grace:
A **he is merciful and kind.**

He sustains those who fear him:
B **he keeps his covenant always.**

All he does is right and just:
A **all his words are faithful.**

They will last for ever and ever:
B **and be kept in faith and truth.**

He provided redemption for his people, and
made an eternal covenant with them:
ALL **holy and awesome is his name!**

The fear of the Lord is the beginning of wisdom;
he gives understanding to those who obey:
ALL **to God belongs eternal praise!**

**Glory to the Father, and to the Son,
and to the Holy Spirit:
as it was in the beginning, is now,
and shall be for ever. Amen.**

The congregation may divide at A *and* B.

113L Psalm 113.1–9

A Praise the Lord:
praise the Lord!

B You servants of the Lord, praise his name:
**let the name of the Lord be praised,
both now and for evermore!**

A From the rising of the sun to the place where
it sets:
the name of the Lord be praised!

B The Lord is exalted above the earth:
his glory over the heavens.

A Who is like the Lord our God?
He is throned in the heights above –

B Yet he bends down:
yet he stoops to look at our world.

A He raises the poor from the dust:
and lifts the needy from their sorrow.

B He honours the childless wife in her home:
he makes her happy, the mother of children.

BOTH Praise the Lord:
Amen.

The ministers/leaders may divide at A *and* B.

116L Psalm 116.1–19

I love the Lord because he heard my voice:
A **the Lord in mercy listened to my prayers.**

Because the Lord has turned his ear to me:
B **I'll call on him as long as I shall live.**

The cords of death entangled me around:
C **the horrors of the grave came over me.**

But then I called upon the Lord my God:
A **I said to him: 'O Lord, I beg you, save!'**

The Lord our God is merciful and good:
B **the Lord protects the simple-hearted ones.**

The Lord saved me from death and stopped
my tears:
C **he saved me from defeat and picked me up.**

And so I walk before him all my days:
A **and live to love and praise his holy name.**

What shall I give the Lord for all his grace?
B **I'll take his saving cup, and pay my vows.**

Within the congregation of his saints:
C **I'll offer him my sacrifice of praise.**

Praise the Lord:
ALL **Amen, amen!**

The congregation may divide at A, B *and* C.

117L Psalm 117.1–2

Praise the Lord, all you nations:
A **praise him, all you people!**

Great is his love towards us:
B **his faithfulness shall last for ever.**

Praise the Lord:
Amen.

The congregation may divide at A *and* B.

118L Psalm 118.1–29

M Give thanks to the Lord, for he is good:
his love endures for ever.

M All those who fear the Lord shall say:
His love endures for ever.

W Open for me the gates of the Temple; I will go in
and give thanks to the Lord.

M This is the gate of the Lord, only the righteous
can come in.

W I will give thanks because you heard me; you
have become my salvation.

C The stone which the builders rejected as worth-
less turned out to be the most important of all:
ALL **The Lord has done this – what a wonderful
sight it is!**

W This is the day of the Lord's victory – let us be happy, let us celebrate:
ALL **O Lord save us – O Lord, grant us success.**

M May God bless the one who comes in the name of the Lord:
ALL **The Lord is God – he has been good to us!**

C From the Temple of the Lord, we bless you.

D With branches in your hands, start the procession and march round the altar:

W You are my God and I will give you thanks:
ALL **You are my God, and I will exalt you.**

M Give thanks to the Lord, for he is good:
His love endures for ever. Amen.

M – *minister*, W – *worshipper – from doorway, then moving through congregation*, C – *choir/chorus*, D – *director – in matter-of-fact tone.*

122L Psalm 122.1–8

I was glad when they said to me:
let us go to the house of the Lord!

Pray for the peace of Jerusalem:
A **may those who love our land be blessed.**

May there be peace in your homes:
B **and safety for our families.**

For the sake of those we love we say:
ALL **Let there be peace! Amen.**

**Glory to the Father, and to the Son,
and to the Holy Spirit:
as it was in the beginning, is now,
and shall be for ever. Amen.**

The congregation may divide at A – *male voices, and* B – *female voices.*

124L Psalm 124.1–8

If the Lord had not been on our side – now let Israel say:
If the Lord had not been on our side –
A **when enemies attacked us,**
B **when their anger flared against us,**
C **they would have swallowed us alive.**
A **The flood would have engulfed us,**
B **the torrent would have swept over us,**
C **the waters would have drowned us.**

Praise the Lord:
A **who has not given us up to their teeth.**
B **We have escaped like a bird from the snare:**
C **the snare is broken and we are free.**

Our help is in the name of the Lord:
ALL **who made heaven and earth. Amen.**

The congregation may divide at A, B *and* C.

126L Psalm 126.1–6

When the Lord brought us back from slavery:
A **we were like those who dream.**

Our mouths were filled with laughter:
B **our tongues with songs of joy.**

Then those around us said, 'The Lord has done great things for them':
A **The Lord has done great things for us,
and we are filled with joy.**

Those who sow in tears
B **shall reap with songs of joy.**

**Glory to the Father, and to the Son,
and to the Holy Spirit:
as it was in the beginning, is now,
and shall be for ever. Amen.**

The congregation may divide at A *and* B, *in which case the* Gloria *should be used.*

128L Psalm 128.1–6

The pilgrims' song:
A **Blessed are those who fear the Lord,**
B **who walk in his ways.**

You will eat the fruit of your work; blessings and prosperity will be yours:
A **Blessed are those who fear the Lord,**
B **who walk in his ways.**

Your wife will be like a fruitful vine within your house; your children will be like young olive trees around your table:
A **Blessed are those who fear the Lord,**
B **who walk in his ways.**

May the Lord bless you all the days of your life; may you have prosperity; may you live to see your children's children:
ALL **Peace be with you. Amen.**

The congregation may divide at A *and* B.

134L Psalm 134.1–3

You servants of the Lord,
who stand in his temple at night:
A **praise the Lord!**

Lift your hands in prayer to the Lord:
B **in his sanctuary, praise the Lord!**

May the Lord who made the heaven and earth bless you from Zion:
ALL **Amen!**

**Glory to the Father, and to the Son,
and to the Holy Spirit:
as it was in the beginning, is now,
and shall be for ever. Amen.**

The congregation may divide at A *and* B, *in which case the* Gloria *should be used.*

136L Psalm 136.1–26

A Give thanks to God, for he is good:
A **his love shall last for ever!**

B Give thanks to him, the God of gods:
B **his love shall last for ever!**

C Give thanks to him, the Lord of lords:
C **his love shall last for ever!**

A For God alone works miracles:
A **his love shall last for ever!**

B The skies were made at his command:
B **his love shall last for ever!**

C He spread the seas upon the earth:
C **his love shall last for ever!**

A He made the stars to shine at night:
A **his love shall last for ever!**

B He made the sun to shine by day:
B **his love shall last for ever!**

C He brought us out from slavery:
C **his love shall last for ever!**

A He leads us onward by his grace:
A **his love shall last for ever!**

B He saves us from our enemies:
B **his love shall last for ever!**

C Give thanks to God, for he is good:
C **his love shall last for ever!**
ALL **Amen!**

*The congregation must divide at A, B and C saying the
whole stanza, OR both ministers and congregation should
divide.*

143L Psalm 143.6–10, and Psalm 51.6–12

O Lord, I spread my hands out to you:
A **I thirst for you like dry ground.**

Teach me to do your will, for you are my God:
B **let your good Spirit lead me in safety.**

You require sincerity and truth in me:
A **fill my mind with your wisdom.**

Create in me a pure heart, O God:
B **and renew a faithful spirit in me.**

Do not cast me from your presence:
A **or take your Holy Spirit from me.**

Give me again the joy of your salvation:
B **and make me willing to obey.**

**Glory to the Father, and to the Son,
and to the Holy Spirit:
as it was in the beginning, is now,
and shall be for ever. Amen.**

*The congregation may divide at A and B, in which case the
Gloria should be used. Psalms 143 and 51 have been
grouped together to provide for an occasion when the person
and work of the Holy Spirit is being considered.*

147L Psalm 147.1–20

O praise the Lord, sing out to God:
such praise is right and good.

The Lord restores Jerusalem:
A **he brings the exiles home.**

He heals all those with broken hearts:
B **he bandages their wounds.**

He counts the number of the stars:
C **he calls them each by name.**

How great and mighty is the Lord:
A **immeasurably wise!**

He raises up the humble ones:
B **and brings the mighty down.**

Sing hymns of triumph to his name:
C **make music to our God!**

He spreads the clouds across the sky:
A **he showers the earth with rain.**

He sends the animals their food:
B **he feeds the hungry birds.**

His true delight is not the strong:
C **but those who trust his love.**

Extol the Lord, Jerusalem:
A **let Zion worship God!**

For God shall keep your people safe:
B **and bring your harvest home.**

He gives commandment to the earth:
C **his will is quickly done.**

He spreads like wool the falling snow:
A **how cold the frosty air!**

He sends the wind, the warming rain:
B **and melts the ice away.**

His laws he gives to Israel:
C **and Judah hears his word.**

He does not favour other lands:
ALL **so, praise the Lord. Amen!**

The congregation may divide at A, B and C.

148L Psalm 148.1–14

Praise the Lord!

Praise the Lord from the heavens:
praise him in the heights above.

Praise him, all his angels:
A **praise him, all his heavenly host.**

Praise him, sun and moon:
B **praise him, all you shining stars.**

Let them praise the name of the Lord:
ALL **Praise the Lord!**

Praise the Lord from the earth:
A **praise him, great sea creatures.**

Praise him, storms and clouds:
B **praise him, mountains and hills.**

Praise him, fields and woods:
A **praise him, animals and birds.**

Praise him, rulers and nations:
B **praise him, old and young.**

Let them praise the name of the Lord:
ALL **Praise the Lord! Amen.**

The congregation may divide at A *and* B.

149L Psalm 149.1–9

Praise the Lord:
praise the Lord!

Sing a new song to the Lord:
A **let the people shout his name!**

Praise your maker, Israel:
B **hail your king, Jerusalem.**

Sing and dance to honour him:
A **praise him with the strings and drums.**

God takes pleasure in his saints:
B **crowns the meek with victory.**

Rise, you saints, in triumph now:
A **sing the joyful night away!**

Shout aloud and praise your God!
B **Hold aloft the two-edged sword!**

Let the judgement now begin:
A **kings shall fall and tyrants die.**

Through his people, by his word:
B **God shall have the victory!**

Praise the Lord:
ALL **praise the Lord!**

Glory to the Father, and to the Son,
and to the Holy Spirit:
as it was in the beginning, is now,
and shall be for ever. Amen.

The congregation – and ministers – may divide at A
and B.

150L 150.1–6

Praise the Lord!

Praise God in his sanctuary:
praise his strength beyond the skies!

Praise him for his acts of power:
A **praise him for his surpassing greatness.**

Praise him with the sounding of the trumpet:
B **praise him with the harp and lyre.**

Praise him with tambourine and dancing:
A **praise him with the strings and flute.**

Praise him with the clash of cymbals:
B **praise him with resounding cymbals.**

Let everything that has breath praise the
Lord:
ALL **Praise the Lord! Amen.**

Glory to the Father, and to the Son,
and to the Holy Spirit:
as it was in the beginning, is now,
and shall be for ever. Amen.

The congregation may divide at A *and* B.

Legal Information, Notes and Acknowledgements

Psalms and Liturgical Texts

Those seeking to reprint material in this book which is the property of Jubilate Hymns or associated authors (attributed '/Jubilate Hymns') may write to The Copyright Secretary, Jubilate Hymns Ltd, 61 Chessel Avenue, Southampton SO2 4DY. In the United States of America these copyrights and those of Timothy Dudley-Smith, Peter Cutts, Fred Kaan and Fred Pratt Green are administered by Hope Publishing Company, Carol Stream, Illinois 60188. Addresses of other copyright-holders can also be supplied.

Jubilate Hymns, Marshall Pickering Communications, Scripture Union, Thankyou Music, Word (UK) Ltd – along with other copyright-holders whose titles they administer (Celebration Services, Maranatha!, Word & Music etc.) have uniform concessions and rates. Details are available from the Copyright Secretary, Jubilate Hymns Ltd.

Most of these publishers also combine to offer a licensing scheme for limited term reproduction. Where this is felt to be an advantage, application should be made to the Christian Music Association at Glyndley Manor, Stone Cross, Pevensey, East Sussex BN24 5BS (0323 440440). Hymns copyrighted Stainer & Bell may not be reprinted or photocopied under any blanket licensing scheme, but should be cleared individually with Stainer & Bell Limited.

Liturgical (Responsive) Psalms

These texts are the copyright of the Editor, and are available for local reproduction subject to acknowledgement of source in the form 'Reprinted from *Psalms for Today* with the permission of Jubilate Hymns Ltd' (or, in the USA, '. . . of Hope Publishing Company, Carol Stream, Illinois 60188').

Recording and Broadcasting

Jubilate Hymns and associated authors, and Word & Music are members of the Mechanical Copyright Protection and Performing Right Societies.

The Alternative Service Book

The Alternative Service Book 1980 (ASB) is © the Central Board of Finance of the Church of England 1980.

The content of Holy Communion Rite A and Morning or Evening Worship is drawn from alternative services authorised for use in the Church of England. The complete alternative services of Holy Communion Rite A, Morning Prayer and Evening Prayer may be found in ASB. These services are authorised for use in the Church of England pursuant to Canon B2 of the Canons of the Church of England until 31st December 2000. The copyright in ASB and in individual alternative services is held by the Central Board of Finance of the Church of England and they may not be reproduced without permission.

The text of the Apostles' Creed, as printed in Morning Prayer and Evening Prayer, is copyright © 1970, 1971, 1975 International Consultation on English Texts (ICET). The Lord's Prayer in its modern form is adapted from the ICET version.

Acknowledgements

We owe our thanks most particularly to those authors and composers who readily created or adapted their work to meet the need for fluent and congregational texts and music settings of quality and relative simplicity. We mention especially those to whom we turned time and again for help and support: John Barnard, Timothy Dudley-Smith, Christopher Idle, Brian Foley, David Mowbray, Norman Warren and Paul Wigmore.

For application of her special expertise to the text of the liturgical (responsive) psalms we thank Rev. Kathleen Bowe of Cliff College.

For the major task of copyright clearance and assistance in preparing the work for publication we thank Bunty Grundy, Ann Darlington and Sylvia Bleasdale of Jubilate Hymns. For their encouragement and professionalism we acknowledge the contribution of publishers and typesetters – especially Hodder and Stoughton's Tim Anderson, Dick Douglas and Kathy Dyke, and Barnes' Michael Mack Smith.

Michael Perry (Editor)
David Iliff (Music Editor)

Themes Index to the Psalms and Canticles

Italics indicate the numbers of canticles and other liturgical hymns

absolution – 24B
acknowledge God – 100D
actions (ours; see also: 'behaviour', 'deeds') – 61A, 139B
acts (of God; see also: 'deeds', 'wonders') – 145B, 150B, 150C
adoration – 19A, 31A, 145A, 146
advent – 16A, 24A, 24B, 28, 44, 50A, 50B, 73, 81, 85A, 96L, 97, 98A, 98B, 98C, 98L, 122B, 132, *156A, 158A, 158B*
Advent services (and Sundays before Christmas; see also: 'advent') – 28, 46A, 46B, 46L, 50A, 50B, 75, 85, 96A, 96L, 97, 97L, 98A, 98B, 98C, 98L, *156A, 158A, 158B, 158C, 160A, 160B, 160C*
adversary (see also: 'enemies', 'oppressor') – 143A
advice – 1C
age (old) – 71A, *162A, 162B, 162C*
ages (see also: 'generations') – 145A, 146
aggression – 43B
aggressors – 76
agony (see also: 'pain') – 22A
All Saints-tide services (see also: 'Saints days') – 1C, 15A, 15B, 33L, 97, 97L, 145A, 145B, 149L, *156A, 156B, 156C, 164B, 164C*
all-seeing (God; see also: 'seeing') – 73
altar – 43A, 84C, 118L
angels – 73, 78, 91A, 103A, 103B, 148A, 148C, 148L, *154A, 154B, 154C, 156B, 156C, 166*
anger (God's) – 30A, 37A, 38, 60, 63B, 80L, 85, 88, 95A, 95C, 103C
anger (God is slow to anger) – 103B
animals – 8A, 8C, 147L, 148A, 148L
anniversary (see also: 'dedication/consecration . . .' etc) – 48A
Annunciation – 113, 113L, 131A, 131B, *160A, 160B, 160C*
anointing – 23A, 23C
anointing (Christ's) – 45
answer to prayer (see also: 'prayer') – 3A, 20A, 22A, 34B, 38, 61B, 65B, 65L, 66A, 91A, 116A, 143A
anthems – 96A, 148B
anxiety – 16A, 55, 127B
anxiety (about the future) – 69A
anxiety (worldly) – 84A
apostles – *156A, 156C, 156D*
approach to God – 24B
approval (God's) – 127A
arm (God's) – 28, 98A, 98C, 98L, 123B, *160A, 160B, 160C, 167*
ascension – 47B, 68A, 93A, 99L, 110, 113L, *152B, 157A, 157B*
Ascensiontide services (see also: 'ascension') – 8C, 21, 24B, 45, 47B, 47L, 68A, 93A, 93B, 93L, 99L, *156B, 156C, 156D, 157A, 157B, 159A, 163A, 163B, 163C, 164A, 164B, 164C*
Ash Wednesday (see also: 'lent services') – 6, 51A, 51B, 90A, 90B
assurance (see also: 'confidence') – 19B, 20A
atheism (see also: 'unbelief') – 1A, 10, 14
atheist – 53, 137

atonement (Jesus') – 116A
autumn – 84C, 148C
awaking – 5
away from home (see also: 'exile') – 61A

babies – 8A, 8C, 107
Baptism (service of thanksgiving for) – 116A, 116B, 116L, *167*
battle – 43A
beasts (see also: 'animals', 'creatures') – 8B, 148A, 148B, 148C
beauty (of God and creation) – 8B, 29A, 52, 90B, 104A
behaviour (see also: 'living') – 19A, 19C, 50A
Bible reading (see: 'receiving . . .')
Bible Sunday – 1A, 1B, 1C, 12B, 19A, 19B, 19C, 62A, 95B, 119A, 119B, 119C
birds – 8A, 8C, 8L, 11, 84A, 84C, 147L, 148A, 148B, 148C, 148L, *154A, 154B*
bitterness – 10
blamelessness (see also: 'innocence') – 15A, 26, 119C
blessing – 1A, 1C, 3A, 14, 20A, 23B, 24C, 24L, 39, 67A, 67C, 67L, 69A, 84A, 84C, 103L, 106A, 107, 112, 115, 123B, 125, 128A, 128B, 128L, 133A, 133B, 134A, 134B, 134C, 134L
blindness (see also: 'light') – 81, 82
blood (see: 'cross', 'ransom', 'redemption')
boasting (see also: 'pride') – 52, 73, 75, 128B
bounty (God's; see also: 'generosity') – 146
bow – 46B, 46L
brass (instruments; see also: 'trumpet') – 149A, 150A
bread – 105L, 146
breath (God's) – 104L
breeze (see also: 'wind') – 147B
bribery – 15B
broken-hearted, the – 51B, 147B, 147L
brokenness (see also: 'contrition', 'penitence', 'repentance') – 51B
brother – 122B
building – 127A, 127B
burdens – 54, 66L, 122A
busy (being busy) – 121B, 121C, 121D, 127B

call, calling – 78, 132
calm – 107L, 121B, 131A
captivity – 126A
care for people (see: 'help', 'kindness')
care (God cares for us) – 8A, 38, 61A, 91A, 103A, 104B, 116A, 121B, 122A
care, lack of (in the world) – 130A
care (negative sense; see also: 'anxiety', 'worry') – 55
cattle – 107, 148A, 148B
cedar – 80, 87, 92A
celebration (see: 'joy', 'praise', 'worship')
changelessness of God – 93A, 93B, 100A, 100B, 103A
changing seasons – 148C
cheer – 31A

chiding (see also: 'discipline', 'scolding') – 103B, 103C

childhood – 71A, 87

children – 8A, 8L, 48A, 76, 78, 102A, 107, 112, 113, 113L, 128A, 128B, 128L

children of God (see also: 'people of God') – 103L, 131A, 133B, 147A

choice – 80L

choice, God's (see: 'choosing', 'ordaining')

choir – 33A, 98B

choosing (God's; see also: 'ordaining') – 4A, 80, 80L

choosing (ours) – 139A

Christ – 1B, 8A, 18A, 18B, 20A, 128A

Christmas Day, Sundays after Christmas – 98B, 98L, 102A, *160A, 160B, 160C, 163A, 163B, 163C, 163D*

Church (see also: 'people of God') – 111L, 128A, 147B, *154B, 156C, 156D*

church, building (see also: 'house of God', 'Temple') – 23A, 24C, 24L, 26, 48A, 84C, 96L, 100A, 100D, 101, 111A, 118A, 118L, 122L, 134A, 134B, 134C, 134L, 149A, 150B, 150C, 150L, *161A, 161B*

church anniversary (see: 'dedication/consecration . . .' etc)

citizens – 122B

city – 87, 122A, 122B

city of God (includes 'Jerusalem', 'Zion' etc; see also: 'holy city') – 24A, 24B, 24C, 46A, 46B, 46L, 48A, 53, 65A, 65B, 76, 84C, 87, 97L, 110, 122B, 122L, 125, 126B, 126C, 133B, 134C, 134L, 137A, 147L, 149L

civic/national occasions – 9, 15B, 44, 60, 67A, 67B, 67C, 67L, 72, 78, 82, 85A, 96A, 96L, 100A, 100B, 100C, 100D, 100L, 111A, 111L, 117A, 117B, 117L, 149A

clap (invitation to 'clap hands') – 47L, 98A, 98C, 98L

cleansing – 19C, 24C, 51A, 51B, 101

clouds – 97, 104B, 105L, 147A, 147B, 147L, 148L, *154A, 154B*

cold – 148C

comfort (God's) – 18A, 23C, 147A

comfortless – 77

command, God's (see also: 'law') – 19A, 19C, 147B

commandments (see also: 'command', 'law') – 19C, 50A, 103B, 112, 119B, 119C, 147L

commissioning/ordination – 37A, 47A

commitment (see: 'lifetime') – 40A

communion (see also: 'Holy Communion') – 23A, 23B, 23C, 76, 78, 81

comparison, God and humanity (see also: 'humanity') – 8A, 8B, 8C, 39

compassion (God's) – 38, 51B, 86A, 103B, 103C, 103L, 116B

confessing (see also: 'proclaiming', 'witness') – 145A, *163A, 163B, 163C*

confession – 32A, 51B

confidence – 20A, 25A, 27A, 63A, 125

confidence in God (see also: 'assurance') – 37A, 112

conflict (see also: 'strife', 'war') – 43B, 56A, 130

congregation – 40A, 116L

conscience – 25A, 32A

consecration (see: 'dedication')

conservation – 122L

conspiracy – 28, 33A

constancy of God (see also: 'faithfulness') – 13A, 102, 103A

constellation (see: 'stars') – 19

contentment – 138A

continents (see also: 'islands', 'lands') – 108A

contrition (see also: 'brokenness', 'penitence', 'repentance') – 52

conversion – 32A

corn – 4A, 65B

cornerstone – 118A

corruption – 14

counsel – 1C

counting our days – 90B

courage (see also: 'fear') 20A, 27

covenant – 50A, 103B, 105L, 111L

creation – 8A, 8B, 8L, 9, 19A, 24C, 33A, 90A, 92A, 103L, 104A, 104L, 136A, 138A, 143A, 146, 147A, 148C, *154A, 154B, 154C, 156A, 156B, 156C, 164B, 164C*

Creation Sunday – 8A, 8B, 8C, 8L, 19A, 19B, 19C, 29A, 100B, 100C, 104A, 104B, 104L, 136, 136L, 147L, 148A, 148B, 148C, 148L, *164B, 164C*

creator, God as – 8A, 19C, 24L, 29A, 33A, 33L, 46A, 49A, 50A, 52, 65A, 68A, 90A, 95A, 95B, 95C, 100B, 100C, 100D, 102A, 104A, 104B, 121C, 121D, 124A, 134B, 134C, 134L, 139B, 145A, 146, 147A, 151, *164B, 164C*

creatures (see also: 'animals', 'beasts' etc) – 8C, 104A, 104B, 117B, 148A, 148C, 149A, *154A, 154B, 154C*

crops – 65L, 107

cross/crucifixion – 22A, *158B, 158C, 163A, 163B, 163C*

cruelty – 56A

cry (see also: 'crying', 'plea', 'prayer'; 'shout') – 3A, 13A, 18A, 28, 30A, 31A, 34A, 40L, 54, 61A, 66L, 77, 80, 84B, 98C, 107L, 123A, 130A, 130B, 130C, 141, 142A, 145B

crying (see also: 'sadness', 'sorrow', 'tears') – 6, 30A

cup – 11, 12A, 23A, 23C, 116L

cymbals – 149A, 150B, 150C, 150L

daily experience of God – 16A, 25A, 40A, 68A, 71A, 145B

dances (instruments) – 150B, 150C

dancing – 30A, 150A

dangers – 18A, 141

dark times – 23A

darkness – 16A, 19C, 20A, 23A, 23B, 23C, 27A, 43B, 49B, 81, 82, 88, 91A, 97L, 112, 116A, 130A, 136A, 139A, 143A, *166*

darkness (powers of) – 10

dawn – 52, 104A, 108, 130A, 130B, *153A, 153B, 153C*

days ('all my days' etc; see also: 'lifetime') – 52, 84A, 121B

death – 6, 13A, 16A, 18A, 18B, 22A, 23A, 23C, 30A, 39, 49A, 49B, 88, 90A, 90B, 104B, 104L, 116A, 116B, 116L, 128A, 137A, 141, *152A, 152B, 162A, 162B, 162C, 165B*

deceit (see also: 'falsehood', 'lies', 'slander') – 10, 62A, 101

decisions – 139A

decree (see also: 'law') – 93A, 93B

dedication (of self) – 26, 37A, 122

dedication/consecration/anniversary of a church – 15A, 24B, 24C, 24L, 48A, 84A, 84C, 89A, 100B, 100L, 118A, 118L, 122A, 122B, 122L, 127A, 127B, 132, 147B, 149A, 149L, 150B, 150C, 150L, *161A, 161B*

deeds (God's; see also: 'wonders') – 46B, 48A, 65B, 66A, 66L, 73, 84B, 86A, 89A, 96B, 96L, 97L, 98A, 98C, 98L, 105L, 107, 107L, 111A, 111L, 126A, 126B, 126C, 126L, 136L, 143A, 145A, 145B, 147B, 150A, 150B, 150C, *155A, 155B, 155C*

deeds (ours) – 19C, 61A, 119A

deer – 42A, 42B

defence – 4A, 12A, 31, 34A, 44, 63A, 72, 76, 78, 84C, 90A, 121C, 121D, 127A, 143A

defender (God as; see also: 'protector') – 3A, 4A, 7A, 8C

delight – 12A, 63A, 92A, 119B, 119C, 128A, 134B

deliverance, God as deliverer – 18A, 18B, 31A, 81, 98C, 106A, 114, 116A, 116B, 118A, 124L, 126A, 126C, 126L, 136A, 136L, *162A, 167*

dependence upon God – 27A, 63A, 108A, 125, 130D

depression (see also: 'despair', 'sadness', 'sorrow') – 39, 40A, 42A, 42B, 61B, 66A, 71A, 116B

depths – 130A, 130B, 130C

desert – 29A, 63A, 63B, 107, 121B, 136A, 143A

designer, God as (see also: 'creator') – 8B, 139B, 147A

desire/desire for God (see also: 'longing') – 12B, 26, 37A, 63A, 84C, 130A, 139B, 145B

desire (evil) – 12B

desolation – 80

despair (see also: 'depression', 'sadness', 'sorrow') – 18A, 22A, 66A, 69A, 76, 77, 80, 88, 107L, 116A, 143A

despise (some despise us; see also: 'mocking', 'taunting') – 123B

destruction – 137A

devil (see also: 'Satan', 'tempter') – 63A, 91A, 141

dew – 133A, 133B

disappointment (dealing with it) – 37A

discipline – 141

disobedience (national) – 60

disobedience (see also: 'obedience') – 50A, 141

disordered lives – 122A

distress (see also: 'depression', 'despair', 'sadness', 'sorrow') – 30A, 31A, 81, 82, 107L, 130B, 143A

divisions – 60

dominion (see also: 'sovereignty') – 145B

doom – 137A

doubt – 22A, 43B, 84B, 116A, 132, *162A*

dove – 55

doxology (metrical doxologies) – 47A, 50B, 60, 62A, 65A, 95A

dread (see also: 'fear') – 143A

dream – 77, 126C, 126L

drink – 4A

drums – 149L

dust – 103B, 103C

duty – 29A

dwelling (God's) – 15B

dying – 6, 116B

dying (Jesus; see also: 'cross/crucifixion') – 139B

eagle – 103B

ears, God's (see also: 'hearing, God hears us') – 34A

earth – 8A, 8B, 24A, 24L, 33L, 46B, 46L, 47B, 47L, 50B, 65A, 66L, 67A, 67B, 67L, 72, 77, 85A, 89A, 93B, 93L, 95B, 95C, 96B, 96L, 97, 97L, 98A, 98B, 98C, 98L, 99A, 99L, 100A, 100L, 102A, 105L, 108A, 114, 124L, 134B, 134C, 134L, 136A, 136L, 147L, 148A, 148L, *159A, 166*

earth shaking/earthquake – 46A, 46B, 68A, 76, 77, 99A

east – 75, 103B, 103C, 103L, 108A, 113A

Easter Day, Sundays after Easter – 8A, 18A, 18B, 105L, 113L, 114, 118A, 118L, *166, 167*

Education Sunday – 1A, 1B, 8A, 8B, 8L, 40L, 104A, 111L, 119A, 119B, 119C, 143L

Egypt – 81, 105L, 114

elderly (see also: 'age, old', 'old age') – 71A, 148A, 148C, *162A, 162B, 162C*

empty words – 4A

encouragement – 46A

endurance – 132

enemies (and their defeat; see also: 'opposition') – 3A, 8C, 8L, 13A, 23A, 27A, 43A, 43B, 44, 47A, 48A, 56A, 61A, 61B, 66L, 68A, 70, 80, 80L, 91A, 97L, 124L, 136L, 143A, *167*

Epiphany services – 110, *153A, 162A, 162B, 162C, 162D*

eternal life – 12B

eternity (including the eternal nature of God) – 89A, 90A, 90B, 92A, 93A, 93B, 93L, 102A, 136L, 138A, 145A

ethical concern (see also: 'justice', 'social responsibility') – 87

Eucharist (see: 'communion')

evening – 52, 134A, 141, *159A, 159B, 159C, 165A, 165B*

evening worship – 36, 36L, 43A, 63A, 63B, 121B, 121C, 121D, 134A, 134B, 134C, 134L, 141, *159A, 159B, 159C, 165A, 165B*

evil – 1C, 7A, 10, 12A, 13A, 23A, 45, 52, 54, 60, 76, 121D, 125, 136A, 141

evil (defeat of) – 125

evil deeds – 37A

exile (see also: 'away from home') – 61A, 137A

exploitation (see: 'poor')

eyes (God's) – 33A, 33L, 119A

eyes (ours) – 19C, 121B, 121C, 123A, 123B, 139A, 141, *153A, 162A, 162B, 162C*

eyes (ours, fixed on God) – 16A, 141, 145B

face (God's) – 11, 13A, 24C, 44, 51A, 61B, 63A, 67A, 67B, 67C, 67L, 80L, 84A, 84B, 90A, 104L, 119A, 143A, *151, 159B, 159C*

failure – 80, 130A

faintness – 27A

fairness – 82

faith (see also: 'trust') – 24B, 34A, 40L, 71A, 76, 78, 81, 90B, 95A, 103A, 115, 122A, 128A, 132

faithful, the – 37A, 50B

faithfulness (God's) – 9, 13A, 25A, 31A, 33L, 36L, 38, 40L, 76, 77, 88, 89A, 97L, 98B, 98C, 100A, 100B, 100C, 100D, 100L, 104B, 107L, 111L, 115, 117B, 117L, 132, 136A, 136L, 138A, 143A, 145B, 147B, *167*

faithfulness (ours) – 34B, 62A, 143L

faithlessness – 81

fall of the wicked (see also: 'wicked, the') – 75

falling – 30A

false advice – 1A

falsehood (see also: 'lies') – 10, 62A

family – 102A, 107, 112, 113A, 122L, 127B, 128A

farmer – 65A, 126A

father (God as) – 103B, 103C, 131B

fatherless (see also: 'orphans') – 82

favour (God's, to us) – 8A, 8B, 14, 23A, 30A, 67A, 84C

fear – 11, 16A, 20A, 23A, 38, 42A, 46B, 46L, 56A, 78, 81, 82, 84B, 91A, 104L, 107L, 116A, 116L, 124A, 131B, 136A, 143A

fear (freedom from) – 23B, 23C, 26, 27A, 46A, 91A, *153A, 153B, 153C, 165B*

feast – 23A, 23B, 23C, 36L, 63A, *153A, 153B*

feeds (God feeds us; see also: 'food', 'providence') – 81, 104B, 136A, 145B

feet (see also: 'footsteps', 'walk', 'way, ours') – 17, 22A, 23A, 25A, 40L, 66L, 73, 116B, 121C, 122B, *153A, 153C*

fellowship (see also: 'love', 'friends') – 84A, 101

fertile – 65B

fields (see also: 'meadow', 'pasture') – 65L, 107, 148A, 148L

fight – 27A

finding God (see also: 'seeking God') – 40A

fine company (see also: 'friends') – 28

fire (see also: 'flame') – 66L, 97, 97L, 104L, 105L, 148A

fire (God's) – 50A

fish – 8C, 8L, *154A, 154B*

flame (see also: 'fire') – 97, 104B

flock (God's people) – 65L, 68, 76, 77, 80L, 81, 100A, 100L

floods (see also: 'rivers', 'sea', 'waters' etc) – 46A, 124L

flourishing – 92A

flowers – 103A, 103B, 103C

flute – 150L

foes (see also: 'enemies') – 27A, 43B, 44, 61A

food (including sense: 'God feeds us') – 4A, 23A, 36L, 73, 104B, 105L, 136A, 147L

foolishness – 14, 36, 38, 53

footsteps (see also: 'feet', 'walk', 'way, ours') – 119A, 119B, 121C, 121D

foreign land – 137A

foreknowledge (God's) – 139A

forest (see also: 'trees', 'woodland') – 124A, 148A

forgiveness (God's, for us) – 23B, 25A, 32A, 38, 51A, 55, 73, 76, 78, 85, 99A, 103A, 103B, 103L, 116A, 122A, 130B, 130C, 145A, *153A, 153C*

forgiveness (ours, for others) – 55

fortress (see also: 'defence', 'refuge', 'rock') – 18B, 46L

foundation (see also: 'rock') – 125

fragrance – 133A

fraud – 10

freedom (see also: 'deliverance', 'liberty') – 13A, 24B, 31A, 66A, 67C, 68A, 114, 116A, 118A, 119A, 122A, 124A, 126A, 126L, 136A, 136L, 143A, *153A, 153C, 164B, 167*

freedom from fear – 84B, 142A

freedom from sin – 19B

friend (God as our friend) – 8A, 25A, 68A, 122B, 142A

friends/friendship – 10, 28, 38, 50A, 88, 101

friends (bad, false, failing, painful) – 50A, 55, 69A, 71A

frost – 154A

fruit – 1C, 67C, 80, 92A

frustration (see also: 'restlessness') – 39, 122A

funeral services – 23A, 23B, 23C, 31A, 39, 42A, 42B, 49B, 71A, 84B, 90A, 90B, 103A, 103B, 103C, 103L, 121A, 121B, 121C, 130A, 130B, 130C, 139A, 139B, *162A, 162B, 162C*

future (see also: 'lifetime') – 36, 47A, 67B, 69A

future secure in God's keeping – 36

galaxy (see also: 'stars') – 19A

generations (see also: 'children') – 78, 90A, 100A, 100C, 103B, 105L, 113A, 128A, 145A, 145B, *161A, 161B*

generosity (God's) – 100B, 103L, 145B, 146

generosity (ours) – 112

gentiles (see: 'nations')

gentleness (God's) – 40A

ghosts/spirits (see also: 'phantoms') – 91A

gifts (from God) – 68A, 81, 87, 127B, 128B, 133A, 145B

girls – 148A

giving – 45, 112, 116

gladness – 100A, 100C, 147A

gladness (see also: 'joy') – 30A, *159A*

glory (God's) – 8L, 19A, 19B, 19C, 29A, 50B, 63B, 85, 93B, 96B, 97L, 102A, 108A, 113A, 113L, 115, 122B, 131A, 145A, *156A, 156C*

glory (to the glory of God) – 127A

godless, the (see also: 'atheism') – 1A, 92A

godlessness – 10, 14, 36

gold – 19C

Good Friday services (see also: 'passiontide') – 13A, 22A, 69A, *158B, 158C, 163A, 163B, 163C, 163D*

good news – 40L, 96B, 122B, 143A

goodness (God's) – 23A, 23B, 23C, 36, 36L, 40A, 51, 65L, 73, 86A, 100B, 100C, 100D, 103B, 103C, 103L, 106A, 107L, 111L, 115, 116L, 118L, 136A, 136L, 142A, 150B, 150C

goodness (ours) – 97L

grace – 4A, 5, 7A, 11, 13A, 19B, 23A, 25A, 30, 49B, 50B, 51A, 52, 57A, 61B, 67A, 67B, 67C, 67L, 73, 78, 84A, 90A, 90B, 95A, 96A, 100A, 103A, 103L, 104B, 111A, 111L, 112, 113A, 116B, 119A, 122A, 122B, 133B, 134A, 134A, 139B, 143A, 147B, 149A, 159B

grain – 65L, 147A

grandchildren – 128A, 128L

grass – 90A, 103A, 103B, 103C, 147A

gratitude (see also: 'thankfulness', 'thanksgiving') – 70, 100A, 122A, 131A, 146 grave (see also: 'death') – 18A, 30A, 49B, 68A, 88, 103L, 116B, 116L

greatness (God's) – 39, 100B, 104L, 145B, 147L, 148C, 150L

grief (see also: 'sadness', 'sorrow') – 10, 28, 116A, *165B*

growth – 104A, 126A

guarded by God (see also: 'defence', 'refuge', 'rock', 'safety', 'strength of God') – 25A, 61A, 86A, 121C, 121D, 127A, 141, *165A, 165B*

guide/guiding/guidance (God guiding us; see also: 'leading') – 16A, 17, 18A, 19A, 20A, 23A, 23B, 23C, 25A, 48A, 56A, 62A, 66A, 67B, 73, 104A, 104B, 116A, 119A, 119B, 123B, 139A, *167*

guidance (for the people) – 72

guilt – 24B, 25A, 38, 51A, 85, 116A, 130B, 147B

guilt (freedom from) – 24B

guiltiness – 69A

hail – 148A

hand (God's) – 8L, 22A, 63A, 80L, 91A, 95C, 97, 98A, 98C, 98L, 102A, 133B, 143A, 145A, 145B

hands (ours) – 22A, 24L, 28, 47A, 84B, 101, 134A, 134B, 134C, 137A, 143A, *165B*

happiness – 89A, 128B, 133A, 137A, 138A

harbour – 107

hardening hearts – 95A, 95C

harp – 33A, 33L, 98A, 98C, 98L, 137A, 150B, 150C, 150L

harvest – 65A, 65B, 65L, 67A, 67B, 67C, 67L, 126A, 126B, 126C, 126L, 127A, 147A, 147L

Harvest Festival services (see also: 'harvest') – 65A, 65B, 65L, 67A, 67B, 67C, 67L, 104A, 104B, 126B, 126C, 126L, 145A, 145B, 147A, 147B, 147L, 148A, 148B, 148C, 148L

haste – 127B

hatred – 22A, 37A, *163B*

head – 141

healing – 11, 19C, 39, 49A, 80, 103L, 122A, 147L, *165B*

healing services (see also: 'healing') – 103B, 103L, 147A, 147B, 147L, *165B*

hearing (God hears us) – 6, 20A, 22A, 28, 34A, 45, 61B, 66L, 69A, 77, 116B, 124A, 136A, 139B

hearing God – 95C, 122B

heart (of God) – 106A

hearts (ours) – 19A, 20A, 40L, 101, 119B, 122A, 134A, 134B, 141

heat – 148C

heathen – 73

heaven – 12B, 21, 23B, 26, 40A, 43A, 49B, 61B, 73, 80L, 84A, 84B, 84C, 85, 89A, 96B, 102A, 108A, 113A, 121A, 123A, 134B, 139B, 148A, *165B*

heavens, the (see: 'sky')

help (God's) – 5, 6, 16A, 18A, 33L, 37A, 46A, 46B, 54, 66L, 70, 73, 77, 105L, 108A, 118A, 121C, 121D, 122A, 124A, 146

hiddenness of God – 121A

hiding (from God, impossibility) – 19A, 139A

hiding-place (see also: 'refuge') – 11

hills – 29A, 65B, 90B, 95C, 98A, 98B, 121B, 121C, 121D, 133A, 148A, 148L, *154B*

holds (God holds us) – 16A, 63A

holiness (God's) – 93B, 95A, 96B, 96L, 99L, 111L

holiness (ours) – 4A, 49B, 134A

holy city (includes 'Jerusalem', 'Zion' etc; see also: 'city of God') – 24A, 24B, 24C, 46A, 46B, 46L, 48A, 53, 65A, 65B, 76, 84C, 87, 97L, 110, 122B, 122L, 125, 126B, 126C, 133B, 134C, 134L, 137A, 147L, 149L

Holy Communion (thanksgiving; see also: 'communion') – 23B, 34A, 116L

home – 66L, 87, 112, 113A, 113L, 122L, 127A, 127B, 128A, 128L

honesty – 119B

honey – 19A, 19B, 19C, 81, 119B, 119C

honour (we honour God) – 50B, 96L, 100A, 103L, 148C, *164A, 164B, 164C*

hope – 16A, 18A, 24A, 25A, 33A, 33L, 39, 42A, 62A, 71A, 91A, 103A, 115, 130A, 130B, 130C, 131A, 147B, *166*

hopelessness (see also: 'hope') – 76, 77, 130C, 143A

horn – 47B, 98B, 98C, 98L, 150B, 150C

house (God's) – 15A, 23A, 23C, 26, 84A, 101, 111A, 118A, 122L, 134A, 134B, 134C

house (ours; see also: 'home') – 127A, 127B, 128L

humanity (ours, contrasted with God's divinity)/ human nature – 8A, 8B, 8C, 8L, 39, 66A, 90B, 108, 117A, 130A, 148B, 148C, 150A, *156A*

humble, the – 76, 116B, 116L, 138A, 147A, 147B, 147L, 149L, *160A, 160B, 160C*

humility (Christ's) – 45, *163A, 163B, 163C*

humility (God's) – 53, 113L, 145A

humility (ours) – 26, 127A, 131A, 147A

hunger – 146, *160A, 160B, 160C, 163B*

hunger for God (see also: 'seeking God', 'thirst') – 63B

hurt – 147A

hurts (see also: 'wounds') – 31A

husband – 128A, 128B

hymn – 19C, 40L, 104B, 145A, 147L

ice – 147L

idolatry (see also: 'idols') – 24C, 95A

idols – 24C, 24L, 40L, 96B, 97L, 101, 106A, 115

illuminating, God's (see also: 'light') – 139A

impartiality (God's) – 89A

impartiality (ours) – 82

impatience – 4A, 6, 13A, 39

impenitent, the – 125

imprisonment (see: 'captivity')

incarnation – 45

incense – 141

injury – 147A

innocence – 15A, 84C

instruments of music (see also: 'cymbals', 'drums', 'flute', 'horn', 'pipe', 'strings', 'trumpet') – 33A, 43A, 47A, 81, 137A, 149A, 150A, 150B, 150C

instruments of war (see also: 'war') – 46B

integrity (see also: 'truth') – 119B

intercession (see also: 'prayer') – 43B, 122A, 122B

invitation – 66L

invitation to worship – 34A, 75, 95A, 95B, 95C, 96A, 98A, 98C, 100A, 100B, 100C, 122A, 134C

invocation of God (or Christ) – 44, 70, 90A, 132, 141, *158A, 158B*

islands (see also: 'continents', 'lands') – 95A, 97L

Israel (see also: 'land', 'people of God') – 80, 81,
98c, 105L, 107, 114, 121D, 130B, 131A, *160A,*
160B, 160C

jeering (see also: 'despise', 'mocking', 'taunting') –
31A
Jerusalem (see: 'holy city')
Jesus – 88, 111A
joy – 4A, 7A, 17, 23A, 25A, 27A, 30A, 32A, 33A, 33L,
36, 38, 43A, 47B, 47L, 51A, 63A, 65L, 66L, 67L,
84B, 85, 86A, 89A, 90B, 92A, 95A, 98c, 98L,
100B, 100D, 105L, 108A, 112, 114, 119c, 123B,
126A, 126B, 126c, 126L, 128A, 132, 136A, 138A,
143L, 147A, 147B, 149L, 150A, *151*
judge (Christ as) – 110, *156B, 156c, 156D*
judge (God as; see also: 'justice') – 25A, 48A, 68A,
81, 82, 96A, 96B, 98c, 139B, *151*
judgement – 1c, 7A, 11, 50A, 51B, 62A, 67L, 75,
81, 92, 96L, 97L, 98A, 98B, 98c, 98L, 99A, 101,
105L, 130c, 137A, 143A, 149L
judgements (God's) – 97, 119c, 122B
judges – 67B
just (God is) – 145B
justice (God's) – 9, 19A, 28, 33A, 33L, 51A, 63B,
67A, 67c, 67L, 68A, 76, 89A, 96B, 97L, 98A, 98B,
103B, 110, 111A, 111L, 119A, 122A, 132, 146,
149A, *154A, 154B, 154C*
justice (in community, nation and world) – 36L,
49L, 60, 72, 82, 85, 87, 99A, 112, 146
justification – 24L, 36

keeping (in God's keeping) – 54, 57A, 121B, 121c,
139A
keeping power of God – 4A, 17, 42A
kindness (God's; see also: 'generosity', 'love',
'mercy') – 23A, 23c, 31A, 100B, 103L, 111L, 145A
kindness (ours) – 112
king (Christ as) – 21, 45, 110, 139B, *159A, 163A,*
166
king (God as; see also: 'majesty', 'sovereignty of
God') – 10, 24B, 24c, 24L, 38A, 47A, 47B, 47L,
53, 75, 82, 86A, 93A, 95A, 95c, 96A, 96L, 97,
97L, 98A, 98L, 99A, 148B, 149A, 149L, *151,*
155A, 155B, 155C
kingdom (Christ's) – 110
kingdom (God's) – 48A, 87, 103B, 128A, 138A,
145A, 145B
knowing (God knows us; see also: 'omniscience') –
139A, 139B, 147B
knowing God (see also: 'seeking God') – 46A

labour – 127A
lambs (see also: 'flock', 'sheep', 'shepherd') – 65A
lamps – 134A
land – 40A, 44, 47B, 60, 65L, 72, 78, 80, 82, 85,
104A, 114, 122L, 148c
lands – 81, 104B, 108A
lantern – 119c
laughter – 114, 126A, 126B, 126c, 126L, 130A
law (God's) – 1B, 1c, 5, 19A, 19B, 19c, 50A, 62A,
68A, 72, 78, 93A, 93B, 93L, 119B, 119c, 122B,
127B, 147A, 147L
leaders (see also: 'rulers') – 47L
leadership – 21, 82

leading (see also: 'guide . . .' etc) – 23B, 56A, 116A,
119A, 132, 136A, 136L
Lent services (and Sundays before Easter) – 10,
11, 13A, 14, 17, 19A, 19B, 26, 27A, 31A, 32A, 38,
40A, 40L, 42A, 42B, 51A, 51B, 54, 61A, 61B, 69A,
70, 84A, 86, 91A, 103c, 103L, 122A, 122B, 122L,
125, 126A, 130B, 130c, 139A, 139B
liberating power of God – 67c
liberty (see also: 'freedom') – 19B, 31A, 68A, 85,
114, 116A, 118A, 124A, 126A, 126L, 136A, 136L,
143A, *153A, 153c, 167*
lies – 1A, 10, 17, 24c, 43B, 53, 123B
life – 18A, 19B, 24B, 31A, 32A, 34A, 36L, 85, 90A,
103A, 104B, 121A, 126B, 133A, 143A
lifetime (our lifetime experience of God) – 22A,
23A, 23B, 23c, 30A, 34A, 40A, 43A, 61A, 63A,
63B, 69A, 84A, 90B, 113, 116L, 121A, 121B, 128A,
128L, 141, 145B, 146
light/light from God – 13A, 19B, 19c, 36, 36L, 44,
50B, 56A, 62A, 67c, 95A, 97L, 104A, 104B, 112,
119A, 119c, 132, 136A, 139A, 139B, 145A, 146,
148B, 148c, *162B, 162c, 166*
light (God as) – 43A
light (lack of) – 81
lightning – 29A, 93B, 97L, 104B, *154A, 154B*
lip-service – 50A
lips – 141
listening (God listening to us) – 66L, 116A, 116B,
116L
listening to God – 95B
lives – 50A
living (see also: 'behaviour') – 19A, 19c, 50A
living (see also: 'life') – 25A
living things (see also: 'creatures') – 148c,
149A
loneliness – 22A, 69A, 71A, 116A, 142A
longing (see also: 'desire') – 37A, 38, 42B, 61B,
84c, 139B
longing (for God) – 6, 13A, 16A, 22A, 42A, 42B,
61B, 63A, 84c
Lord's Supper (see: 'communion')
lordship/lordship of Christ (see also: 'sovereignty')
– 24B, 45, *163A, 163B, 163C*
lost (the) – 113A
love (God's) – 1B, 7A, 8A, 13A, 17, 23B, 23c, 26,
27A, 31A, 33A, 33L, 34A, 36, 36L, 38, 40L, 42B,
45, 49B, 51A, 57A, 60, 61A, 66A, 66L, 68A, 71A,
84A, 84B, 85, 86A, 89A, 90A, 91A, 97, 98B, 98L,
100A, 100B, 100c, 100D, 100L, 103A, 103L, 106A,
107L, 108A, 111A, 113A, 115, 116A, 117A, 117B,
117L, 118L, 119A, 119B, 121A, 122A, 131B, 136A,
136L, 137A, 138A, 139A, 139B, 141, 145A, 147B,
147L, *160A, 165B*
love (ours for God) – 5, 18A, 18B, 20A, 54, 66A, 78,
86A, 91A, 116A, 116L, 119A, 134B, 143A
love (ours, for one another) – 85A, 122L, 128A,
133A
loving-kindness, God's (see: 'kindness', 'mercy',
'love, God's')
lute – 150B, 150c
lyre – 33A, 150L

majesty, Christ's (see also: 'ascension',
'sovereignty') – *166*

najesty, God's (see also: 'sovereignty', 'reign', 'throne') – 8A, 8C, 20A, 21, 24B, 76, 77, 89A, 93A, 93B, 93L, 96B, 96L, 104B, 104L, 111L, 113A, 147A, *167*

naker (God as; see also: 'creator') – 18A, 19C, 24L, 33L, 95B, 100D, 104A, 121D, 124A, 134C, 134L, 139B, 149L, *151*

nalice – 17

narriage/marriage services – 67B, 121B, 121D, 127B, 128A, 128B, 128L

nartyrs – *156A, 156B, 156C, 156D*

narvels (God's; see: 'deeds', 'wonders')

neadow (see also: 'fields', 'pasture') – 65B, 90A, 147B

neditation (see also: 'thoughts') – 119A, 119B, 119C

neek (see: 'humble')

nelodies – 137A

nemory (see: 'recalling', 'Remembrance')

nen – 148A, 148B, 148C

nercy – 1C, 4A, 21, 25A, 27A, 36, 37A, 40A, 40L, 42B, 43B, 47A, 51A, 51B, 56A, 60, 61A, 61B, 62A, 63A, 67A, 71A, 76, 78, 88, 98A, 98B, 98C, 100C, 101, 103A, 103B, 103C, 103L, 106A, 107, 111L, 116L, 119A, 123A, 130B, 130C, 133B, 134A, 134B, 139B

nercy (God's) – 19A, 33A, 117B, 145A, 146, *153A, 153C, 159A, 165A, 167*

nerit – 115

night (God's; see also: 'strength') – 147A

nighty, the – 147L

nind (God's/Christ's) – 1B, 49A, *163A, 163B, 163C*

nind (ours) – 16A, 122A, 133B, 143L, *165B*

ninisters – 134A, 134B

niracles – 105L, 136L

nisery – 130B

nisrepresentation – 56A

nission/missionary occasions (see also: 'proclaiming', 'witness') – 46A, 46B, 46L, 47A, 47L, 67A, 67B, 67L, 68A, 87, 96A, 96B, 96L, 97, 98B, 98L, 100B, 100C, 100L, 117A, 117B, 117L, 138A, *157A, 164C*

nisuse of God's gifts – 28

nocking/mockery (see also: 'scorn', 'taunting') – 3A, 22A, 42B, 56A, 61B, 123A

noon – 8A, 8B, 8C, 19B, 33L, 97, 104B, 121C, 121D, 148A, 148B, 148C, 148L, *154A, 154B*

norning (see also: 'waking') – 5, 88, 143A

norning worship – 5, 16A, 19B

nortality (see also: 'humanity') – 49A, 90A, 90B, 146

nother – 113L, 131A, 131B

nothering Sunday – 67B, 100L, 112, 113L, 121B, 122L, 127A, 127B, 128A, 128B, 128L, 131A, 131B, *160A, 160B, 160C*

nountains – 11, 36L, 46A, 46B, 46L, 61B, 65A, 95A, 95B, 97, 97L, 98C, 98L, 99L, 104A, 108A, 121A, 125, 147A, 148A, 148L, *151, 154B*

nouth (see also: 'lips', 'speech', 'voice') – 126B, 141, 145B

nurmuring – 81

nusic – 33A, 33L, 43A, 92A, 98L, 147L, 149A

nusicians – 68A, 137A

name (God's) – 8A, 8C, 8L, 21, 23A, 30A, 33L, 34B, 50A, 52, 57A, 66A, 66L, 67A, 68A, 70, 75, 76, 77, 84B, 91A, 96A, 96B, 96L, 97, 99L, 100A, 100D, 103A, 103B, 104B, 105L, 111L, 113L, 115, 116A, 116L, 118A, 124L, 130B, 131A, 138A, 143A, 145A, 145B, 148A, 148B, 148C, 148L, 149A, 149L, *161A, 161B*

name (Jesus'; see also: 'Jesus') – *163C*

name (ours) – 115, 121A

nation (see also: 'land') – 12A, 33L, 44, 60, 76, 78, 99L, 105L, 128A, 130A, 130B

national occasions – 76, 130A

nations, the – 45, 46A, 46B, 46L, 47B, 47L, 50B, 66L, 67A, 67B, 67L, 68A, 81, 96A, 96B, 96L, 98A, 98C, 99A, 117A, 117B, 117L, 148L, 149A, *154B, 155A, 155B, 155C, 162A, 162B, 162C, 167*

nations (freedom for) – 67C

nearness (see also: 'presence of God') – 11, 20A, 22A, 26, 28, 34A, 46L, 121A, 124, 145A, 145B

need (God sees our needs) – 31A

need (ours) – 13A, 23A, 70, 73, 104B, 122A, 127B, 145A, 147B

need (our need of God) – 86A

needy (see also: 'poor', 'weakness') – 82

neighbour – 15A, 15B, 24A

new life – 126B, 126C

New Year services – 47A, 67C, 67L, 102A

news/good news – 96B, 143A

night – 52, 63A, 63B, 92A, 104A, 119B, 121B, 134A, 134B, 134C, 136L, 148B, 149L, *154A, 154B*

nightmares – 91A

noise – 31A

nourishment – 4A

oath (see also: 'promises, ours') – 15B

obedience – 5, 37A, 40L, 53, 62A, 76, 78, 86A, 90B, 95B, 111L, 116A, 127B, 131B, 141, 143L

objectives – 26, 37A, 43A, 73

ocean (see also: 'sea', 'waters') – 29A, 33A, 61B, 93L, 97, 107L, 148A, 148B, *154A*

offences (see also: 'sin') – 51A

offering(s) – 40L, 50A, 51B, 54, 66L

oil of anointing – 133B, 141

old age (see also: 'age', 'elderly') – 90B, 92A, 119B, 148C, 148L

omnipotence (God's; see: 'power', 'strength')

omniscience (God's) – 37A, 38, 139A, 139B, 147B

opposition – 22A, 23A

oppression/the oppressed – 9, 14, 125, 136A, 146

oppression (triumph over) – 125

oppressor – 143A

orphans – 81, 82

ownership (God's) – 108A, 139B

pain – 12A, 18A, 22A, 43B, 54, 84A, 90B, 136A, 147A, 165B

Palm Sunday – 8L, 22A, 24A, 24B, 24C, 24L, 45, 69A, *163A, 163B, 163C, 163D*

palm tree – 92A

paradise (see also: 'heaven') – 102A

pardon (see also: 'forgiveness') – 85

parents (see also: 'children', 'family', 'father', 'mother') – 128A, 128B

partner/partnership – 127B

passing years – 71A
Passiontide services/passiontide – 13A, 22A, *158A, 158B, 158C, 163A, 163B, 163C, 163D*
pasture (see also: 'fields', 'meadow') – 23A, 23B, 65B, 107, 147A, 147B
path – 16A, 17, 23A, 25A, 32A, 62A, 78, 119C
patience – 40L, 126A
peace (personal, God-given) – 3A, 4A, 23B, 27A, 34A, 57A, 95B, 103A, 121B, 131A, 134A, 134B, 138A, 147A, 147B, *153A, 153B, 153C, 162A, 162B, 162C, 165A*
peace (from conflict/war) – 46A, 46B, 66A, 68A, 85, 125, *157*
peace in God's presence (see also: 'peace, God-given') – 84A, 122A, 131A
peace (in the nation/prayer for peace) – 60, 122B, 122L, 125
peace (losing) – 95A
peace (in heaven) – 43A
peace of mind – 3A, 4A, 25A, 32A, 38, 55, 57A, 131A
peace with each other – 53, 122L, 128A, 128L, 133A, *157A, 157B*
peacemakers – 37A, 133A
penitence (see also: 'remorse', 'repentance') – 36, 69A, 80
Pentecost (see also: 'Spirit') – 104L, 143A, 143L
Pentecost services – 51L, 104L, 143L
people of God (see also: 'flock', 'sheep') – 10, 12A, 34A, 45, 50B, 65A, 67A, 67B, 68A, 77, 78, 80L, 81, 84A, 85, 87, 89A, 93B, 95A, 95B, 98B, 100A, 100B, 100C, 100D, 102, 103A, 103C, 103L, 105L, 106A, 107, 108A, 111L, 114, 116L, 118A, 121C, 125, 126A, 130B, 131A, 132, 133A, 133B, 136A, 147A, 148B, 149A
percussion (see also: 'cymbals', 'drums', 'instruments') – 150A
peril – 12A
perish (earth and sky) – 102A
permanence of God (see also: 'eternity') – 102A, 116A
persecutors (see also: 'enemies', 'mocking', 'opposition', 'taunting') – 137A
phantoms – 91A
PILGRIMS 128L, *153A*
pipe (see also: 'instruments') – 81, 150B, 150C
plains – 108A
plan (see also: 'story') – 19B
planets (see also: 'stars') – 148A
plans, ours (see also: 'desire', 'objectives') – 20A
plants (see also: 'flowers', 'trees') – 148C
play – 33L
plea for our prayers to be heard (see also: 'answer', 'cry', 'hearing', 'listening', 'prayer') – 3A, 6, 13A, 22A, 25A, 30A, 39, 44, 54, 61A, 61B, 70, 76, 77, 84B, 84C, 86A, 88, 90A, 106A, 116B, 122A, 123A, 130B, 130C, 141, 143A, 145B, *157A, 157B*
politics (see also: 'rulers', 'social responsibility') – 72
pomp, human (see also: 'power', 'pride') – 146
poor, the (see also: 'hunger', 'needy'; 'justice', 'social responsibility') – 4A, 10, 12A, 14, 34A, 49B, 68A, 72, 81, 113L, *160A, 160B, 160C*
port – 107
power (God's; see also: 'strength') – 18A, 33A, 49B, 67B, 70, 75, 77, 81, 82, 90B, 91A, 93A, 93L, 95, 96A, 96L, 98A, 104B, 150B, 150C, 150L, *152A, 155A, 160A, 160B, 160C*
power (human) – 146, 147A
power (of Christ) – 21
powers – 10, 148B
praise (of God/injunction to praise) – 1B, 3A, 5, 8A, 18A, 19B, 19C, 20A, 21, 25A, 26, 28, 29A, 42B, 47A, 48A, 53, 66L, 67A, 67B, 67L, 72, 75, 84A, 84B, 87, 92A, 93L, 95B, 96L, 97L, 98B, 98L, 100B, 100C, 100L, 103A, 103B, 103L, 104B, 105L, 107L, 113L, 114, 115, 116L, 117A, 117B, 117L, 118A, 128A, 128B, 138A, 145A, 146, 147B, 147L, 148A, 148B, 148C, 149A, 150A, 150B, 150C, 150L, 166
prayer – 3A, 4A, 5, 6, 9, 18A, 20A, 22A, 25A, 26, 28, 31A, 32A, 34A, 39, 43B, 54, 61A, 61B, 62B, 65B, 65L, 66A, 66L, 69A, 70, 76, 84A, 84C, 86A, 91A, 95B, 103A, 106A, 107L, 116A, 116B, 116L, 118A, 121B, 122A, 122B, 128A, 130A, 130C, 131B, 134L, 141, 142A, 143A, 143L, 145B, 146, *157B*
prayer (for deliverance) – 3A, 4A, 6, 10, 12A, 13A
prayer, heard by God (see: 'answer', 'hearing', 'listening')
pre-existence of God – 90A
precept (see also: 'law') – 19C
presence of God (see also: 'nearness') – 6, 8B, 10, 11, 16A, 20A, 22A, 23A, 23B, 26, 27A, 28, 34A, 38, 46A, 46B, 46L, 61B, 71A, 95C, 100B, 100C, 100D, 121A, 122A, 124A, 125, 143L, 145A, 145B
presence of God (in worship) – 95B
pride – 14, 19A, 19C, 30A, 52, 73, 75, 81, 101, 127A, 128B, 131A, 131B, 146, 147A
priesthood of Christ – 110, 139B
priests – 99A, 134A, 134B, *154A, 154C, 164A, 164C*
princes (see also: 'rulers') – 148A
procession – 118L
proclaiming (acts of God, faith, salvation etc; see also: 'witness') – 24, 34A, 37A, 40L, 66A, 68A, 71A, 73, 76, 78, 89A, 96L, 97L, 98B, 103A, 108A, 111A, 118A, 119C, 131A, 138A, 145A, 145B, 147A, *160A, 160C*
promise/promises (God's) – 12B, 18A, 25A, 34A, 37A, 111A, 116A, 119A, 130A, *160A, 160B, 160C, 162A, 162B, 162C*
promise/promises (ours) – 15A, 15B, 50A
promised land – 114
prophecy – 104B
prophet (Christ as) – 139B
prophets – 1B, 62A, 99A, *153A, 153B, 153C, 156A, 156C, 156D*
prosperity (under God) – 72, 128L
protection (God's/God as protector; see also: 'defence', 'defender', 'refuge', 'rock', 'safety') – 3A, 4A, 12A, 23A, 36, 56A, 61A, 63A, 121B, 121D, 123B, 127A, 143A, *165A*
proud, the – 75, 123A, 138A, *160A, 160B*
providence (God's) – 20A, 23A, 23C, 76, 90B, 111A, 127A, 136A, 145B, 147B
proving God's goodness – 19A, 19B, 34A, 34B, 81, 119B, 119C
psalms – 47B, 47L, 95C, 122B
punishment (God's) – 7A, 37, 85, 103L
punishment (God not punishing us) – 103B, 103C

purifying (God's) – 51B

purity – 15B, 24C, 24L, 51A, 73

purpose, God's (see also: 'guiding', 'leading', 'plan', 'will') – 137A, 138A

questioning – 22A, 39

quietness – 25A, 121B, 131A

races – 68A, *155A*, *164C*

rain – 84C, 104A, 147A, 147B, 147L, *154A*, *154B*, *154C*

ransom – *164B*, *164C*

reaping – 126A, 126B, 126C, 126L, 127A

rebelling – 78

rebels – 92A, 108A

recalling (see: 'remembering', 'Remembrance')

receiving God's word – 40L, 95B

redeemer – 38, 49A, 88, 107L, 111L, *159B*

redemption – 19B, 34B, 49B, 52, 66A, 73, 103B, 107L, 111L, 119A, 126A, 130B, *153A*, *153C*, *156A*, *156B*, *156C*, *156D*, *164A*, *164B*, *164C*

refreshment – 23A, 23C, 36, 42A, 84A, 133A

refuge (see also: 'shelter') – 7A, 11, 14, 18A, 18B, 19C, 28, 31A, 34B, 36, 40A, 46A, 46B, 46L, 51A, 57A, 61A, 62B, 84C, 90A, 91A, 92A, 95A, 122A, 130C, 142A

reign, God's (see also: 'king', 'majesty', 'sovereignty' etc) – 21, 45, 47L, 54, 68A, 90A, 93L, 96A, 99L, 103B, 115, 122B, 148B

rejecting God – 95A

rejoicing (and injunction to rejoice; see also: 'joy', 'praise') – 21, 34A, 47B, 96L, 97, 97L, 98B, 100A, 100L, 105L, 111A, 115, 116A, 122A, 126A, 126B, 126C, 145A, 147B

release (see also: 'deliverance', 'freedom', 'liberty' 'redemption' etc) – 18A, 118A, 122A, 126C, 136L, *153A*, *153B*, *153C*, 167

remembering (God's blessings etc) – 66L, 71A, 77, 87, 95B, 100L, 103B, 103L, 105L, 111A, 119B, 143A

Remembrance services (see also: 'peace', 'remembering', 'civic' etc) – 44, 46A, 46B, 47A, 47L, 93, 93L, 111A, 111L, 124A, 124L, 126B, 126C, 126L, 130A, 130B, 130C, 137A

remorse – 38

remoteness of God – 121A

renewal – 19B, 25A, 51A, 51B, 62A, 85, 88, 104L, 143L

repentance (see also: 'brokenness', 'contrition', 'penitence', 'remorse') – 52, 80

repentance (national) – 85

reputation (God's) – 44

rescue (see also: 'deliverance', 'freedom', 'liberty', 'release' etc) – 3A, 84B, 116A, 124L, 126L, 139B

resolve – 26, 119B

response to God's love – 116A, 116B

responsibility (for creation) – 8B, 8C, 8L

rest – 3A, 23C, 25A, 31A, 32A, 37A, 43A 55, 61A, 62A, 62B, 66A, 84A, 95C, 116B, 122A, 131A, 134A, 134B

rest (losing) – 95A

restlessness – 122A

restoration (see also: 'renewal') – 30A, 88, 122A, 126B, 147L

restraint/restraining – 46L, 131B

resurrection – 8A, 18A, 30A, 49B, 68A, *152A*, *152B*, *166*, *167*

returning (Christ's) – *156A*, *158A*, *158B*

revelation (of God to us; see also: 'deeds', 'wonders' etc) – 44, 84B, *162B*, *162C*

reverence for God – 131A, 134A

revival (see: 'renewal')

reward – 7A, 9, 12B, 19A, 37A, 62A, 68A, 78, 89A, 97L, 116B, 128A

riches (God's) – 19B

riches (see also: 'wealth') – 17, 49A, 49B, 62A, 81, 119C, *160A*, *160B*

righteous, the – 14, 15A, 33A, 33L, 92A, 118L, 125

righteousness – 10, 72, 97L, 118A, 125, *151*

righteousness (God's) – 14, 33A, 36, 40L, 45, 51A, 67A, 88, 89A, 98A, 98C, 98L, 99, 111L, 116B, 138A, 143A, 145A

righteousness (ours) – 51B, 97L, 119A

rivers – 36L, 42A, 46A, 46B, 93A, 98A, 98C, 98L, 114, 137A, 148B, *154A*, *154B*

robes (of God) – 104B

rock (see also: 'defence', 'refuge') – 18B, 28, 40A, 40L, 61A, 61B, 62A, 62B, 92A, 95A, 95B, 105L, 141

rogation – 65L, 67C, 107, 126A, 126L, 147A

Rogation services (see also: 'rogation') – 65A, 65L, 67B, 67C, 67L, 107, 126B, 126C, 126L, 147L

rule, God's (see: 'king, God as', 'sovereignty')

rulers – 21, 47L, 72, 81, 82, 138A, 148A, 148L, 149L

sacrifice – 40L, 50A, 51B, 116L, 141

sadness (see also: 'sorrow') – 6, 10, 30A, 61B, 126A, 137A, 147A, 147B

safety (in God) – 3A, 61B, 62B, 66L, 67B, 91A, 122A, 122B, 122L

sailors – 107

saints – 34A, 52, 65A, 73, 85, 93B, 97, 97L, 103A, 116L, 139B, 148A, 148B, 149L, *154B*, *156A*, *156B*, *156C*, *166*

Saints' days – 32A, 34A, 34B, 112, *156A*, *156B*, *156C*, *164B*, *164C*

salvation – 3A, 7A, 18A, 18B, 20A, 24B, 24L, 27A, 33A, 34A, 37A, 40L, 49B, 50B, 51A, 53, 54, 60, 62A, 62B, 67A, 76, 78, 80L, 85, 95A, 95B, 95C, 96A, 96B, 96L, 98A, 98B, 98C, 98L, 108A, 116B, 116L, 118L, 124A, 124L, 130C, 136L, 139B, 143L, 145A, 146, *162C*

sanctification – 49A

sanctuary (see also: 'church', 'heaven') – 11, 96B, 134L, 150B, 150C, 150L

sanctuary (see also: 'defence', 'refuge', 'rock', 'shield') – 122A

Satan (see also: 'devil', 'tempter') – 10, 48A, 63A, 91A, 141, *165A*

satisfaction – 103B

saviour – 18A, 19A, 38, 40A, 42A, 42B, 68A, 76, 77, 88, 95A, 124A, 138A, 147B, *153A*, *153B*, *153C*, *158A*, *158B*, *159C*, *160A*, *160B*, *160C*, *164A*

sceptre – 108A

scheming – 28

scolding (see also: 'discipline', 'chiding') – 103B, 103C

scorn (see also: 'mocking', 'taunting') – 3A, 56A, 123A

sea (see also: 'ocean', 'waters') – 24L, 29A, 33A, 46A, 46B, 46L, 65A, 66, 66L, 89A, 93A, 93B, 93L, 95A, 95B, 95C, 98A, 98B, 98C, 104A, 104B, 107, 107L, 113A, 136A, 136L, 148A, 148B, 148C, *154A*, *154B, 167*

sea (Red Sea) – 76, *167*

Sea Sunday – 57, 93B, 93L, 107, 107L, *151*

seasons – 147A, 148C

secret (see also: 'hiding') – 19C, 38, 139B

secret (known to God; see also: 'omniscience') – 38

security (ours, in God; see also: 'defence', 'refuge', 'rock' etc) – 63B, 121B

seed – 126B, 126C

seeing (God seeing us; see also: 'all-seeing') – 1B, 14, 33A, 34A, 53, 73, 90A, 124A, 139A

seeking God (see also: 'longing for God') – 9, 34B, 40A, 42A, 63A, 63B, 119B

self-dedication (see: 'dedication')

selfishness – 19C

sentence (see also: 'judgement') – 51B, 75

servant, Christ as – *163A*, *163B*, *163C*

servants of God (see also: 'serving God') – 1A, 19A, 19C, 34B, 51A, 102A, 103B, 113A, 113L, 123A, 134B, 134L, 139B, 143A, *162A*, *162B*, *162C*

serving God (see also: 'servants of God') – 19C, 53, 84B, 84C, 100A, 100C, 122A, 143A

shadow (see: 'darkness', 'night')

shame – 11, 50A, 147B

sheaves – 126B, 126C

sheep (see also: 'flock', 'lamb', 'shepherd') – 8C, 65A, 65B, 65L, 68A, 77, 80L, 81, 95B, 95C, 100A, 100B, 100C, 100L, 107, 121B, *162B*

shelter – 25A, 31A, 61A

shelter (see also: 'refuge', 'rock') – 57A

shepherd (God as) – 23A, 23B, 68A, 76, 77, 80L, 81, 95A, 100A, 100B, 100C, 100L, 121B, *162B*

shield (see also: 'defence' etc) – 3A, 7A, 19A, 33L, 46L, 47A, 62A, 84C, 89A, 115

ships – 107, 107L

shout (including injunction to shout) – 26, 33L, 47B, 47L, 65B, 65L, 66A, 66L, 67A, 98C, 98L, 100C, 100D, 105L, 149L, *151*

showers – 65L, *154A*, *154B*, *154C*

sight – 136A, 139A

sign – 86A, 115

sin – 5, 10, 14, 15A, 19A, 19B, 19C, 36, 38, 51A, 51B, 52, 66L, 78, 84B, 103A, 103B, 103C, 103L, 106A, 116A, 119C, 124A, 130B, 130C, *152A*, *152B*, *156B*, *156C*, *156D*, *163B*, *165A*

sincerity – 143L

sing (including injunction to sing) – 21, 47A, 53, 57A, 67A, 87, 96A, 96B, 98A, 98B, 98C, 100B, 105L, 146

singing – 43A, 45, 63B, 81, 100B, 122B, 149A

sinners – 1A, 1C, 4A, 15B, 103A, *153A*

sister – 122B

skill – 137A

sky (including 'heavens') – 8A, 8B, 8C, 8L, 19A, 19B, 19C, 33A, 33L, 36L, 89A, 93B, 96B, 96L, 97, 97L, 102A, 104A, 104B, 108A, 113A, 121C, 124A, 124L, 134C, 134L, 136L, 138A, 147A, 147L, 148L, 149A, *167*

slander/slanderer (see also: 'lies') – 50A, 56A

slavery (see also: 'deliverance', 'freedom', 'liberty' etc) – 126L, 136L

sleep/sleeping (see also: 'quietness', 'rest') – 3A, 4A, 57A, 107, 121B, 131A, 134A, *165A*, *165B*

snare (see also: 'trap') – 25A, 43A, 57A, 116B, 124L

snow – 147A, 147L, *154A*

social responsibility (see also: 'justice', 'poor' etc) – 72, 87, 113L, 130A

Social responsibility services – 4A, 9, 12A, 72, 76, 82, 87, 99A, 130A, 146, *160A*, *160B*, *160C*

Son of God – 110

song/songs (see also: 'sing', 'singing') – 14, 31A, 33A, 34A, 40L, 51A, 61A, 68A, 76, 77, 87, 88, 89A, 92A, 95B, 96A, 96B, 96L, 98A, 98B, 98C, 98L, 100A, 100C, 100D, 101, 108A, 123B, 126A, 126B, 126C, 126L, 128A, 137A, 145A, 149A, 149L, 150A, *153A*, *157A*, *159C*

sons and daughters of God – 131B

sorrow (see also: 'sadness', 'tears' etc) – 6, 10, 22A, 30A, 31A, 38, 42B, 43B, 51A, 61B, 80L, 84B, 85, 113L, 116A, 116B, 126A, 126L, 137A, 147B

sorrow (God's) – 138A

sovereignty of God/Christ – 7A, 9, 20A, 21, 24A, 24B, 24C, 33L, 45, 47A, 47B, 47L, 53, 66L, 67A, 68A, 75, 76, 81, 90A, 92A, 93A, 93B, 93L, 95B, 95C, 96A, 96L, 97L, 98L, 99A, 103A, 103B, 104B, 107L, 110, 113L, 138A, 139B, 145A, 145B, 147A, 147B, 148B, 149A, *156A*, *156B*, *156C*, *156D*, *164A*, *164B*, *164C*

sowing – 126A, 126B, 126C

space – 8A, 19B, 103A, 113A, 145A

sparrow (see also: 'birds') – 84A, 84C

speaks, God (see also: 'voice', 'word') – 95B, 127A

spear – 46A, 46B, 46L

speech (ours; see also: 'words') – 10, 12A, 15A, 19A, 19C, 52, 61A, 139B, 141, 150A

Spirit, Holy – 3A, 11, 18A, 47A, 51A, 51B, 51L, 88, 104L, 143L

spite – 3A

splendour – 96L, 104L

spring (season) – 136A, 147A, 148C

spring (water) – 104B

standard (God's) – 139B

stars – 8A, 8B, 8C, 19A, 33L, 93B, 97, 103A, 104B, 113A, 124A, 136A, 136L, 147A, 147B, 147L, 148A, 148B, 148C, 148L, *154A*, *154B*

steps (see also: 'footsteps') – 119B

stillness – 121B, 122A

stone – 118L

stooping (God, to save/help; see also: 'humility, God's') – 45, 53

storm – 29A, 48A, 89A, 93B, 104A, 104B, 107, 107L, 126A, 127B, 147B, 148A, 148L, *154A*, *154B*, *154C*

story – 19B, 34A, 44, 48A, 89A, 111, 145A

straying – 95A

stream (see also: 'rivers', 'water') – 1C, 23A, 23B, 42A, 46B, 46L, 65L, 98L, 104B

strength (God's) – 7A, 18A, 18B, 19C, 20A, 23B, 24L, 27A, 37A, 39, 40A, 46A, 46B, 46L, 47A, 48A, 54, 56A, 60, 61B, 62A, 62B, 66A, 68A, 71A, 78, 80L, 81, 84A, 84C, 93B, 97L, 104B, 108A, 121B, 124A, 127B, 130A, 136A, 138A, 147A, 147L

strength/strengthening (from God) – 73, 121B, 141

tress – 127B

rife (see also: 'conflict', 'war') – 56A

rings (see also: 'instruments') – 33L, 81, 108A, 149A, 149L, 150A, 150B, 150C, 150L

tumbling (see also: 'feet') – 73, 116B

uccess – 127A

uffering (ours; see also: 'sorrow' etc) – 39

uffering (Jesus') – 139B

uffering, the (those who suffer; see: 'distress', 'hunger', 'justice', 'needy', 'oppression', 'poor', 'social responsibility', 'weakness')

ummer – 148C

un – 8A, 8B, 19A, 19B, 19C, 90A, 97, 104B, 113A, 113L, 121C, 121D, 136A, 136L, 148A, 148C, 148L, *154A, 154B*

unshine – 147A

upper (the Lord's – see: 'communion')

ustaining power of God (see also: 'providence') – 54, 66L, 90A, 111L, 145B, 147B

ustenance – 19C, 23A

wallow (see also: 'birds') – 84C

weetness – 19B

word – 108A, 115, 149L

ambourine (see also: 'instruments') – 150L

aste (see: 'proving God's goodness')

aunting (see also: 'mocking', 'scorn') – 22A, 42B, 61B

eaching (God's) – 40L, 86A, 143L

ears (see also: 'sadness', 'sorrow' etc) – 6, 30A, 32A, 42A, 42B, 56A, 80L, 116A, 116B, 116L, 126A, 126B, 126C, 126L, 130A

empest (see also: 'storm', 'wind') – 148A

Temple (see also: 'church building', 'house of God', 'sanctuary') – 15A, 15B, 23A, 23C, 24C, 24L, 26, 48A, 84A, 84C, 96B, 96L, 100A, 100B, 100C, 100D, 100L, 101, 108A, 111A, 118A, 118L, 122L, 134A, 134B, 134C, 134L, 138A, 150L, *161A, 161B*

emporary nature of life – 146

emptation – 1A, 5, 19A, 26, 27A, 63A, 119C, 141

empter (see also: 'Satan', 'devil') – 63A

enderness of God – 103B, 103C

error (see also: 'fear') – 27A, 78

esting – 54, 66A, 66L, 107

esting God – 95A, 95B, 95C

hankfulness – 100D, 116A, 146

hanksgiving – 5, 7A, 22A, 34A, 62A, 67B, 69A, 70, 75, 76, 77, 87, 95A, 95B, 95C, 98A, 100A, 100B, 100C, 100D, 100L, 105L, 107, 107L, 111L, 118A, 118L, 128B, 131A, 136A, 136L

hanksgiving for deliverance – 7A, 9

Thanksgiving for the birth of a child – 20A, 116B, 116L

Thanksgiving services – 89A, 136L, 145A, 145B, 147A, 147B, 147L, 148A, 148L, 149A, 149L, 150A, 150B, 150L, *155B, 155C*

hief – 50A

hirst – 22A, 42A, 42B, 63A, 63B, 84C, 143A, 143L

houghts – 19C, 61B, 119A, 119B, 119C, 139A, 139B, *165B*

hreats – 3A, 13A, 76

hrone (God's/Christ's; see also: 'king, God as', 'majesty', 'sovereignty of God') – 21, 26, 45,

47A, 47L, 48A, 49A, 61A, 67B, 68A, 75, 80L, 89A, 92A, 93A, 93B, 93L, 97, 97L, 99L, 103B, 113A, 113L, 121B, 123A, 138A, 145A, 148C, *160B, 161B, 164A, 166, 167*

thunder – 29A, 75, 76, 93B, 97L, *167*

timbrel (see also: 'instruments') – 150B, 150C

time – 93A, 93L, 113A, 145A, 147A

time (as contrasted with eternity) – 102A

tiredness (see also: 'weariness') – 73, 142A

toil (see also: 'labour', 'work') – 84A, 127B

tongue – 52, 126B, 126C

tormentors (see also: 'enemies' etc) – 137A

Transfiguration services (see also: 'face of God') – 84A

transgression (see also: 'sin') – 51A

trap (see also: 'snare') – 25A, 43A, 57A, 66L, 118A, 124L

treasure (in heaven) – 17

trees (see also: 'forest', 'woodland'; compare: 'flowers', 'plants') – 1A, 1C, 29A, 52, 80, 87, 92A, 124A, 148A, 148C

trials – 107

trinity – 31A, 47A, 50B, 60, 62A, 65A, 76, 77, 88, 95A, 99L, 123B, *153B, 155A, 155B, 156A, 156B, 156C, 156D, 159A, 159B, 159C, 160B, 164A, 165A, 165B*

Trinity Sunday services – 93, 93L, 97, 97L, 99L, 149A, *153B, 156A, 156B, 156C, 156D, 161A, 164A, 167*; evening – *159A, 159B, 159C, 165A, 165B*

triumph (God's) – 63A, 67A, 98A, 98C, 98L, 100C, 108A, 118A, 139B, 145A, 149L, *156A, 156B, 156C, 156D*

triumph (ours) – 25A

troubles – 13A, 46B, 46L, 66L, 88, 107A, 138A, 142

trumpet (see also: 'instruments') – 47A, 47L, 81, 87, 98A, 98B, 98C, 98L, 149A, 150L, *166*

trust in God – 13A, 18A, 18B, 22A, 24A, 24B, 25A, 26, 33L, 34A, 36, 40A, 40L, 42B, 47A, 49A, 49B, 51A, 56A, 62A, 62B, 71A, 84A, 84B, 84C, 90B, 91A, 95B, 112, 113A, 116A, 122A, 128B, 131A, 131B, 132, 143A, 146, 147B, 147L

truth – 1A, 10, 11, 19B, 25A, 26, 27A, 29A, 36, 37A, 43A, 43B, 61A, 63A, 72, 76, 85, 86A, 89A, 93B, 96B, 96L, 97L, 98A, 98C, 104B, 108A, 111, 111L, 112, 117A, 119A, 119B, 138A, 143L

truthfulness – 15A, 145B

turn (to God) – 146

tyrants – 76, 126A, 137A, 149A, 149L

unbelief (see also: 'atheism') – 10, 73, 115

ungodliness – 84C

unity/Unity services – 122A, 122B, 122L, 133A, 133B

untruth (see also: 'falsehood', 'lies') – 17

valleys – 65B, 147A

vanity – 4A

vice (see also: 'sin') – 10

victory (Christ's) – 139B, *166*

victory (God's) – 24C, 44, 47B, 48A, 63B, 66A, 68A, 95A, 98C, 118L, 145A, 149L

victory (ours, with God's help) – 108A, 124A, 149L

vine – 80

Virgin Mary – *156B, 156C, 156D*
voice (God's) – 29A, 46B, 46L, 50B, 68A, 76, 77, 95A, 95C, 107L, 108A, 110
voice (ours) – 6, 50B, 108A, 116L, 137A, 141
voices (together in praises) – 53, 98B, 122B, 146, 149A
vows – 50A, 50B, 61A, 61B, 65B, 66L, 116L

waiting on God – 37A, 162A
waking (see also: 'morning') – 57A, 165B
walk – 56A, 81, 86A, 116L, 119A, 119C, 128A, 128B, 128L, 147A
wandering (see also: 'straying') – 78, 95A
war – 46A, 46B, 46L, 68A, 76, 78, 130A, 138A
warning (to those who reject God) – 149A
washing (see also: 'cleansing') – 51A, 51B
waste – 28
watchfulness (God's) – 36
watching (God) – 121C, 121D, 127A, *162A*
watching (us) – 127A, 127B, 130A, 134A, 134B
water/waters (see also: 'ocean', 'river', 'sea', 'stream', 'waves') – 1A, 1C, 8C, 23C, 33A, 46B, 46L, 65L, 69A, 77, 98A, 104A, 124L, 147A, 148B, *167*
waves (see also: 'waters' etc) – 18A, 88, 93L, 107L
Way (God the) – 43A
way (God's) – 14, 16A, 23B, 25A, 32A, 50A, 67C, 67L, 78, 84B, 86A, 88, 95A, 95B, 95C, 102A, 111A, 128A, 128L, 145B, 147A, *154B, 154C*
way (ours) – 1B, 66L, 119A, 119B, 119C, 139A, 141
waywardness – 19A
weakness – 10, 12A, 44, 76, 81, 82, 90B, 103B, 146
wealth (see also: 'riches') – 17, 49A, 49B, 62A, 81, 119C, *160A, 160B*
wealth (spiritual) – 112
wealth (transient nature of) – 39
weariness (see also: 'tiredness') – 73, 142A
weather – 34A
weddings (see: 'marriage')
weeping (see also: 'tears') – 126B, 126C, 130A
west – 75, 103B, 103C, 103L, 108A, 113A
whole (see: 'healing') – 122A
wicked, the – 9, 12B, 75, 92, 97L, 112, 145B
wickedness – 43B, 51B, 80, 101, 103C, 141
wife – 113L, 128A, 128B, 128L
wilderness (see also: 'desert') – 65B, 107
will, God's (see also: 'purpose of God') – 1B, 5, 40L, 61A, 90B, 115, 119A, 121A, 121B, 122A, 123B, 137A, 143L, 148C, *165B*
wind – 29A, 34A, 76, 89A, 93B, 103A, 103B, 103C, 104A, 104B, 104L, 147A, 147B, 147L, 148A, *154A, 154B*

wind instruments (see also: 'instruments', 'pipe' etc) – 149A
wine – 4A, 128B
winter – 136A, 147A, 148C
wisdom (God's/from God) – 19A, 19B, 19C, 32, 49A, 49B, 50B, 51A, 68A, 81, 82, 92A, 104A, 111L, 138A, 143L, 147A
witness (see also: 'proclaiming') – 34B, 40A, 40L, 46A, 48A, 49B, 66A, 67A, 67B, 70, 71A, 73, 76, 78, 89A, 96L, 97L, 98B, 100A, 103A, 111A, 118A, 119B, 119C, 131A, 138A, 145A, 145B, 147A, *160A, 160C*
women – 148A, 148B, 148C
wonder – 8B
wonders, God's (see also: 'deeds') – 46B, 48A, 65B, 66L, 86A, 88, 89A, 92A, 96B, 96L, 98A, 98B, 98C, 105L, 107, 107L, 111L, 118L, 126A, 126B, 126C, 126L, 136L, 143A, 145A, 145B, *155A, 155B, 155C*
woods/woodland (see also: 'forest', 'trees') – 124A, 148L
word (God's) – 1A, 1B, 10, 12A, 12B, 15B, 19A, 19B, 33A, 33L, 37A, 39, 40L, 44, 50A, 52, 62A, 68A, 85, 90B, 100B, 102A, 103B, 110, 111L, 116A, 119A, 119B, 119C, 127A, 130A, 130B, 130C, 145A, 147A, 147B, 148, 149A, 149L
word (receiving God's word; see: 'receiving')
words (ours; see also: 'speech') – 15A, 19A, 19C, 61A, 119A, 127A, 139A, 139B, 141, 150A
work – 47A, 84A, 90B, 104L, 127A
works (of God; see also: 'deeds', 'wonders') – 8B, 8C, 46A, 92, 111A, 111L
world (see also: 'nations') – 21, 104B, 110, 150A
worry (see also: 'anxiety') – 54
worship – 15B, 19B, 21, 24A, 24B, 24C, 25A, 26, 28, 30A, 40L, 47A, 63A, 66L, 67B, 75, 86A, 93B, 95A, 95B, 95C, 97L, 98A, 99L, 100A, 100L, 104A, 104B, 105L, 117A, 118A, 122A, 123B, 134A, 134B, 134C, 134L, 138A, 141, 145A, 145B, 147A, 148A, 148B, 148C, 149A, 157A, 157B
worship, unacceptable – 50B
worshippers – 84C
wounds (see also: 'hurts') – 22A, 147A, 147L
wrath (see also: 'anger') – 30A, 85, 88, 95C
writing – 45
wrong – 85, 108A
wrong succeeding – 37A

youth – 71A, 103B, 119B, 148A, 148C, 148L

Zion (see: 'holy city')

Liturgical Index to the Psalms and Canticles

Italicised subjects refer to the Themes Index

Advent (and Sundays before Christmas; see also: *'advent'*) – 28, 46A, 46B, 46L, 50A, 50B, 75, 85, 96A, 96L, 97, 97L, 98A, 98B, 98C, 98L, 122B, 132, 153A, 153B, 153C, 156A, 158A, 158B, 158C, 160A, 160B, 160C

All Saints-tide (see also: 'Saints Days') – 1C, 15A, 15B, 33L, 97, 97L, 145A, 145B, 149L, 156A, 156B, 156C, 164B, 164C

Anniversary (see: 'dedication/consecration')

Annunciation Festival – 113A, 113L, 131A, 131B, 160A, 160B, 160C

Ascensiontide (see also: *'ascension'*) – 8C, 21, 45, 47A, 47B, 47L, 68A, 93A, 93B, 93L, 99L, 155A, 155B, 155C, 156A, 156B, 156C, 157A, 157B, 159A, 163A, 163B, 163C, 163D, 164A, 164B, 164C

Ash Wednesday (see also: 'Lent') – 6, 51A, 51B, 90A, 90B

Baptism (service of thanksgiving for; see also: *'baptism'*) – 116A, 116B, 116L, 167

Bible Sunday – 1A, 1B, 1C, 12B, 19A, 19B, 19C, 62A, 95B, 119A, 119B, 119C

Christmas Day, Sundays after Christmas – 98B, 98L, 102A, 160A, 160B, 160C, 163A, 163B, 163C, 163D

church anniversary (see: 'dedication/consecration')

civic/national occasions – 9, 15B, 44, 60, 67A, 67B, 67C, 67L, 72, 78, 82, 85, 96A, 96L, 100A, 100B, 100C, 100D, 100L, 111A, 111L, 117A, 117B, 117L, 149A

commissioning/ordination – 37A, 47A

Communion (see: 'Holy Communion')

Creation Sunday – 8A, 8B, 8C, 8L, 19A, 19B, 19C, 29A, 100B, 100C, 104A, 104B, 104L, 136A, 136L, 147L, 148A, 148B, 148C, 148L, 151, 154A, 154B, 154C, 159B (evening), 164B, 164C

dedication/consecration (anniversary) of a church – 15A, 24B, 24C, 24L, 48A, 84A, 84C, 89A, 100B, 100L, 118A, 118L, 122A, 122B, 122L, 127A, 127B, 132, 147B, 149A, 149L, 150B, 150C, 150L, 161B

Easter Day, Sundays after Easter – 8A, 18A, 18B, 105L, 113L, 114, 118A, 118L, 152A, 152B, 166, 167

Education Sunday – 1A, 1B, 8A, 8B, 8L, 40L, 104A, 111L, 119A, 119B, 119C, 143L

Epiphany – 110, 153A, 162A, 162B, 162C, 162D

evening worship – 36, 36L, 43A, 63A, 63B, 121B, 121C, 121D, 134A, 134B, 134C, 134L, 141, 159A, 159B, 159C, 165A, 165B

funeral services – 23A, 23B, 23C, 31A, 39, 42A, 42B, 49B, 71A, 84B, 90A, 90B, 103A, 103B, 103C, 103L, 121A, 121B, 121C, 130A, 130B, 130C, 139A, 139B, 162A, 162B, 162C

Good Friday (see also: *'passiontide'*) – 13A, 22A, 69A, 158A, 158B, 158C, 163A, 163B, 163C, 163D

Harvest Festival (see also: *'harvest'*) – 65A, 65B, 65L, 67A, 67B, 67C, 67L, 104A, 104B, 126B, 126C, 126L, 145A, 145B, 147A, 147B, 147L, 148A, 148B, 148C, 148L

healing services – 103B, 103L, 147A, 147B, 147L, 165B

Holy Communion (Thanksgiving for; see also: *'communion'*) – 23B, 34A, 116L, 157A, 157B

Lent (and Sundays before Easter) – 10, 11, 13A, 14, 17, 19A, 19B, 26, 27A, 31A, 32A, 38, 40A, 40L, 42A, 42B, 51A, 51B, 54, 61A, 61B, 69A, 70, 84A, 86A, 91A, 103C, 103L, 122A, 122B, 122L, 125, 126A, 130B, 130C, 139A, 139B

marriage services – 67B, 121B, 121D, 127B, 128A, 128B, 128L

missionary occasions (see also: *'proclaiming'*, *'witness'*) – 46A, 46B, 46L, 47A, 47L, 67A, 67B, 67L, 87, 96A, 96B, 96L, 97, 98B, 98L, 100B, 100C, 100L, 117A, 117B, 117L, 138A, 157A, 164C

morning worship – 5, 16A, 19B

Mothering Sunday – 67B, 100L, 112, 113L, 121B, 122L, 127A, 127B, 128A, 128B, 128L, 131A, 131B, 160A, 160B, 160C

New Year services – 47A, 67C, 67L, 102A

Palm Sunday – 8L, 22A, 24A, 24B, 24C, 24L, 45, 69A, 163A, 163B, 163C, 163D

Passiontide – 13A, 22A, 158A, 158B, 158C, 163A, 163B, 163C, 163D

Pentecost (see also: *'Spirit'*) – 51L, 104L, 143A, 143L

Remembrance services (see also: 'civic/national occasions', *'remembrance'*) – 44, 46A, 46B, 47A, 47L, 93, 93L, 111A, 111L, 124A, 124L, 126B, 126C, 126L, 130A, 130B, 130C, 137A

Rogation-tide (see also: *'rogation'*) – 65A, 65L, 67B, 67C, 67L, 107, 126B, 126C, 126L, 147L

Saints' days – 32A, 34A, 34B, 112, 156A, 156B, 156C, 164B, 164C

Sea Sunday – 57A, 93B, 93L, 107, 107L, 151

social responsibility services – 9, 12A, 72, 76, 82, 87, 99A, 113L, 130A, 146, 160A, 160B, 160C

Thanksgiving for the birth of a child – 20A, 116B, 116L

Thanksgiving services – 89A, 136L, 145A, 145B, 147A, 147B, 147L, 148B, 148L, 149A, 149L, 150A, 150B, 150L, 154A, 155B, 155C

Transfiguration (see also: *'face of God'*) – 84A

Trinity Sunday – 93, 93L, 97, 97L, 99L, 149A, 155A, 156A, 156B, 156C, 156D, 157A, 157B, 161A, 161B, 164A, 164B, 164C; evening: 159A, 159B, 159C, 165A, 165B

unity services – 122A, 122B, 122L, 133A, 133B

Morning and Evening Prayer Index to the Canticles

MORNING CANTICLES

Venite (Psalm 95.1–7, Psalm 98.9)
Come with all joy to sing to God – 95A
Come worship God who is worthy of honour – 95B
O come, let us sing out to the Lord (ASB) – 95C, 151
Come, let's joyfully praise our God (LIT) – 95L

Jubilate (Psalm 100)
Come, rejoice before your maker – 100A
Sing, all creation – 100B
O shout to the Lord in triumph
all the earth (ASB) – 100C
With joyful shouts acclaim the Lord – 100D
Rejoice in the Lord, all the earth (LIT) – 100L

The Easter Anthems (1 Corinthians 5.7–8;
Romans 6.9–11; 1 Corinthians 15.20–22)
Now lives the Lamb of God – 152A
Christ our passover
has been sacrificed for us (ASB) – 152B

FIRST LESSON

Benedictus (The Song of Zechariah – Luke 1.68–79)
O bless the God of Israel – 153A
O praise our great and faithful God – 153B
Blessed be the Lord the God of Israel (ASB) – 153C

A Song of Creation/Benedicite (The Song of the
Three Children 35–64 – The Greek Old
Testament)
Bless the Lord, created things – 154A
Angels, praise him – 154B
Bless the Lord, all created things (ASB) – 154C

Great and wonderful (Revelation 15.3–4)
Great and wonderful your deeds – 155A
Wonderful your deeds, Lord – 155B
Great and wonderful are your deeds (ASB) – 155C

SECOND LESSON

Te Deum (A Christian hymn from the fourth
century)
God of gods, we sound his praises – 156A
God, we praise you! God, we bless you – 156B
You are God and we praise you (ASB) – 156C
Great is the Lord we now acclaim – 156D

Gloria in excelsis (A Christian hymn from the
fourth century – based on Luke 2.14)
All glory be to God on high – 157A
Glory to God in the highest (ASB) – 157B

Saviour of the world (A free church hymn from
the nineteenth century)
Saviour Christ, in mercy come – 158A
Jesus, saviour of the world – 158B
Saviour of the world (ASB) – 158C

EVENING CANTICLES

Psalm 134
Bless the Lord as day departs – 134A
Come, praise the Lord, all you his servants – 134B
Come bless the Lord all you servants of the Lord
(ASB) – 134C
You servants of the Lord (LIT) – 134L

O gladsome light (A Christian hymn from the
third century)
Light of gladness, Lord of glory – 159A
Light of gladness, shining radiance – 159B
O gladdening light, O grace (ASB, adapted) – 159C

The Easter Anthems (1 Corinthians 5.7–8;
Romans 6.9–11; 1 Corinthians 15.20–22)
Now lives the Lamb of God – 152A
Christ our passover has been sacrificed for us (ASB)
– 152B

FIRST LESSON

Magnificat (The Song of Mary – Luke 1.46–55)
My soul proclaims
the greatness of the Lord – 160A
With Mary let my soul rejoice – 160B

My soul proclaims
the greatness of the Lord (ASB) – 160C

Cantate Domino (Psalm 98)
Sing to God new songs of worship – 98A
Sing a new song to the Lord – 98B
O sing to the Lord a new song (ASB) – 98C
Sing to the Lord a new song (LIT) – 98L

Bless the Lord (The Song of the Three Children
29–32 – The Greek Old Testament)
Bless the Lord, our fathers' God – 161A
Bless the Lord the God of our fathers – 161B
Bless the Lord the God of our fathers (ASB) – 161C

SECOND LESSON

Nunc dimittis
(The Song of Simeon – Luke 2.29–32)
Faithful vigil ended – 162A
Lord, now let your servant go his way in peace –
162B
Lord now let your servant go in peace (ASB) – 162C
Now at last your servant
can depart in peace – 162D

Deus misereatur (Psalm 67)
Mercy, blessing, favour, grace – 67A
May God be gracious, may we see his face – 67B
May God be gracious to us and bless us (ASB) – 67C
May God be gracious to us and bless us (LIT) – 67L

The Song of Christ's glory (Philippians 2.6–11)
All praise to Christ – 163A
Before the heaven and earth – 163B
Christ Jesus was in the form of God (ASB) – 163C
Though Christ put on our frail humanity – 163D

Glory and honour
  (Revelation 4.11; 5,9,10,12,13)
Heavenly hosts in ceaseless worship – 164A
Glory and honour – 164B
Glory and honour and power (ASB) – 164C

Saviour of the world (A free church hymn from
  the nineteenth century)
Saviour Christ, in mercy come – 158A
Jesus, saviour of the world – 158B
Saviour of the world (ASB) – 158C

OTHER LITURGICAL HYMNS

Before the ending of the day (From a Latin hymn
  of before the eighth century)
Before the ending of the day – 165A
Now evening comes to close the day – 165B

Exsultet (Song of praise
  from the Western Easter liturgy)
Exult, creation round God's throne – 166

Exodus 15 (Song of praise
  from the Western Easter liturgy)
I will sing the Lord's high triumph – 167

Lectionary Index to the Psalms and Canticles

Italics indicate Lectionary appointed psalms; italicised words indicate references to the Themes Index

9 before Christmas (The Creation) – 8A, 8B, 8C, 8L, 19A, 19B, 19C, *29A*, 100B, 100C, *104A, 104B, 104L*, 136A, 136L, 147L, *148A, 148B, 148C, 148L, 150A, 150B, 150C, 150L*, 151, 154A, 154B, 154C, 159B (evening), 164B, 164C

8 before Christmas (The Fall) – 5, 10, 14, 15A, 19A, 19B, 19C, *25A*, 36, 38, 51A, 51B, 52, 78, 84B, 103A, 103B, 103C, 103L, 106A, 116A, 119C, 124A, *130B, 130C, 139A, 139B*

7 before Christmas (The Election of God's People: Abraham) – *1A, 1B, 1C*, 4A, *32A*, 34A, *36A, 36L*, 50B, 67B, 80, 80L, 89A, 98A, 98B, 100A, 100B, 100C, 100D, 102A, 103C, 103L, *105L*, 111L, *136A, 136L*

6 before Christmas (The Promise of Redemption: Moses) – 10, 12A, 65A, *66A, 66L*, 67A, 68A, 77, 78, 81, 84A, 85, 87, 93B, 95A, 95B, 105L, *106A*, 107, 114, 136A, 167

5 before Christmas (The Remnant of Israel) – 1B, 37A, 39, 40A, 42A, 42B, 50B, 61B, 62A, 66A, 71A, *75, 76, 80, 80L*, 99A, 116B, *147A, 147B, 147L*, 153A, 153B, 153C, 156A, 156C, 156D, 158A, 158B

Advent 1 (The Advent Hope) – *18A, 18B*, 28, 46A, 46B, 46L, *50A, 50B, 68A*, 75, 82, 85, 96A, 96L, 97, 97L, 98A, 98B, 98C, 98L, 132, 153A, 153B, 153C, 156A, 158A, 158B, 158C, 160A, 160B, 160C

Advent 2 (The Word of God in the Old Testament) – 1A, 1B, 1C, 12A, *19A, 19B, 19C*, 49A, 49B, 50B, 62A, 95B, *119A, 119B, 119C*

Advent 3 (The Forerunner) – *11, 14*, 46A, 46B, 46L, 47A, 47L, *80, 80L*, 96A, 96B, 96L, 97, 98B, 98L, *126A, 126B, 126C, 126L*, 153A, 153B, 153C, 157A, 164C

Advent 4 (The Annunciation) – *40A, 40L(i), 40L(ii)*, 45, 113A, 113L, 123A, 123B, 131A, 131B, 160A, 160B, 160C

Christmas 1 (The Incarnation) – 47A, 67C, 67L, *84A, 84B, 84C*, 98B, 98L, 102A, *116A, 116B, 116L*, 122A, 122B, 122L, 132, 160A, 160B, 160C, 163A, 163B, 163C, 163D

Christmas 2 (The Holy Family) – 27A, 67B, 85, 87, *89A*, 100L, 112, 113L, 121B, 122L, 127A, 127B, 128A, 128B, 128L, 131A, 131B, 160A, 160B, 160C, *162A, 162B, 162C, 162D*

Epiphany 1 (Revelation: The Baptism of Jesus) – *29A, 30A, 36A, 36L, 46A, 46B, 46L, 47A, 47B, 47L, 89A*, 110, 116A, 116B, 116L, 117A, 117B, 117L, 153A, 155A, 162A, 162B, 162C, 162D

Epiphany 2 (Revelation: The First Disciples) – 4A, *15A, 15B, 16A*, 34B, 78, 80, 80L, 95B, 96A, 98B, *100A, 100B, 100C, 100D, 100L*, 111A, *121A, 121B, 121C, 121D, 126A, 126B, 126C, 126L*, 127A, 132, 138A, *145A, 145B*, 155B, 155C

Epiphany 3 (Revelation: Signs of Glory) – 8L, 19A, 19B, 19C, 29A, *33A, 33L*, 46A, 46B, 46L, 50B, 81, 85, 93B, 96B, 97L, 102A, 104B, *107, 107L*, 108A, 113A, 113L, 115, 131A, *136, 136L*, 145A, 145B, 156A, 156C

Epiphany 4 (Revelation: The New Temple) – 15A, 24B, 24C, 24L, *34A, 34B, 48A, 50A, 50B, 84A, 84C*, 100B, 100L, 118A, 118L, 122A, 122B, 122L, 127A, 127B, 147B, 149A, 149L, 150B, 150C, 150L, 161B

Epiphany 5 (Revelation: The Wisdom of God) – 19A, 19B, 19C, 32A, *36A, 36L, 49A, 49B*, 50A, 51A, 68A, 81, 82, 92A, 104A, 111L, *119A, 119B, 119C, 119L*, 138A, 143L, 147A

Epiphany 6 (Revelation: Parables) – *25A, 43A, 43B*, 75, 76, 127A, 127B, 128A, 128B, 128L, 133A, 133B

9 before Easter (Christ the Teacher) – 1A, 1B, 8A, 8B, 8L, *34A, 34B*, 40L, *71A*, 73, *103A, 103B, 103C, 103L*, 104A, 111L, 119A, 119B, 119C, 143L

8 before Easter (Christ the Healer) – 103B, 103L, *131A, 131B, 137A, 139A, 139B*, 142A, *146, 147A, 147B, 147L*, 165B

7 before Easter (Christ, the Friend of Sinners) – 8A, *25A, 32A, 56A, 57A*, 68A, *103A, 103B, 103C, 103L, 119A, 119B, 119C, 119L*, 122B

Lent 1 (The King and the Kingdom: Temptation) – 10, 11, 13A, 14, 17, 19A, 19B, 26, 27A, 31A, 32A, 38, 40A, *40L(i), 40L(ii)*, 42A, 42B, *51A, 51B*, 54, 61A, 61B, 69A, 70, 84A, 86A, 90A, 90B, *91A*, 103C, 103L, *119A, 119B, 119C, 119L*, 122A, 122B, 122L, 125, 126A, 130B, 130C, 139A, 139B, 142A

Lent 2 (The King and the Kingdom: Conflict) – 1A, 5, *18A, 18B*, 19A, 20A, 26, 27A, 43B, 56A, 63A, *119C*, 130A, 141

Lent 3 (The King and the Kingdom: Suffering) – *31A*, 39, *40L(i), 40L(ii)*, 46A, 46B, 47A, 50A, 51B, 84A, 90B, 104L, *115*, 116L, *119A, 119B, 119C, 119L*, 127A, 139B, 141 (see also: *'prayer'*)

Lent 4 (The King and the Kingdom: Transfiguration) – 11, 13A, *18A, 18B, 23A, 23B, 23C*, 24C, 27, 44, 51A, 61B, 63A, 67A, 67B, 67C, 67L, 80L, 84A, 84B, 90A, 104L, *119A, 119B, 119C*, 143A, 151, 159B, 159C

Lent 5 (The King and the Kingdom: The Victory of the Cross) – 19B, *22A*, 34B, 49B, 52, *66A*, 73, 76, 103B, 107L, 111L, 119A, 126A, *130B*, 142A, *143A, 143L*, 153A, 153C, 156A, 156B, 156C, 156D, 158B, 158C, 163A, 163B, 163C, 164A, 164B, 164C (see also: *'freedom'*, *'liberty'*, *'release'*)

Palm Sunday (The Way of the Cross) – 8A, 8B, 8C, 8L, 13A, 19B, *22A, 24A, 24B*, 24C, 24L, 45, *61A, 61B, 62A, 62B, 69A*, 100B, 158A, 158B, 158C, 163A, 163B, 163C, 163D

Easter – *18A, 18B*, 105L, *113L*, 114, *117A, 117B, 117L, 118A, 118L, 152A, 152B, 156A, 156B, 156C, 156D*, 166, 167

Easter 1 (The Upper Room / The Bread of Life) – Year 1: 18A, *30A, 34A, 34B*, 42A, 42B, *48A*, 49B, 115, *145A, 145B*, 152A, 166, 167. Year 2: *30A,*

34A, 34B, 48A, 104B, 105L, *115,* 136A, *145A, 145B,* 146

Easter 2 (The Emmaus Road / The Good Shepherd) – Year 1: *8A, 8B, 8C, 8L, 23A, 23B,* 30A, 42A, 42B, *49B,* 63A, 63B, 68A, *111, 111L,* 152B, 166. Year 2: *8A, 8B, 8C, 8L, 23A, 23B, 49A, 49B,* 68A, 76, 77, 80L, 81, 95A, 100A, 100B, 100C, 100L, *111A, 111L,* 121B, 162B

Easter 3 (The Lakeside, The Resurrection and the Life) – *16, 18A, 18B, 30A,* 42A, 42B, 49B, 63A, 63B, *121A, 121B, 121C, 121D, 126A, 126B, 126C, 126L,* 152A, 152B, 166, 167

Easter 4 (The Charge to Peter / The Way, the Truth and the Life) – Year 1: 8B, 8C, 8L, 15A, 18B, *33A, 33L, 37A, 57A, 63A, 63B,* 77, 131A, 131B, 139A. Year 2: 1A, 1C, 12B, 19B, 19C, 26, *33A, 33L, 37A,* 43A, *57A, 63A, 63B,* 77, 119A, 119B

Easter 5 (Going to the Father) – 12B, *15A, 15B,* 21, 23B, 26, 40A, 43A, 49B, 61B, *65A, 65B, 65L, 67A, 67B, 67C, 67L,* 73, 80L, *84A, 84B,* 84C, 89A, 96B, 102A, *107, 107L,* 108A, 113A, 121A, 123A, 134B, 139B, 148A, 165B

Ascension 1 (The Ascension of Christ) – 8C, 21, *24A, 24B, 24C, 24L,* 45, *47A, 47B, 47L,* 68A, 93A, 93B, 93L, 97, 99L, *108A, 110, 138A,* 155A, 155B, 155C, 156A, 156B, 156C, 157A, 157B, *159A, 159B, 159C,* 163A, 163B, 163C, 163D, 164A, 164B, 164C

Pentecost – 11, 29A, *36A, 36L,* 47A, 50B, 51A, 51L, 67B, *68A, 104A, 104B, 104L,* 108A, *122A, 122B, 122L,* 143A, 143L

Trinity – 29A, *33A, 33L, 93, 93L,* 97, *97L, 99L, 145A, 145B, 149A, 149L,* 155A, 156A, 156B, 156C, 156D, 157A, 157B, 161A, 161B, 164A. Evening: 159A, 159B, 159C, 165A, 165B

Pentecost 2 (The People of God, the Church's Unity and Fellowship) – 15A, 24B, 24C, 24L, 48A, 84A, 84C, *85, 89A,* 95A, *95B, 95C, 95L,* 100B, 100L, 118A, 118L, 122A, 122B, 122L, 127A, 127B, 132, *133A, 133B,* 147B, 149A, 149L, 150B, 150C, 150L, 161B

Pentecost 3 (The Life of the Baptised / The Church's Confidence in Christ) – Year 1: *11,* 19C, *20A, 32A, 36A, 36L, 44,* 50A, 103B, 112, 116A, 116B, 116L, 119A, 119C, 147L, *150A, 150B, 150C, 150L,* 167. Year 2: *11,* 19C, *20A,* 24B, *32A,* 34A, *36A, 36L,* 37A, 40L(i), 40L(ii), *44,* 71A, 76, 78, 81, 90B, 95A, 103A, 115, 122A, 128A, 132, *150A, 150B, 150C, 150L*

Pentecost 4 (The Freedom God Gives / The Church's Mission to the Individual) – Year 1: 13A, 24B, 31A, *42A, 42B, 43A, 43B, 63A, 63B,* 66A, 67C, 68A, 114, 116A, 118A, 119A, 122A, 124A, 126A, 126L, 136A, 136L, 143A, *147A, 147B, 147L, 153A, 153C,* 164B, 167. Year 2: 32A, 34A, 40L(i), 40L(ii), *42A, 42B, 43A, 43B, 63A, 63B,* 71A, 76, 78, 81, 90B, 95A, 103A, 115, 128A, 132, *147A, 147B, 147L, 153A, 153C* (see also: Pentecost 5: 'The Church's Mission to All')

Pentecost 5 (The New Law / The Church's Mission to All) – Year 1: 19C, 50A, *67A, 67B, 67C, 67L, 98A, 98B, 98C, 98L,* 103B, 112, *119B,*

119C, 147L. Year 2: 4, 46A, 46B, 46L, 47A, 47L, *67A, 67B, 67C, 67L,* 87, 96A, 96B, 96L, 97, *98A, 98B, 98C, 98L,* 100B, 100C, 100L, 117A, 117B, 117L, 157A, 164C (see also: Pentecost 4: 'The Church's Mission to the Individual')

Pentecost 6 (Made New in Christ) – *1A, 1B, 1C,* 4A, 49B, 55, 67C, 77, 97L, *102A,* 103B, 105L, 111L, *112*

Pentecost 7 (The More Excellent Way) – 26, 55, *62A, 62B, 81,* 85A, *99A, 99L, 100A, 100B, 100C, 100D, 100L, 101, 103A, 103B, 103C, 103L,* 112, 122L, 128A, 133A

Pentecost 8 (The Fruit of the Spirit) – *25A, 27A,* 40L(i), 40L(ii), 53, 73, 84A, *91A,* 97L, 122A, 122L, 126A, 127A, 128A, 128L, 131A, 133A, 147A, 157A, 157B

Pentecost 9 (The Whole Armour of God) – 3A, 4A, 7A, 12B, *18A, 18B,* 19A, *24A, 24B, 24C, 24L,* 27A, 31A, *33A, 33L,* 34A, 44, 46A, 46L, 47A, 62A, 63A, 72, 76, 78, 84C, 89A, *90A, 90B,* 115, 121C, 121D, 127A, 143A (see also: *'faith', 'salvation'*)

Pentecost 10 (The Mind of Christ) – *1A, 1B, 1C, 4A, 19A, 19B, 19C,* 26, 45, 53, 55, *71A,* 113L, 126A, 126B, 126C, 126L, 127A, 131A, 145A, 147A, 163A, 163B, 163C, 165B

Pentecost 11 (The Serving Community) – *31A, 40A, 40L(i), 40L(ii),* 82, 103B, 103L, *112, 123A, 123B, 124, 124L,* 125, 147A, 147B, 147L, *165A, 165B* (see also: *'social responsibility'*)

Pentecost 12 (The Witnessing Community) – *34A, 34B,* 46A, 46B, 46L, 47A, 47L, 67A, 67B, 67L, 87, 96A, 96B, 96L, 97, 98B, 98L, 100B, 100C, 100L, 117A, 117B, 117L, 138A, *145A, 145B, 150A, 150B, 150C, 150L,* 157A, 164C

Pentecost 13 (The Suffering Community) – 3A, 9, 13A, 14, *22A, 23A,* 27A, *31A,* 39, *43A, 43B,* 56A, 61A, 61B, 70, 80, 80L, 91A, 97L, 124L, 125, *130A, 130B, 130C,* 136A, 136L, *137A,* 142A, 143A, 146, 167

Pentecost 14 (The Family) – *45,* 67B, 100L, *103A, 103B, 103C, 103L,* 112, 113L, 121B, 122L, *127A, 127B, 128A, 128B, 128L,* 131A, 131B, 160A, 160B, 160C

Pentecost 15 (Those in Authority) – 9, 15B, *20A,* 44, *50A, 50B,* 60, 67A, 67B, 67C, 67L, 72, 78, 82, 85, 96A, 96L, 100A, 100B, 100C, 100D, 100L, 111A, 111L, 117A, 117B, 117L, 149A

Pentecost 16 (The Neighbour) – 9, 12A, 15A, 15B, 17, 24A, 24C, 24L, *34A, 34B,* 49A, 49B, 72, 76, 81, 82, 87, 99A, *107, 107L,* 113L, 119C, 130A, *133A, 133B,* 146, 160A, 160B, 160C

Pentecost 17 (The Proof of Faith) – *19A, 19B, 19C, 20A,* 24B, 34A, 40L(i), 40L(ii), 52, *56A, 57A,* 71A, 76, 78, 81, 90B, *91A, 93A, 93B, 93L,* 95A, 95B, 103A, 115, 122A, 126B, 126C, 128A, 132

Pentecost 18 (The Offering of Life) – 45, *90A, 90B,* 112, *116A, 116B,* 118A, *118L,* 127A, 127B, *145A, 145B*

Pentecost 19 (The Life of Faith) – 13A, 18A, 18B, 22A, 24A, 24B, 25A, 26, 33L, 34A, 36, *37A,* 40A, 40L(i), 40L(ii), 42B, 47A, 49A, 49B, 51A, 56, 62A, 62B, *65A, 65B, 65L,* 71A, 84A, 84B, 84C, *85,* 90B, 91A, 95B, *111A, 111L,* 112, 113A, 116A, 122A, 128B, 131A, 131B, 132, *139A, 139B,* 143A, 146, 147B, 147L

Pentecost 20 (Endurance) – 1c, 15A, 15B, 32A, 33L, 34A, 34B, *37A, 39, 51A, 51B*, 97, 97L, 112, *121A, 121B, 121C, 121D*, 142A, 145A, 145B, 149L, 156A, 156B, 156C, 164B, 164C

Pentecost 21 (The Christian Hope) – *11, 15A, 15B, 16A, 23A, 23B, 23C, 24A, 24B, 24C, 24L*, 31A, 42A, 42B, 49B, 71A, *78*, 84B, 90A, 90B, 103A, 103B, 103C, 103L, 121B, 121C, *126A, 126B, 126C, 126L*, 130A, 130B, 130C, 139A, 139B, 162A, 162B, 162C

Pentecost 22 (The Two Ways) – 14, 25A, 32A, *40A, 40L(i), 40L(ii), 42A, 42B, 43A, 43B*, 50A, 67C, 67L, 78, 84B, 86A, 88, 95A, 95B, 95C, 102A, 111A, *112, 119A, 119B, 119C, 119L*, 128A, 128L, 145B, 147A, 154B, 154C

Last Sunday after Pentecost (Citizens of Heaven) – 12A, 12B, *15A, 15B*, 21, 23A, 26, 43A, 49B, 61B, 73, 80L, *84A, 84B, 84C, 89A*, 96B, 102A, 108A, 113A, 121A, 123A, 134B, 139B, *146*, 148A, 165B (see also: *'holy city'*)

Alphabetical Index to Tunes

A babe is born – 50A
Aberystwyth – 51A
Acclamation – 156D(i)
Ach, Gott und Herr – 8A(ii)
Agincourt – 166(ii)
Alicia – 165A(i)
Alleluia – 34A
Anderson – 124A(i)
Andrew Mark – 160A
Antiphoner – 154A
Asthall – 134A
Astwood – 53
Attercliffe – 22A(i)

Bangor – 13A, 56
Bedfordshire May-Day Carol – 23A(i)
Belgravia – 131B
Bennelong – 65A
Berkswell – 139B
Bertem – 162D
Bibury – 1B(i)
Billing – 130A
Bishop Tucker – 30A
Bishopthorpe – 92A(ii)
Blaenwern – 164A
Blunham – 88
Bolnhurst – 5(i)
Boundless love – 57A
Bramdean – 12B
Brightwell Baldwin – 104B
Brother James' Air – 23A(ii)
Bugeilio'r Gwenith Gwyn – 141
Burgate – 147B(i)
Buttermere – 32A(i)

Calon Lân – 73
Camberwell – 148A
Canterbury Cathedral – 146
Capetown – 124A(ii)
Carsaig – 43B
Carter Knowle – 116A(i)
Catherine – 80(i)
Charnwood – 165B(i)
Chorus Angelorum – 118A(ii)
Christchurch – 147B(ii)
Christmas Eve – 50B
Christus der ist mein Leben – 27A
Church Triumphant – 18B(ii)
Cogenhoe – 17
Coln Rogers – 1C
Come rejoice – 100A(i)
Confitebor tibi – 9
Cople – 75
Cornwall – 133B
Covenanters – 153B(i)
Crail – 93B
Creator God – 91A(i)
Cross Deep – 112(i)
Crucifer – 24B
Crüger – 145A
Culbach – 158A(ii)

Cwm Rhondda – 107

Dam Busters March – 46A
Daniel – 5(ii)
Darwall's 148th – 152A
Davos – 121B
Detroit – 14
Doncaster – 128B
Dundee – 114
Durrow – 122B

Easter Song – 111A
Elmore – 132
Engelberg – 163A
Epiphany Hymn – 95B(ii)
Erlestoke – 155B
Es ist kein Tag – 8B(ii)
Eureka – 121A
Everberg – 11
Eythorne – 104C

Faithful vigil – 162A
Fenny Stratford – 166(i)
Flanders – 52
Fulda – 95A
Fullness – 1A

God of gods – 156A
Golden Hill – 49A
Goodwyn's Vale – 99A
Gopsal – 47A
Gott Will's machen – 100A(ii)
Great Cheverell – 34B
Great Glen – 44
Great Oxendon – 85
Grendon – 102A(ii)
Growing – 130C

Haresfield – 104A(i)
Harts – 66A
Hawkhurst – 32A(ii)
Heather – 54(i)
Heinlein – 10(ii)
Hemsby – 127B
Herongate – 131A
Hiding-place – 7A
Highwood – 138A
Horsell – 108A
Howerton – 42A

Ibstone – 119B
Innocents – 128A
Innsbruck – 90A

Jacob's Well – 8A(i)
Jane – 18A
Jerusalem – 149A
Jesmian – 95B(i)
Joyous Peace – 39

Kingly majesty – 93A
Knightwood – 54(ii)

La Corbière – 48A
Land of Rest – 127A(i)
Langleigh – 38
Lardergate – 33A
Laudate Dominum – 117B
Leoni – 63A
Les Commandemens – 134B
Lewknor – 10(i)
Light of gladness – 159B
Limburg – 102A(i)
Listening – 61A
Little Barrington – 154B
Little Venice – 123B
Littlebourne – 98B(ii)
Liverpool – 4A
Llanymawddwy – 82
Long Crendon – 100B
Lord of the years – 96A
Love's Gift – 61B(i)
Luther – 29A
Lux Eoi – 115
Lyminge – 136A

Macpherson's Farewell – 130B
Maiden Way – 72
Maisemore – 139A
Manton Hollow – 8B(i)
Marlborough Gate – 45
McKee – 127A(ii)
Melchbourne – 84A
Melcombe – 1B(ii)
Michael – 62A
Morning Hymn – 112(ii)
Morning Light – 153A
Mow Cop – 103A

Nannerch – 40A
Narenza – 163B
Neville Court – 97
Nicolaus – 157A
North Coates – 162B(ii)
Northwood – 18B(i)
Norwich – 43A
Now join we – 77
Nunc dimittis – 159C

Oakmount – 162B(i)
Ode to Joy – 98A
Old 100th – 156D(ii)
Ombersley – 22A(ii)
Onslow Square – 98B(i)
Orientis partibus – 150A, 161A
Orphan Girl – 90B

Palace Green – 16A
Pamela – 86A(i)
Passons – 71A
Patrixbourne – 89A(i)
Plumstead – 76(ii)
Pokesdown – 110
Potterne – 60

QEGS – 84B
Queen's Terrace – 20A
Quem pastores laudavere – 159A

Regent Square – 147A
Restoration – 78
Ridley – 87(i)
Rodmell – 92A(i)
Rustington – 156B

Salvator mundi – 158A(i)
Salvum me – 69A
Salvum me fac – 12A
Schönster Herr Jesu – 164B
Sennen Cove – 118A(i)
Shepherd Boy's Song – 55
Sherington – 36
Slovenia – 113A
Solothurn – 3A
Somerset – 28(i)
Song 46 – 68A
South Ormsby – 106A
Southwell (Irons) – 104A(ii)
Speen – 81
Splendour – 70
St Albinus – 158B
St Alphege – 6

St Austin – 21
St Bartholomew's Pico Rivera –
   76(i)
St Bees – 80(ii)
St Bernard – 28(ii)
St Ethelwald – 87(ii)
St George's, Windsor – 122A
St Helens – 148B
St Matthias – 116A(ii)
St Michael – 123A(ii)
St Patrick – 19C
St Petersburg – 25A
St Stephen – 160B
Stanton – 91A(ii)
Steeple Ashton – 133A(i)
Stowey – 61B(ii)
Stracathro – 165B(ii)
Streets of Laredo – 137A
Summercourt – 37A
Sursum Corda – 163D

Talbot Woods – 26
Tallis' Canon – 165A(ii)
Tamié Tone – 42B
Temple Guiting – 63B
The Linden Tree – 19A
The Truth from above – 143A

Thursford Green – 86A(ii)
Timeless love – 89A(ii)
Tyddyn Llwyn – 167(i)
Tyrol – 100D

Universa Laus – 67B
University – 119A
Upton Scudamore – 148C
Urchfont – 67A

Veni Sancte Spiritus – 117A
Venice – 133A(ii)
Vossem – 126A

Was lebet – 125
Water-End – 19B
Webster – 101
Wells House – 15B
West Wickham – 123A(i)
Westminster Abbey – 167(ii)
Wharfdale – 49B
Willard – 23B
Wiltshire – 153B(ii)
Withington – 15A
Wootton – 24A
Württemberg – 155A

Ye banks and braes – 31A
You are my refuge – 142A

First Lines Index to the Psalms and Canticles

Italics indicate titles of canticles and liturgical hymns

A Song of Creation/Benedicite – 154A, 154B, 154C
All glory be to God on high – 157A
All my soul to God I raise – 25A
All praise to Christ, our Lord and king divine – 163A
All things I see, Lord, call to me – 104A
All things that are, praise God – 148C
Alleluia! Love eternal – 106A
Angels, praise him – 154B
As a deer longs for running brooks (O put your trust in God) – 42B
As David took no rest – 132

Be gracious to me, Lord – 57A
Be merciful to me, O God – 56A
Before the ending of the day – 165A
Before the ending of the day/Te lucis ante terminum – 165A, 165B
Before the heaven and earth – 163B
Before the Lord my soul is bowed – 131A
Behold how pleasant it shall be – 133B
Benedicite/A Song of Creation – 154A, 154B, 154C
Benedictus – 153A, 153B, 153C
Bless all who trust in God – 128B
Bless the Lord – 161A, 161B, 161C
Bless the Lord all created things – 154C
Bless the Lord as day departs – 134A
Bless the Lord, created things – 154A
Bless the Lord, our fathers' God – 161A
Bless the Lord the God of our fathers – 161B, 161C
Blessed are they who listen not to evil counsel – 1C
Blessed are those who fear the Lord – 128A
Blessed are those whose way is blameless – 119C
Blessed be the Lord the God of Israel – 153C
Bring songs of joy to God the Lord – 33A
Bring to the Lord a glad new song – 149A
By rivers of sorrow we sat and remembered – 137A

Cantate Domino – 98A, 98B, 98C, 98L
Christ Jesus was in the form of God – 163C
Christ our passover is sacrificed for us – 152B
Clothed in kingly majesty – 93A
Come, bless the Lord – 134C
Come, praise the Lord/Psalm 134 – 134A, 134B, 134C, 134L
Come, praise the Lord, all you his servants – 134B
Come quickly, Lord, to rescue me – 70
Come, rejoice before your maker – 100A
Come with all joy to sing to God – 95A
Come, worship God who is worthy of honour – 95B
Commit your way to God the Lord – 37A

Deus misereatur – 67A, 67B, 67C, 67L

Easter Anthems – 152A, 152B
Easter Liturgy – 167
Easter Song of Praise/Exsultet – 166
Exult, creation round God's throne – 166

Faithful vigil ended – 162A
Fill your hearts with joy and gladness – 147A
Flawless are God's mighty words (God will arise because the weak are crying) – 12A
Fling wide the gates – 24B
For all your boundless gifts – 87
From time beyond my memory – 71A

Give God thanks for he is gracious – 107
Give thanks to God, the Lord of all – 136A
Gloria in excelsis – 157A, 157B
Glory and honour – 164A, 164B, 164C
Glory and honour and power – 164C
Glory and honour, wisdom and splendour – 164B
Glory and praise to God – 19B
Glory to God in the highest – 157B
God, be merciful to me – 51A
God everlasting, at your word – 90B
God is king – be warned, you mighty – 82
God is king! The Lord is reigning – 93B
God is king – the nations tremble – 99A
God is my great desire – 63A
God is my strong salvation – 27A
God is our refuge and strength – 46B
God is our strength and refuge – 46A
God is the king of all the earth – 47B
God of gods, we sound his praises – 156A
God of hosts, you chose a vine – 80
God, we praise you! God, we bless you – 156B
God whose praise is sung in Zion – 65A
God will arise (Flawless are God's mighty words) – 12A
God's glory fills the heavens – 19C
God's holy ways are just and true – 111A
Great and wonderful – 155A, 155B, 155C
Great and wonderful are your deeds – 155C
Great and wonderful your deeds – 155A
Great is the Lord! His praise is great – 48A
Great is the Lord we now acclaim – 156D

Have mercy on me O God – 51B
He speaks – the Lord of all the earth – 50B
He will not let your foot slip (I will lift up my eyes) – 121D
Hear me, O Lord, and respond to my prayer – 86A
Hear me, O Lord, in my distress – 143A
Heavenly hosts in ceaseless worship – 164A
How blessed are those who trust in God – 112
How can I repay the Lord – 116B
How glad are those with peace of mind – 32A
How good a thing it is – 133A
How long will you forget me, Lord – 13A
How lovely is your dwelling-place: O Lord God of hosts – 84C
How lovely is your dwelling-place, O Lord most high – 84A
How many are against me, Lord – 3A

I come to you for shelter, Lord – 31A

I cried to my Saviour to hear me – 77
I find my refuge in the Lord – 11
I have no strength but yours (I will give thanks to the Lord most high) – 7A
I lift my eyes to the quiet hills – 121C
I lift my eyes to you – 123A
I lift up my eyes to the hills – 121C
I love the Lord because he heard my voice (How can I repay the Lord) – 116B
I love the Lord, he heard my voice – 116A
I love you Lord, my strength and rock – 18B
I love you, O Lord, you alone – 18A
I praise you, Lord, with all my heart (Your justice is perfect) – 9
I rejoiced to hear them say – 122A
I see the mountains far away – 121A
I set the Lord before my eyes – 16A
I will exalt you O God – 145B
I will give thanks to the Lord most high (I have no strength but yours) – 7A
I will lift up my eyes to the hills – 121D
I will sing the Lord's high triumph – 167
I worship you, O Lord – 30A
If God is building when we build – 127A
If the Lord had not been near – 124A
If we love the word of God – 1A
I'll praise the Lord for ever and ever – 34B
I'll praise you Lord with heart content and joyful – 138A
In God is my safety and glory (My soul is at rest in God) – 62B
In my hour of grief or need – 10

Jerusalem! how glad I was – 122B
Jesus, saviour of the world – 158B
Jubilate – 100A, 100B, 100C, 100D, 100L

Laughter and song – 126A
Let all in heaven and earth unite – 29A
Let God arise! His enemies, be gone – 68A
Let everything that has breath – 150B
Let God be gracious to us – 67C
Let God who called the worlds to be – 50A
Let those with voices sing – 45
Lift up your heads, eternal gates – 24A
Light of gladness, Lord of glory – 159A
Light of gladness, shining radiance – 159B
Like the deer, athirst and questing – 42A
Listen to my prayer, Lord – 61A
Lord all-knowing, you have found me – 139B
Lord, as I wake I turn to you – 5
Lord, how majestic is your name – 8A
Lord, now let your servant go his way in peace – 162B
Lord now you let your servant go in peace – 162C
Lord of all my footsteps – 17
Lord, this thing I ask you – 131B
Lord, who may dwell within your house – 15A
Lord, who may venture where you dwell – 15B
Lord, will you turn from your anger – 38

Magnificat – 160A, 160B, 160C
Make music to the Lord most high – 92A
Master, we lift our eyes – 123B

May God be gracious – 67B
May the Lord God hear you pray – 20A
Mercy, blessing, favour, grace – 67A
My heart is ready, O my God – 108A
My soul is at rest in God (In God is my safety and glory) – 62B
My soul proclaims the greatness of the Lord, and my spirit sings for joy – 160A
My soul proclaims the greatness of the Lord: my spirit rejoices – 160C

No fear of God before the eyes – 36
Not to us be glory given – 115
Now all the world (Fling wide the gates) – 24B
Now at last your servant can depart in peace – 162D
Now evening comes to close the day – 165B
Now lives the Lamb of God – 152A
Nunc dimittis – 162A, 162B, 162C, 162D

O bless the God of Israel – 153A
O bless the Lord, my soul – 104B
O clap your hands (God is the king of all the earth) – 47B
O come let us sing out to the Lord – 151
O come let us sing unto the Lord – 95C
O for the wings to fly afar – 55
O gladdening light – 159C
O gladsome light – 159A, 159B, 159C
O God, defender of the poor – 4A
O God, hear me calling – 61B
O God, we thank you – 75
O God, you are my God – 63B
O gracious Lord, be near me – 6
O let the Church rejoice – 147B
O light and truth of God – 43A
O Lord, come quickly when I call – 141
O Lord, my rock, to you I cry – 28
O Lord my shepherd, lead me in your ways – 23B
O Lord our Governor: how glorious is your name – 8C
O Lord, the God who saves me – 88
O Lord, the mansions where you dwell – 84B
O people, listen; hear God's wisdom crying – 49B
O praise God in his sanctuary – 150C
O praise our great and faithful God – 153B
O put your trust in God (As a deer longs for running brooks) – 42B
O shout to the Lord in triumph – 100C
O sing to the Lord a new song: for he has done marvellous things – 98C
O sing to the Lord a new song: sing to the Lord all the earth – 96B
Only the fool will say, 'There is no God' – 53
Open the gates of righteousness – 118A
Our God eternal, reigning – 90A
Out of our failure to create a world of love and care – 130A
Out of the depths I cry – 130C

Praise him, praise him, praise him – 148B
Praise him, you nations (Praise the Lord, all you nations) – 117B
Praise our God with shouts of joy – 66A

Praise the God of our salvation – 146
Praise the Lord, all nations, praise – 117A
Praise the Lord, all you nations (Praise him, you nations) – 117B
Praise the Lord and bless his name – 103A
Praise the Lord O my soul – 103B
Praise the Lord of heaven – 148A
Praise the Lord with joyful cry – 150A
Psalm 134 – 134A, 134B, 134C, 134L

Rest in God, our God most mighty – 62A

Safe in the shadow of the Lord – 91A
Save me, O God, hear my prayer – 54
Saviour Christ, in mercy come – 158A
Saviour of the world – 158A, 158B, 158C
Saviour of the world come to us – 158C
Servants of the living Lord – 113A
Silent, I have waited – 39
Silent the earth when God arose – 76
Sing a new song of God and his salvation – 96A
Sing a new song to the Lord – 98B
Sing, all creation, sing to God in gladness – 100B
Sing merrily to God – 81
Sing to God new songs of worship – 98A
Sing to the Lord (O sing to the Lord a new song) – 96B
Song of Christ's Glory – 163A, 163B, 163C, 163D
Song of Creation/Benedicite – 154A, 154B, 154C
Song of Mary/Magnificat – 160A, 160B, 160C
Song of Simeon/Nunc dimittis – 162A, 162B, 162C, 162D
Song of Zechariah/Benedictus – 153A, 153B, 153C
Surely God the Lord is good – 73

Take heart and praise our God – 47A
Te Deum – 156A, 156B, 156C, 156D
Tell his praise in song and story – 34A
The earth is the Lord's – 24C
The everlasting Lord is king – 97
The fool whose heart declares in pride – 14
The law of God is life to choose – 1B
The Lord is full of compassion and mercy – 103C
The Lord is my shepherd: therefore can I lack nothing – 23C
The Lord my shepherd rules my life – 23A
The majesty of mountains – 104C
The promises of God are pure – 12B
The will of God to mark my way – 119A
There is no moment of my life – 139A
This is the word of God's decree – 110

Those who rely on the Lord are unshakeable – 125
Though Christ put on our frail humanity – 163D
Timeless love! We sing the story – 89A
To God our great salvation a triumph-song we raise – 145A
To lead a blameless life, O Lord – 26
To the Lord I looked in patience – 40A
To those who rule our land – 72

Unless the Lord has built the house – 127B
Up from the depths I cry to God – 130B

Venite – 95A, 95B, 95C, 95L, 151

We are a land divided – 60
We have heard, O Lord our God, the story of your grace – 44
We look into your heavens and see your glory – 19A
We will tell each generation what the Lord our God has done – 78
What riches on this earth can buy one human breath – 49A
When Israel broke their cruel chains – 114
When my bitter foes surround – 43B
When the Lord turned again the captivity of Sion – 126C
When the Lord turned again the fortunes of Zion – 126B
When the waters cover me – 69A
When this land knew God's gracious love outpoured – 85
Why, God, have you forsaken me – 22A
Why in the dawning of another day – 52
With all my heart I seek the true and living way – 119B
With all your heart rejoice – 21
With heart and hands washed clean – 101
With joyful shouts acclaim the Lord – 100D
With Mary let my soul rejoice – 160B
With wonder, Lord, we see your works – 8B
Wonderful your deeds, Lord – 155B

You are God and we praise you – 156C
You are my refuge – 142A
You are to be praised O God – 65B
You laid the foundations of earth – 102A
Your justice is perfect (I praise you, Lord, with all my heart) – 9

The Order for Holy Communion Rite A
from The Alternative Service Book 1980

The Prayers of the Congregation

THE PREPARATION

The Lord be with you
and also with you.

Almighty God,
to whom all hearts are open,
all desires known,
and from whom no secrets are hidden:
cleanse the thoughts of our hearts
by the inspiration of your Holy Spirit,
that we may perfectly love you,
and worthily magnify your holy name;
through Christ our Lord. Amen.

There is no other commandment greater than
these.
Amen. Lord, have mercy.

Almighty God, our heavenly Father,
we have sinned against you
 and against our fellow men,
in thought and word and deed,
through negligence, through weakness,
through our own deliberate fault.
We are truly sorry,
and repent of all our sins.
For the sake of your Son Jesus Christ,
 who died for us,
forgive us all that is past;
and grant that we may serve you
 in newness of life
to the glory of your name. Amen.

Or

Almighty God, our heavenly Father,
we have sinned against you,
through our own fault,
in thought and word and deed,
and in what we have left undone.
For your Son our Lord Jesus Christ's sake,
forgive us all that is past;
and grant that we may serve you
 in newness of life
to the glory of your name. Amen.

Lord, have mercy. Christ, have mercy.
Lord, have mercy. **Christ, have mercy.**

    Lord, have mercy.
    Lord, have mercy.

Glory to God in the highest,
and peace to his people on earth.

Lord God, heavenly King,
almighty God and Father,
we worship you, we give you thanks,
we praise you for your glory.

Lord Jesus Christ,
 only Son of the Father,
Lord God, Lamb of God,
you take away the sin of the world:
have mercy on us;
you are seated at the right hand of the Father:
receive our prayer.

For you alone are the Holy One,
you alone are the Lord,
you alone are the Most High,
Jesus Christ,
with the Holy Spirit,
in the glory of God the Father. Amen.

THE MINISTRY OF THE WORD

This is the word of the Lord.
Thanks be to God.

Glory to Christ our Saviour.

This is the Gospel of Christ.
Praise to Christ our Lord.

We believe in one God,
the Father, the almighty,
maker of heaven and earth,
of all that is,
seen and unseen.

We believe in one Lord, Jesus Christ,
the only Son of God,
eternally begotten of the Father,
God from God, Light from Light,
true God from true God,
begotten, not made,
of one Being with the Father.
Through him all things were made.
For us and for our salvation
he came down from heaven;
by the power of the Holy Spirit
he became incarnate of the Virgin Mary,
 and was made man.
For our sake he was crucified
 under Pontius Pilate;
he suffered death and was buried.
On the third day he rose again
in accordance with the Scriptures;
he ascended into heaven
and is seated at the right hand of the Father
He will come again in glory
to judge the living and the dead,
and his kingdom will have no end.

We believe in the Holy Spirit,
the Lord, the giver of life,
who proceeds from the Father and the Son.
With the Father and the Son
  he is worshipped and glorified.
He has spoken through the Prophets.

We believe in one holy catholic
  and apostolic Church.
We acknowledge one baptism
  for the forgiveness of sins.
We look for the resurrection of the dead,
and the life of the world to come.   Amen.

Lord, in your mercy
hear our prayer.

Merciful Father,
accept these prayers
for the sake of your Son,
our Saviour Jesus Christ.   Amen.

We do not presume
to come to this your table, merciful Lord,
trusting in our own righteousness,
but in your manifold and great mercies.
We are not worthy
so much as to gather up the crumbs
  under your table.
But you are the same Lord
whose nature is always to have mercy.
Grant us therefore, gracious Lord,
so to eat the flesh of your dear son Jesus Christ
and to drink his blood,
that we may evermore dwell in him
and he in us.   Amen.

Or

Most merciful Lord,
your love compels us to come in.
Our hands were unclean,
our hearts were unprepared;
we were not fit
even to eat the crumbs
  from under your table.
But you, Lord,
  are the God of our salvation,
and share your bread with sinners.
So cleanse and feed us
with the precious body and blood of your Son,
that he may live in us and we in him;
and that we, with the whole company of Christ,
may sit and eat in your kingdom. Amen.

THE MINISTRY OF THE SACRAMENT

The peace of the Lord be always with you
and also with you.

Yours, Lord, is the greatness, the power,
the glory, the splendour, and the majesty;
for everything in heaven and on earth is yours.
All things come from you,
and of your own do we give you.

The Lord is here.
His Spirit is with us.

Lift up your hearts.
We lift them to the Lord.

Let us give thanks to the Lord our God.
It is right to give him thanks and praise.

We proclaim your great and glorious name,
for ever praising you and saying:
Holy, holy, holy Lord,
God of power and might,
heaven and earth are full of your glory.
Hosanna in the highest.

Blessed is he who comes
  in the name of the Lord.
Hosanna in the highest.

Do this, as often as you drink it,
in remembrance of me.
Christ has died:
Christ is risen:
Christ will come again.

[We worship you, Father almighty,
in songs of everlasting praise:
Blessing and honour and glory and power
be yours for ever and ever.]
Amen.

As our Saviour taught us, so we pray.
Our Father in heaven,
hallowed be your name,
your kingdom come,
your will be done,
on earth as in heaven.
Give us today our daily bread.
Forgive us our sins
as we forgive those who sin against us.
Lead us not into temptation
but deliver us from evil.
For the kingdom, the power,
  and the glory are yours
now and for ever.   Amen.

We break this bread
to share in the body of Christ.
Though we are many, we are one body,
because we all share in one bread.

AFTER COMMUNION

Father of all,
we give you thanks and praise,
that when we were still far off
you met us in your Son
    and brought us home.
Dying and living,
he declared your love,
gave us grace,
and opened the gate of glory.
May we who share Christ's body
live his risen life;
we who drink his cup
bring life to others;
we whom the Spirit lights
give light to the world.
Keep us firm
in the hope you have set before us,
so we and all your children
    shall be free,

and the whole earth
live to praise your name;
through Christ our Lord.   **Amen.**

**Almighty God,
we thank you for feeding us
with the body and blood of your Son
    Jesus Christ
Through him we offer you our souls and bodies
to be a living sacrifice.
Send us out
in the power of your Spirit
to live and work
to your praise and glory.   Amen.**

Go in peace to love and serve the Lord.
In the name of Christ.   Amen.

Or

Go in the peace of Christ.
Thanks be to God.

Morning or Evening Worship
drawn from The Alternative Service Book 1980

INTRODUCTION
We have come together
  as the family of God
in our Father's presence
to offer him praise and thanksgiving,
to hear and receive his holy word,
to bring before him
  the needs of the world,
to ask his forgiveness of our sins,
and to seek his grace,
that through his Son Jesus Christ
we may give ourselves to his service.

SENTENCE
If we say we have no sin,
we deceive ourselves,
and the truth is not in us.
If we confess our sins,
God is faithful and just,
and will forgive us our sins,
and cleanse us
  from all unrighteousness.

CONFESSION
Let us confess our sins to almighty God:

**Almighty God, our heavenly Father,
we have sinned against you
  and against our fellow men,
in thought and word and deed,
through negligence,
  through weakness,
through our own deliberate fault.
We are truly sorry
and repent of all our sins.
For the sake of your Son Jesus Christ,
  who died for us,
forgive us all that is past;
and grant that we may serve you
  in newness of life
to the glory of your name. Amen.**

Or

**Almighty God, our heavenly Father,
we have sinned against you,
through our own fault,
in thought and word and deed,
and in what we have left undone.
For your Son our Lord Jesus Christ's sake,
forgive us all that is past;
and grant that we may serve you
  in newness of life
to the glory of your name. Amen.**

ABSOLUTION
Almighty God, who forgives all who truly repent,
have mercy upon *you*, pardon and deliver *you* from
all *your* sins, confirm and strengthen *you* in all goodness, and keep *you* in life eternal; through Jesus
Christ our Lord. **Amen.**

LITANY
O Lord, open our lips:
and our mouth shall proclaim your praise.

Let us worship the Lord:
all praise to his name.

**Glory to the Father, and to the Son,
and to the Holy Spirit:
as it was in the beginning, is now,
and shall be for ever. Amen.**

RESPONSES TO READINGS
This is the word of the Lord:
thanks be to God.

THE APOSTLES' CREED
**I believe in God, the Father almighty,
creator of heaven and earth.
I believe in Jesus Christ, his only Son, our Lord.
He was conceived
  by the power of the Holy Spirit
and born of the Virgin Mary.
He suffered under Pontius Pilate,
was crucified, died, and was buried.
He descended to the dead.
On the third day he rose again.
He ascended into heaven,
and is seated at the right hand of the Father.
He will come again
  to judge the living and the dead.
I believe in the Holy Spirit,
the holy catholic Church,
the communion of saints,
the forgiveness of sins,
the resurrection of the body,
and the life everlasting. Amen.**

Lord, have mercy upon us.
Christ, have mercy upon us.
Lord, have mercy upon us.

THE LORD'S PRAYER
**Our Father in heaven,
hallowed be your name,
your kingdom come,
your will be done,
on earth as in heaven.
Give us today our daily bread.
Forgive us our sins
as we forgive those
  who sin against us.
Lead us not into temptation
but deliver us from evil.
For the kingdom, the power, and the glory
  are yours
now and for ever. Amen.**

385

RESPONSES
Show us your mercy, O Lord;
and grant us your salvation.

O Lord, save the Queen;
and teach her counsellors wisdom.

Let your priests be clothed with righteousness;
and let your servants shout for joy.

O Lord, make your ways known upon the earth;
let all nations acknowledge your saving power.

Give your people the blessing of peace;
and let your glory be over all the world.

Make our hearts clean, O God;
and renew a right spirit within us.

MORNING COLLECTS
Almighty and everlasting Father,
we thank you
that you have brought us safely
to the beginning of this day.
Keep us from falling into sin

or running into danger;
order us in all our doings;
and guide us to do always
what is right in your eyes;
through Jesus Christ our Lord.   **Amen.**

Or

Eternal God and Father,
you create us by your power
and redeem us by your love:
guide and strengthen us by your Spirit,
that we may give ourselves in love and service
to one another and to you;
through Jesus Christ our Lord.   **Amen.**

EVENING COLLECT
Lighten our darkness,
Lord, we pray;
and in your mercy defend us
from all perils and dangers of this night;
for the love of your only Son,
our Saviour Jesus Christ.   **Amen.**